Longman M

GEOMORPHOLOGY

pton

Longman
London and New York

Longman Group UK Limited
*Longman House, Burnt Mill, Harlow, Essex
CM20 2JE, England and Associated companies
throughout the world.*

*Published in the United States of America
by Longman Inc., New York.*

First published 1989
Fifth impression 1994
ISBN 0 582 35589 3

*Set in 10/12 Times, Linotron 202
Produced by Longman Singapore Publishers Pte Ltd.
Printed in Singapore*

The Publisher's policy is to use paper manufactured from sustainable forests.

All photographs supplied by
Landform Slides.
Cover: Helambu, Nepal; C S Caldicott

British Library Cataloguing-in-Publication Data

Small, R. J. (Ronald John) 1930–
Geomorphology and hydrology.
1. Geomorphology. 2. Slopes.
I. Title.
551.4
551.4′36

ISBN 0-582-35589-3

Library of Congress Cataloging-in-Publication Data

Small, R. J. (Ronald John)
Geomorphology and hydrology/by R. J. Small.
p. cm. — (Longman's modular geography series)
Bibliography: p.
Includes index.
ISBN 0-582-35589-3
1. Geomorphology. 2. Hydrology.
I. Title. II. Series.
GB401.5.S57 1989 88-21530
551.4 — dc19 CIP

Contents

Preface 4

1 The Hydrological System 5

The hydrological cycle 5
Precipitation and the hydrological cycle 8
The effect of vegetation on rainfall 8
Run-off 10
The groundwater system 16
Conclusion 23

2 Fluvial Processes and Landforms 25

River energy and flow 25
Erosion, transport and deposition by rivers 26
The form of river channels 34
The form of river valleys 38
The form and development of drainage patterns 44
Conclusion 49

3 Weathering and Slope Recession 51

The processes of weathering 51
The patterns of weathering 56
Slope recession 63
Slope transportational processes 66
Slope profile analysis 70
Slope evolution 74

4 The Landforms of Cold Environments 81

Glacial environments 82
Processes of glacial erosion, transport and deposition 86
The landforms of glaciated regions 91
Periglacial environments 100
Periglacial landscapes 108

5 The Landforms of Hot Environments 111

Landform development in the humid tropics 114
Landform development in the seasonally humid tropics 118
Landform development in the arid and semi-arid tropics 124
Conclusion 133

6 Coastal Processes and Landforms 135

Wave processes 136
Coastal depositional landforms 143
Coastal erosional landforms 147
Changes of sea level and related coastal landforms 152

7 Landforms on a Global Scale 159

Major structural features of continental land masses 159
Major structural features of the ocean basins 168
The structural evolution of the continents and oceans 170

Index 176

Preface

This modular series of nine separate but interlocking geography texts is designed primarily for sixth form students in the 1990s in the UK. The series is written by a team of authors who, with the Joint Editors, are Chief Examiners and Moderators for a number of GCE Examining Boards, and have been actively involved with sixth form teaching of geography at GCE 'A', and now 'A/S' Levels, as well as at college and university level.

In any modular system, self-standing parts are complementary to each other and to the series as a whole which caters, in its full range of systematic studies, for the needs of any conventional UK geography 'A' Level syllabus. In this series, there are nine texts: three physical and three human, together with three which focus on the interfaces (a) within physical geography, (b) within human geography and (c) between physical and human geography. Thus, the traditional compartmentalisation of the subject is challenged and new interdisciplinary syllabus and educational developments anticipated. Moreover, real case-studies on global and local scales abound throughout, providing a continuing, but ordered and necessary, real-world perspective. Assignments of varying types are to be found in each chapter, providing stimulating work at the sixth form level as well as maintaining the spirit and approaches of GCSE.

Above all, this series offers a representative range of geography books, covering most of the subject, from which individuals may select their own combination for study. A combination of selected physical, human or interface texts can be tailored to suit any teaching programme and designed to meet the special requirements of a specific 'A' or 'A/S' Level syllabus, including those 'A/S' Levels which concentrate on physical or human topics alone. Again, the available expertise and preferences in any given sixth form centre could govern the selection of texts adopted for study. Such selections could favour specialisation (either in physical or human geography) or the interdisciplinary approach (based primarily on the interface volumes). The choice is yours.

Geography is a changing academic subject in a changing world, a changing society and a changing environment, creating great interest and new challenges at all educational levels. The inquisitive and illustrative style of these texts will provide sixth formers with the opportunities to learn, by self-discovery, how theory matches practice and how the local, or distant, geographies can come alive in the classroom. Geography is in a unique position, straddling the humanities and the sciences, yet maintaining a strong academic and professional identity of its own. This series of texts serves to promote and advance that identity, in both the pure and applied senses, providing a contribution to training for good citizenship, and environmental awareness, as well as perspectives on human opportunities and environmental issues the world over.

B. P. Price
J. A. Taylor
(Joint Editors)

1

The Hydrological System

Water is arguably the earth's most vital substance. Humans, animals and plants cannot exist without it, though some plants and animals are adapted to live successfully even where quantities of available water are very small, notably in the hot deserts. To the geographer water is of prime importance because it constitutes a major element in the earth's environment, in the form of the oceans and seas (which are considerably more extensive than the land areas), as well as lakes, rivers, swamps and groundwater. Moreover, water plays an active role in shaping the earth's surface features, aiding most weathering and erosional processes. It follows that physical geographers in particular must understand the principles of the science of *hydrology*, the study of water associated with the earth's land areas, and including both surface and underground water. In addition, the utilisation and management of water resources, or *applied hydrology*, is of concern to both physical and human geographers, and is likely to become of increasing importance as the world's population, and its demand for water for drinking, agriculture, industry and a variety of other purposes, continues to expand.

THE HYDROLOGICAL CYCLE

This is the most fundamental of all hydrological concepts, helping us to understand the 'flows' and 'exchanges' of water that are continually taking place between the earth's water bodies, the atmosphere, the soil and the land surface (Fig. 1.1). By far the greatest amount of the earth's water is stored in the oceans and seas. These constitute a vast reservoir which is being

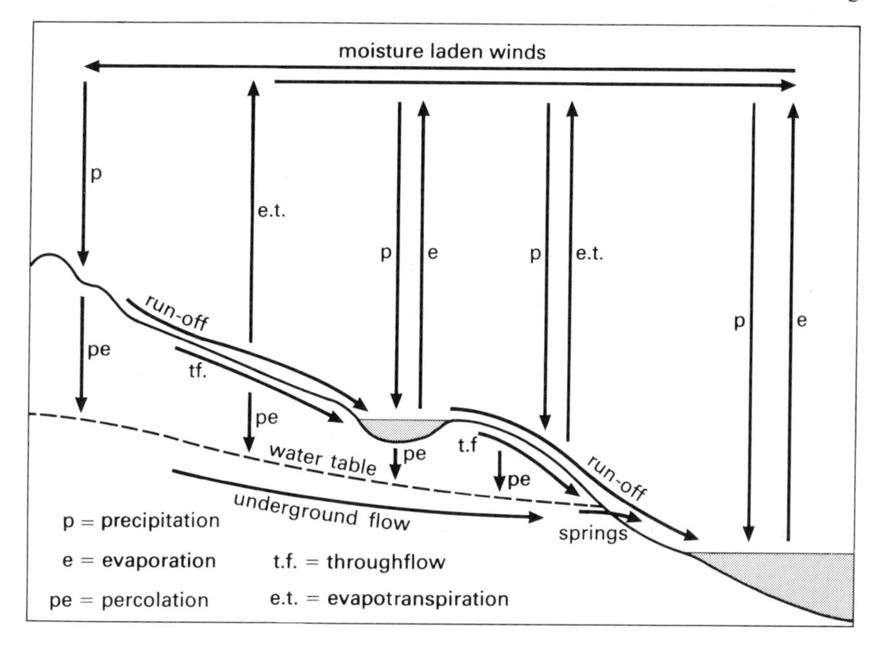

Figure 1.1 *Main flows and exchanges of the hydrological cycle (see pp. 5–7)*

constantly depleted by evaporation from the water surface into the atmosphere, particularly in low latitudes where solar heating is at a maximum. The resultant water vapour is either condensed to form rain clouds whilst still over the oceans, leading to a direct return of the water to its source, or is transported by the planetary winds (such as the Westerlies of the mid-latitudes) over the continental land masses, where again condensation and precipitation occur, particularly in coastal regions or over high mountains. Precipitation over the land may be in the form of snow. As such, water is 'stored' either for a short period, until released rapidly by a period of thaw, or for a longer time span, sometimes up to many thousands of years, in the form of glacier ice. Precipitation as rain may run off the ground surface relatively rapidly; or it may be stored temporarily in lakes, evaporated from soil surfaces, transpired by growing plants, or sink into the ground.

Surface water will mostly be returned to the oceans by way of river flow, though there may be some losses by percolation, as in deserts and limestone terrains, and by evaporation from the surfaces of rivers and lakes, especially in hot climates. There will thus be a simple 'circularity of flow': evaporation from the ocean – precipitation on the land – surface flow back into the oceans. As a result, the initial losses from the ocean, due to evaporation, will be compensated for, and the hydrological system as a whole will tend towards a condition of *equilibrium* or *steady state*.

The water that is evaporated or transpired from the land-surface, known as *evapotranspiration*, may be condensed again in the atmosphere, and then be precipitated back onto the land, where it may increase run-off, be evaporated yet again, or percolate into the ground. Alternatively, it may be carried by offshore winds and precipitated in the oceans. The water that sinks into the soil and subsoil, if it is retained at relatively shallow depths, may be tapped by the roots of growing plants, and thus contribute to evapotranspiration. However, in areas of highly permeable rocks, such as limestone or sands, water will penetrate much more deeply, to form a zone of saturated rock some tens or even hundreds of metres beneath the surface (p. 18). This deep *groundwater* can, however, escape again to the ground surface. For example, it can emerge at the base of an escarpment or on the floor of a deeply incised valley, where the *zone of saturation* intersects the land surface. The resultant springs and seepages will then augment the flow of rivers and, in this way, groundwater will eventually be returned to the oceans. It will be apparent that, within the framework of the hydrological cycle as a whole, there are several subsidiary 'circularities of flow', all of which help to maintain the equilibrium of the hydrological system.

The concept of the water balance

Attempts have been made to quantify the actual amounts of water following the main routes within the hydrological cycle. For instance, it is possible to calculate, albeit somewhat approximately, the global *annual water balance* (otherwise termed the *hydrological balance budget*) in the following simple equation:

$$P = E + R \pm S$$

in which P is annual precipitation, E is evapotranspiration, R is surface run-off, and S reflects gains or losses (and is thus a positive or negative quantity) due to changes in *storage*. Over a period of many years S may tend to be constant, and for that reason is sometimes omitted from the equation. However, it is necessary to remember that, within a single year, more groundwater may be drained by springs than is replenished by percolation of rainwater; hence one of the stores within the hydrological system will become depleted. In contrast, over a very long time span, as during the Quaternary period, extensive ice-sheets may accumulate over the land to thicknesses of thousands of metres. In these circumstances, the land water store will be considerably increased at the expense of the ocean water store.

It has been estimated that, at the present time, annual precipitation over the earth as a whole amounts to some 560 000 km^3, 117 000 km^3 falling over the land and 443 000 km^3 falling over the oceans. To maintain equilibrium, an amount of water equal to this global figure must be evaporated from oceans, seas and lakes each year. Of the water precipitated on the continental surfaces, 67 000 km^3 is consumed by evapotranspiration, and the remaining 50 000 km^3 is lost to surface run-off. However, in terms of real situations the global water balance, involving as it does the averaging of conditions over the earth's surface as a whole, is a somewhat theoretical concept. It is more realistic to calculate the annual water balances for particular regions or locations. These will differ greatly from the global balance, owing to the influence of local factors such as amount and type of precipitation, prevailing temperatures, vegetation, relief and rock type. Moreover, such balances are best expressed in terms of water depth rather than volume. For example, of an annual precipitation of 1000 mm, 300 mm may be used up by evapotranspiration, 670 mm may run off the surface, and 30 mm may enter groundwater storage.

In tropical rainforests the well distributed, high annual precipitation, often exceeding 2000 mm, is disposed of by both large scale evapotranspiration (reflecting the large biomass of the forests, and the high prevailing temperatures) and considerable run-off throughout the year. By contrast, in the sub-tropical hot deserts, where annual rainfall is mainly less than 250 mm, evapotranspiration is overwhelmingly dominant, and run-off, except for short lived flows over short distances, is minimal. In high latitudes, such as the tundra regions of northern Canada and the USSR, annual precipitation is generally very low, 300 mm or less. However, it is mainly lost during a short period of intense run-off in early summer, resulting from the sudden melting of the accumulated winter snow cover; evapotranspiration, on the other hand, is greatly reduced by the scanty vegetation and low temperatures.

It is even more valuable to consider fluctuations in water balance occurring in a particular region or location within the year. In climates that are markedly seasonal in terms of rainfall and/or temperature (for example, Mediterranean, tropical savanna and tropical monsoon climates), evapotranspiration will greatly exceed rainfall during the dry season, with the result that run-off, except where fed by springs, ceases and stream beds become dry (Fig. 1.2). Even in Britain, a much greater proportion of the precipitation is lost to run-off in winter than in summer, when rainfall is somewhat reduced in amount and evapotranspiration, which is negligible in winter, is enhanced by the higher temperatures and the growing vegetation. Indeed, in the drier south-east and east of

Figure 1.2 *A dry stream valley in the rift valley of southern Kenya. The photograph was taken in November during the dry season; in the wet season (commencing in April) surface run-off is intense, and capable of transporting coarse sediment, as can be seen from the floor of the channel*

Britain, evapotranspiration will actually exceed summer rainfall in most years, leaving the soil deficient in moisture and rendering irrigation desirable for optimum grass and crop growth.

PRECIPITATION AND THE HYDROLOGICAL SYSTEM

Precipitation, mainly in the form of rain and snow but including also small amounts of hail, sleet, dew and frost, provides the initial input of water to the hydrological system, but also helps to determine the manner in which the system operates.

1 Total annual precipitation varies widely from almost nil in the 'hyper arid' hot desert interiors to over 10 000 mm/annum^{-1} in some tropical uplands, as in Cameroun, Assam and Hawaii. Clearly the sheer amount of rainfall must influence the overall scale of evapotranspiration and run-off losses. However, there is no straightforward relationship between annual precipitation and the volume of run-off. Indeed, run-off losses are proportionately at a maximum in tropical semi-arid regions, where annual rainfall is low but rainfall intensity is high (see below) and the vegetation cover is scanty. Moreover, the seasonality of precipitation influences the way in which the hydrological system operates at different times within the year. In some climates run-off is a purely seasonal occurrence (p. 13), and fluctuations in the water table are primarily a response to differences in rates of percolation between the wet and dry seasons (p. 20).

2 Type of precipitation closely controls the amount and timing of run-off. For instance, in cold temperate and polar climates there is a considerable build up of the surface snow cover during winter, when the hydrological system becomes virtually inactive. However, in the spring or early summer thaw, this large store of precipitation is released, quite suddenly, leading to rapid and intense run-off, known as the *nival flood*, especially where the soil is still frozen and infiltration thus impeded (p. 107). This process has a major impact in areas such as Siberia, where the largest rivers, the Ob and Yenesei, flow *northwards*. The thaw commences in the south, at a time when in their lower courses the rivers remain frozen, thus hindering the escape of the meltwater and making the problems of flooding even more severe.

3 Intensity of precipitation is another factor of major importance in determining the amount and rate of run-off. In humid temperate regions, most rainfall is associated with the warm fronts of depressions, and much occurs as steady light rain or even drizzle over a prolonged period, usually lasting for several hours. A typical situation is one in which 10–20 mm of rain falls in 5–10 hours, giving a low rate of 0.5–4 mm/hour^{-1}. Heavier rainfall is derived from infrequent convective thunderstorms, but even in these the precipitation intensity rarely exceeds 10 mm/hour^{-1}. However, in tropical latitudes rainfall rates tend to be much greater. The high temperatures and rapid evaporation from land and sea promote high atmospheric humidity. When tropical air is cooled, usually by rapid ascent to great heights as a result of atmospheric instability, condensation occurs on a large scale, and the resultant rainfall is often exceptionally heavy. On 1 December 1978, at the onset of the north-east monsoon, 512 mm of rain fell on Singapore in an 18-hour period – the wettest day in the city's history! The mean rainfall intensity was thus 28 mm/hour^{-1}, and at the height of the rainstorm probably exceeded 50 mm/hour^{-1}. Detailed analysis of thunderstorms of much briefer duration at Kampala, Nairobi and Dar-es-Salaam in East Africa has revealed rates as high as 100–150 mm/hour^{-1}.

THE EFFECT OF VEGETATION ON RAINFALL

The impact of rain at the earth's surface may be greatly affected by the presence of vegetation, which in effect reduces both rainfall intensity and also the proportion of total precipitation that reaches ground level. When, for example, rain falls in an area of forest, much is retained by leaf surfaces and branches; this is referred to as *interception*. The intercepted water is then either evaporated or absorbed, or – as rain continues and the capacity of leaves for surface storage is reached – will begin to drip to the ground resulting, together with the raindrops that penetrate gaps in the canopy, in *throughfall*. Also, some raindrops will run down branches and the trunks of trees as *stemflow*.

The precise effects of all these processes will depend on many factors, including the type of vegetation (whether forest, bush or grassland), the size and nature of individual trees, the actual density of the tree cover, and seasonal changes in the forest, such as the annual shedding of leaves by deciduous trees. *Interception losses* are particularly high in tropical rainforests, but may be significant even in grasslands. Measurements in a Brazilian rainforest have shown that only 60 per cent of the rainfall ever reaches the ground, 20 per cent being evaporated from the tree crowns and 20 per cent being evaporated from or absorbed by the tree trunks. It has also been shown that in coniferous forests up to 30 per cent of the total rainfall is intercepted. The general effect of vegetation cover is to facilitate infiltration, both indirectly by reducing rainfall intensity at ground level, and more directly by way of plant root systems which open up the soil structure to allow the easy passage of rainfall. In vegetated areas, excess surface flow (p. 11) is therefore unlikely under most rainfall conditions.

Evapotranspiration

Precipitation accumulates on the ground surface in a variety of forms, ranging from small puddles to large rivers and lakes. This surface water is in turn depleted by *evaporation*, the physical process of molecular transfer whereby a liquid, in this case water, is changed into a gas, atmospheric water vapour. The precipitation which succeeds in infiltrating the soil can also be lost by evaporation, involving the upward movement of capillary moisture (p. 16), particularly when the soil surface temperature is high. However, greater amounts are consumed usually by the process of *transpiration*, resulting from the *absorption* of soil water by roots, *translocation* up the plant stem, and *evaporation* into the atmosphere through minute pores, known as *stomata*, on leaf surfaces. Rates of transpiration are variable in both space and time, depending on such factors as vegetation and climate. For example, the xerophytic plants of hot deserts, such as cacti, are physically adapted to reduce transpiration and to store water internally, whilst prevailing climatic conditions may increase transpiration rates by high atmospheric temperatures, strong winds, and low relative humidity. A large tree, such as a fully grown oak in southern England, may transpire several hundreds of litres of water a day during summer; on the other hand a maize plant in southern France will transpire only 2–3 litres/day^{-1}.

In hydrology, evaporation and transpiration are grouped together as *evapotranspiration* (sometimes referred to more simply as water loss), mainly because the two processes, but more particularly transpiration, are difficult to measure separately. Indeed, one way of determining evaporation loss is by the formula:

$$E = P - R$$

where E is evapotranspiration, P is precipitation (as measured by a rain gauge) and R is run-off (as measured at river gauging stations). More directly, evaporation can be measured by the use of a percolation gauge, a metal cylinder inserted into the ground and containing soil. Rainwater passing through the soil to the base of the cylinder is collected and measured, and deducted from the rainfall as recorded in a near-by rain gauge to give the amount of evaporation. Where the soil surface in the percolation gauge is vegetated, evapotranspiration can be determined. For practical purposes, such as estimating the need for irrigation, evapotranspiration is usually calculated by complex mathematical equations, such as that derived by H L Penman, which takes into account controlling factors such as solar radiation, mean air temperature, mean air humidity and mean wind speed.

Hydrologists make a distinction between *potential evapotranspiration* and *actual evapotranspiration*. The former relates to evapotranspiration losses at times when the soil moisture is maintained at *field capacity* (p. 17); in other words, it is the maximum rate at which evapotranspiration can take place, because water is continually available within the soil. Actual evapotranspiration refers to measured rates at times when there may even be a deficit of soil moisture, or in other words the soil moisture is below field capacity. Clearly, these rates are lower than those associated with potential evapotranspiration, and reach a minimum when the soil moisture content is so low that plants begin to wilt, or attain *wilting point*. In the USA, annual potential evapotranspiration may exceed 150 cm/annum^{-1} in the hot deserts of the south-west, is generally above 75 cm/annum^{-1} in the southern states as a whole, and ranges from 40–60 cm/annum^{-1} in New England and the Great Lakes Region. Since, in the hot deserts in particular, the annual rainfall received is considerably less than the potential evapotranspiration, the actual evapotranspiration rates are much below potential evapotranspiration rates. Indeed, for much of the year there is a large soil moisture deficit, which greatly restricts plant growth except under conditions of irrigation.

RUN-OFF

Run-off comprises the rainwater which leaves the drainage basin by surface routes, either as *overland flow* (water running down slopes in the form of *sheet wash, rills* and *rivulets*) or *channel flow* (water concentrated into streams and rivers). Run-off is initially a direct product of rainfall or melting snow and ice, but may be considerably augmented by spring and seepage flow which taps soil water and groundwater sources (pp. 21 and 22). The total amount of water available to run-off is the residue of total precipitation, once evapotranspiration has taken its toll.

Overland flow

This is a process which leads to soil erosion (both sheet and gully erosion), and is widely regarded as active in the shaping of slopes (p. 66). It normally comprises a very thin layer of flowing water, rarely more than a few mm in depth, and covering all or much of the slope surface. On the upper part of the slope, it maintains its character as *sheet flow*, otherwise

Figure 1.3 *The effects of surface run-off on sandy soils near Southampton. Such run-off is rare, but can result from heavy rainstorms; the uncompacted soils can then be subjected to significant amounts of erosion*

sheet wash or *unconcentrated wash*, but on the lower part of the slope may become concentrated into rills or rivulets, forming *concentrated wash*. The latter may incise small channels into the slope surface which can, in time, develop into sizeable gullies (Fig. 1.3). It has been estimated that, given a run-off rate of 25 mm/hour^{-1} (a generous assumption, since precipitation intensity is rarely that high) and a flow velocity of 7 m/sec^{-1}, a slope 30 m in length will generate at its base a depth of run-off of 25 mm at maximum. It should be emphasised that overland flow is a temporary process, active only during, and for a relatively short time after, rainstorms of sufficient magnitude.

One theory to account for overland flow is that proposed by R E Horton in 1945 (Fig. 3.14). Horton accepted that when rain falls at a low or even moderate intensity on a slope, as in humid temperate regions experiencing frontal rainfall, the resultant surface water will sink readily into the ground. This is simply because the intensity, perhaps in the order of 1–2 mm/hour^{-1}, will be below the infiltration capacity of the soil, which may have a capacity to absorb rainwater at a rate of 5–50 mm/hour^{-1}. However, if rainfall intensity, sometimes abbreviated to i, is high, as during tropical thunderstorms, or the soil's infiltration capacity f is low, as in clay soils which have been baked by the sun's heat, then surface water cannot penetrate the soil sufficiently rapidly. The excess water therefore accumulates on the soil surface, where initially it will occupy small irregularities, giving rise to *depression storage*. However, these will quickly fill and then overflow to form a continuous sheet of water flowing down the slope.

This type of surface run-off is termed *infiltration excess flow* or *Hortonian overland flow*. The layer of water produced when i exceeds f will thicken downslope, as the excess surface water at any one point is added to by the water arriving from upslope; in other words there is a cumulative *downslope increment* of surface water. The actual velocity of flow will also increase downslope, not only because of increased gradient in many instances, but because the energy losses due to friction between the water and the soil surface become proportionately less as depth of flow increases. At the slope base, overland flow enters the stream or river channel, thus contributing to channel flow.

However, the Horton model is now recognised as having limitations. The model works well in some situations, such as semi-arid environments in which rainfall intensity is often high but, in the absence of an effective vegetation cover which aids infiltration and impedes surface flow, infiltration capacity is low. In other situations, infiltration excess flow is rarely generated under natural conditions, that is, where the vegetation cover has not been seriously disturbed or destroyed, or where the upper soil layers have not been compacted by agriculture or removed altogether to expose the less permeable sub-soil. Under temperate humid conditions, as in Britain, f usually exceeds i by a wide margin, so that Hortonian overland flow is rarely encountered, especially where there is a chalk or sandstone substratum.

Nevertheless, in such temperate environments the downward movement of rainwater through the soil may not be unimpeded. The presence of less permeable layers in the soil, or a relatively impermeable B-horizon, can cause the build-up of water as the rainstorm proceeds. Throughflow will become active (p. 17), resulting in the downslope migration of soil water. This will cause the soil to become saturated at the base of the slope, and then, with the passage of time, the saturated zone will be gradually extended upslope. When rain continues to fall on saturated soil, it cannot be absorbed, with the result that surface water accumulates and hence overland flow will begin; this is known as *saturation overland flow* (Fig. 1.4). On the lower parts of the slope, this surface flow will be increased because soil water which has migrated from upslope, by way of throughflow, will tend to seep out again. If a rainstorm is particularly prolonged, the area of the basin experiencing saturation overland flow can be increased very considerably. Moreover, since individual storms differ in duration,

Figure 1.4 *Saturation overland flow (see p. 11)*

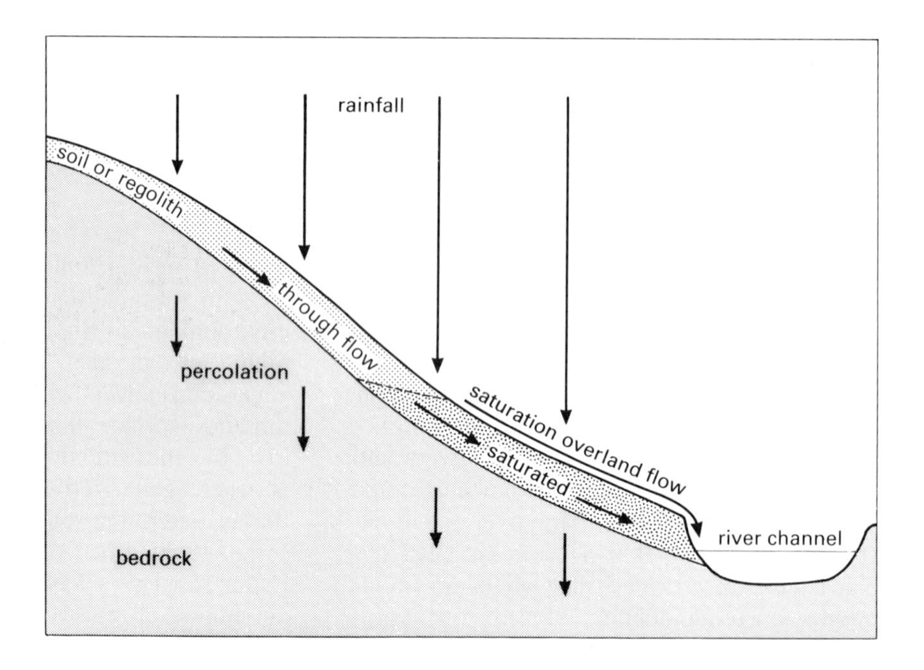

Figure 1.5 *An intermittent channel (winterbourne) in the chalk, near Micheldever, Hampshire. Taken at the time of highest water table levels in March 1988, this shows the stream at bank-full stage; the channel is completely grassed, and the absence of bank erosion reflects the short period each year of surface flow*

different extents of the drainage basin will be subjected at different times to overland flow of this type.

Channel flow

Stream and river channels (the terms are usually regarded as synonymous by hydrologists) comprise the 'arteries' of the surface run-off system. However, they do not necessarily carry water at all times. Some channels are dry for most of the time, and become occupied only after a rainstorm; these are known as *ephemeral channels*. Others are seasonally occupied by flowing water. For instance, the chalk valleys of England contain streams when the water table rises to the surface in winter; these are known as *intermittent channels* (Fig. 1.5). However, many channels are always occupied by some flowing water, and these are known as *permanent* or *perennial channels*. In these, since there is a lapse of time between the entry of the water and its exit to a lake or the sea, large quantities of water are stored; this is referred to as *channel storage*, which is at its maximum during times of flood.

Hydrologists study variations of channel flow, or *discharge*, over time, partly for the possible application of this knowledge in the solution of problems posed by rivers. Discharge (Q) is measured in terms of the *volume* of water (in m^3) passing a point in the river channel in a *unit of time* (one second); for further explanation, see p. 26. Discharge studies are of potential value in the prediction and forecasting of river floods.

Flood prediction represents an attempt to say whether a flood of a particular *magnitude* will occur during a specified future time span. The method is based on the study of *recurrence intervals*, or *return periods*, of floods which have been recorded in the past. From this record, the peak discharges are plotted on a graph according to (a) magnitude (in m^3/s^{-1}), and (b) the average time intervals between floods of particular magnitudes (Fig. 1.6). This graph can then be used to predict, say, that a flood with a discharge of 100 m^3/s^{-1} is likely to recur within a future ten-year period, hence the term *10-year flood*; or that a flood with a discharge of 1000 m^3/s^{-1} is likely within a hundred-year period, hence the term a *100-year flood*. However, reality is not quite as simple as this, since floods of a given magnitude do not actually occur at regular time intervals. In the example given, it is possible that floods of 100 m^3/s^{-1} might occur in successive years, and then not recur for 20 or 30 years. Again, long term changes in flood frequency may be taking place, in response to climatic changes or human modification of the drainage basin by deforestation, agriculture and urbanisation, all of which tend to accentuate run-off and render floods of a certain magnitude more frequent. *Flood forecasting* relates to shorter time intervals, and is undertaken when a rainstorm

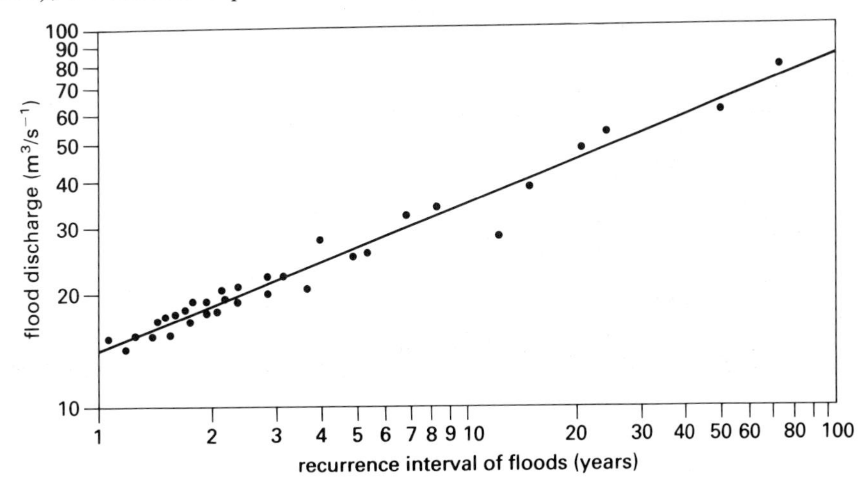

Figure 1.6 *A typical flood frequency graph*

actually occurs within a drainage basin. If the hydrological characteristics of the basin and its channel flow have previously been studied, and the distribution, amount and intensity of precipitation have been accurately recorded, it should be possible to calculate when the resultant flood will reach a particular point along the river channel, and what the height of the flood will be. Any precautions needed to safeguard life and property can then be taken.

Seasonal fluctuations of channel flow are characteristic of many of the world's rivers, but are most pronounced in those types of climate (for example, the Mediterranean or tropical savanna) with a distinct rainy season, and an equally distinct dry season during which run-off is derived from sub-surface water stores by way of springs and seepages (*base flow*). Even in Britain there is usually a marked difference in discharge from winter (maximum) to summer (minimum), reflecting not only differences in rainfall amounts but also losses to evapotranspiration during the summer growing season (Fig. 1.7). Thus, in 1980 the average mean discharge of the River Thames at Teddington ranged from a minimum of 17.6 m^3/s^{-1} (August) to a maximum of 143.3 m^3/s^{-1} (February). Under similar climatic conditions, seasonal contrasts of flow can, however, be much reduced by geological factors. For example, in limestone and chalk terrains, much of the wet season rainfall does not produce direct surface run-off, but percolates into the ground, to re-emerge during the dry season as base flow. For example, in 1980 the maximum recorded discharge on the Itchen, a chalk stream measured near Eastleigh in Hampshire, was 5.1 m^3/s^{-1} (on 1 January) and the minimum was 2.3 m^3/s^{-1} (on 28 July).

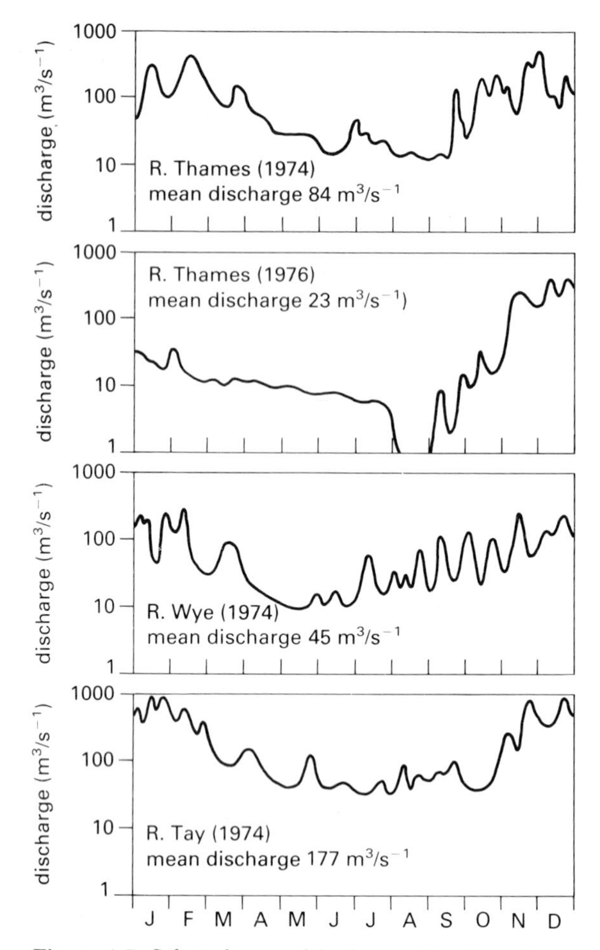

Figure 1.7 *Selected annual hydrographs. Note the effect of the 1976 drought on the discharge of the Thames*

Short term fluctuations of channel flow are related to 'events' such as rainstorms of short duration, or the sudden melting of a snow cover which had accumulated over a period of days or weeks. The resultant peaks on the *hydrograph*, a graph on which variations in river discharge are plotted against time, are characterised by *rising limbs* which are concave, and increase sharply in steepness once run-off from valley side slopes begins to enter the river in large quantities (Fig. 1.8a). The *falling limbs*, or *recession curves*, are usually much gentler, and although generally concave in shape may at a later stage approximate to a straight line. This reflects the ending of direct surface run-off, and a return to base flow, which is derived not only from true groundwater reserves, but at least for a time comprises water from the rainstorm which enters the channel via the process of throughflow (p. 17). It should also be noted from Fig. 1.8a that there will be a time interval, referred to as the *lag time*, between the peak of rainfall intensity and the peak of channel discharge. This reflects the

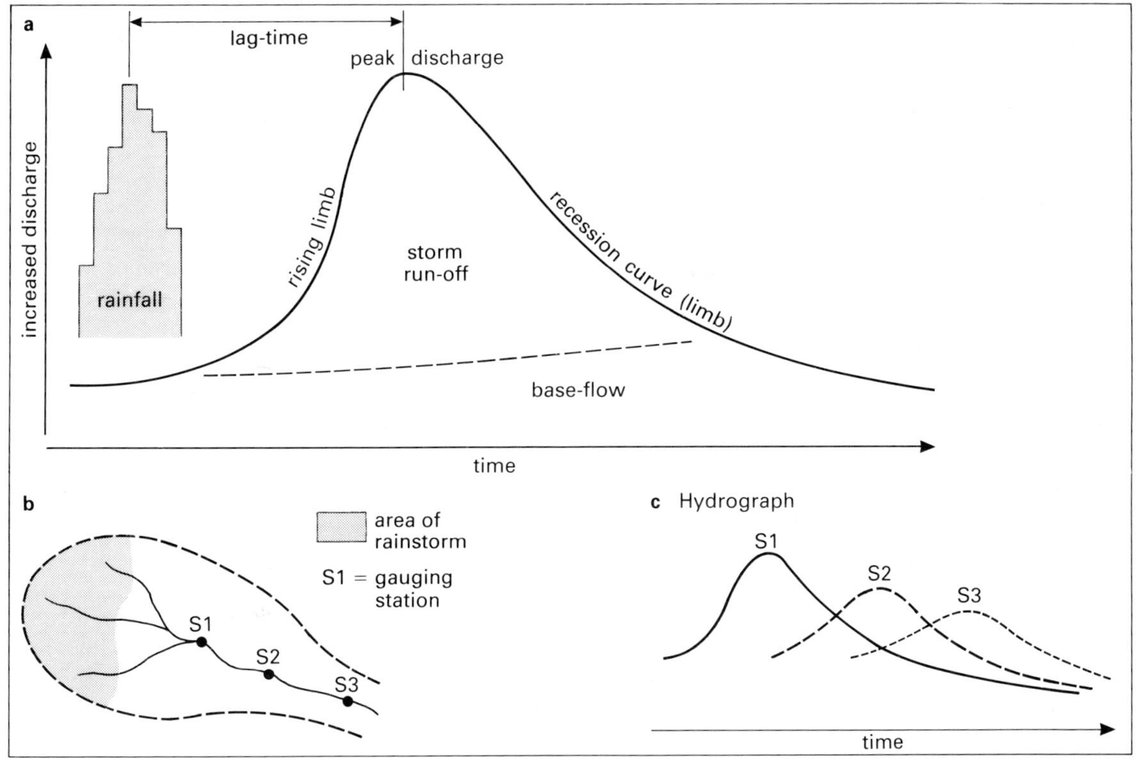

Figure 1.8 *The form of the river hydrograph (see pp. 14–16)*

time needed both for the rain to generate overland flow, and for that overland flow to pass downslope into the channel. In some instances, the hydrograph may display a double peak, and hence two lag times. The first, and major peak, will represent the relatively rapid arrival of rainwater at the channel via the overland flow route; the second, a lesser and more protracted peak, will result from the passage of rainwater via the slower throughflow route.

Various other factors also influence both the form of individual hydrograph peaks and the lag time. In a particular river basin, the rainstorm may be confined to the upper part of that basin (Fig. 1.8b). The peak of run-off thus generated will pass down the main channel within the basin, so that lag time will be increased towards the point at which the river leaves the basin (Fig. 1.8c). Moreover, in such an instance the peak itself will become less pronounced, or will be 'damped', in a down-channel direction. Where a rainstorm occurs in a basin characterised by steep slopes, sparse vegetation cover, and soils which are either compacted or are already saturated as a result of previous rainfalls, run-off will be generated very rapidly. The peak discharge will thus be high, the rising limbs steep and short lived, and the lag time brief. This phenomenon, sometimes referred to as 'flashy' discharge, can also be observed in urbanised areas, where roads and paved surfaces, associated with storm drains leading into natural river channels, give rise to very rapid and considerable run-off. It has been noted that, as river basins become increasingly urbanised, the danger of flooding increases, since the existing channels are adjusted to handle smaller discharges than are being generated by the new conditions. The artifical enlargement of these channels, to increase their capacity, and the stabilisation of the banks by concrete or brick walls, to prevent serious erosion by the more powerful flows, often becomes necessary. By contrast, where the impact of the storm is reduced by gentle slopes, the presence of a thick forest cover, and the occurrence of porous soils with a high moisture storage capacity, . the peak discharge in the channel will be lower, the rising limb will be more gentle in angle, lag time will be increased, and the recession curve greatly extended.

Perhaps the most striking short term variations of flow, giving a very distinctive river hydrograph, are associated with meltwater from glaciers and ice-sheets. During summer in regions such as the Alps, surface melting of ice reaches its maximum during the early afternoon, when atmospheric temperatures are highest, and its minimum shortly before dawn, when temperatures are lowest. As a result, the hydrographs of streams draining from glaciers show pronounced *daily* peaks, with maximum discharge occurring in the late afternoon (Fig. 1.9). In this instance, the lag time, usually an hour or two in the high summer season, reflects the time taken for the meltwater to flow off the ice surface, or through tunnels within and beneath the glacier, to the glacier snout.

THE GROUNDWATER SYSTEM

Infiltration and soil moisture

When rain falls on to the land surface, a proportion will, under most circumstances, sink directly into the soil; this is known as *infiltration*. Entry of the rainwater is facilitated by the fact that soil comprises mineral and organic particles which are separated from each other by small spaces known as *pores*. These vary in size from less than 0.001 mm to several mm in diameter, and interconnect to a greater or lesser extent, depending on the size and shape of the soil particles. They thus provide narrow passages, or capillaries, through which the rain water can pass vertically downwards or laterally on slopes under the pull of gravity (*gravity water*). Alternatively the water forms *capillary water*, held as thin films adhering to individual soil particles by surface tension. The ability of a soil to allow the entry of water is referred to as its *infiltration capacity*; this is expressed in terms of the depth of water (in millimetres) that can infiltrate the soil in a unit of time (one hour).

Several factors control the infiltration capacity of a soil. Of particular note is the *soil texture*, which is determined primarily by the proportions of the constituent particles, such as sand, silt or clay, present in the soil. Where the texture is coarse, as in gravels and sands, the pore spaces are large and have a high degree of connectivity. In this case the soil is both *porous* and *permeable*, or in other words readily allows the entry and passage of rain water. However, where the texture is fine, as in clay soils, the pore spaces, though possibly very numerous, are much smaller. Water which succeeds in entering the soil actually becomes trapped within the pores by surface tension,

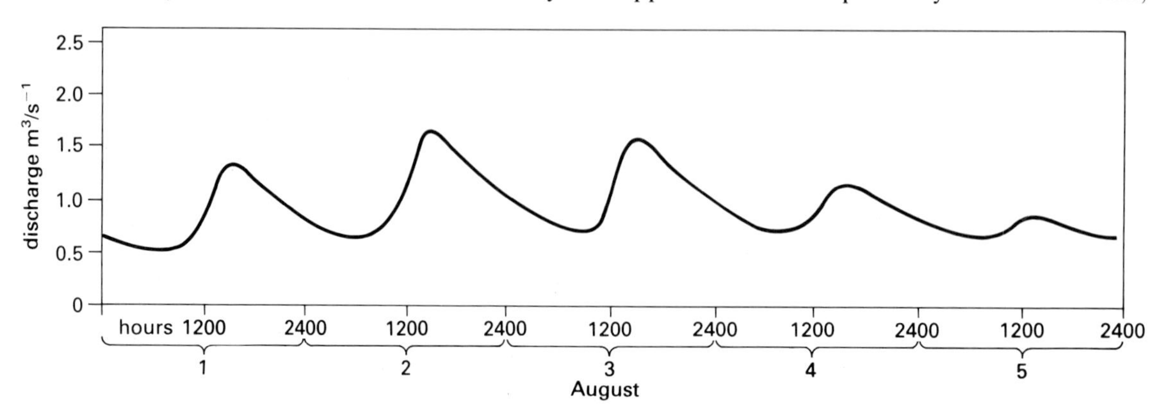

Figure 1.9 *A hydrograph of a meltwater stream from an Alpine glacier. Note the steep rising limb each day, and the gentler recession curve, arising from the drainage of meltwater stored within the glacier (see above)*

rather than passing through them, so that the soil is relatively *impermeable*. Four other factors influencing infiltration capacity are: *soil structure*, or the manner in which individual soil grains are aggregated into *peds*, which may be 'crumb-like' and allow good drainage, or comprise horizontal 'plates' impeding downwards water movement; the presence of plant roots, animal burrows and worm-holes, which provide ready made passages for infiltrating rainwater; the degree to which the soil has been compacted, for instance, by agricultural vehicles such as tractors and combine-harvesters, or trampling by humans and animals along well used tracks; and the presence of antecedent moisture, that is, water from a previous rainstorm which still fills the soil pores, and thus impedes the entry and passage of fresh rainwater.

The rate at which the soil absorbs rainfall, the *infiltration rate*, varies over time as the storm proceeds. When the rain begins to fall it usually infiltrates at a relatively rapid rate. There are some exceptions to this rule, for example, when the soil is already saturated, or has been baked hard by a drought. However, after a period of some ten to twenty minutes, the infiltration rate becomes reduced, as the soil pores become filled by water and the entry of additional water is dependent on the loss of water at the base of the soil profile. Other factors which reduce the infiltration rate are the washing in by raindrops of fine particles which block the pores, and the swelling of clay minerals in the soil when these become wetted. After the initial period of relatively rapid infiltration, the rate settles down and becomes more or less constant (Fig. 1.10). Median rates are in the order of 25 mm/hour^{-1}; however in a sandy soil the rate may be as high as 50 or more mm/hour^{-1}, and in a clay soil less than 5 mm/hour^{-1}.

The permeability of the soil is frequently greater than that of the underlying parent material or bed rock, as in granite, which is itself largely impermeable but often weathers to give a sandy soil or regolith. Again, the B horizon of the soil may contain a *clay pan*,

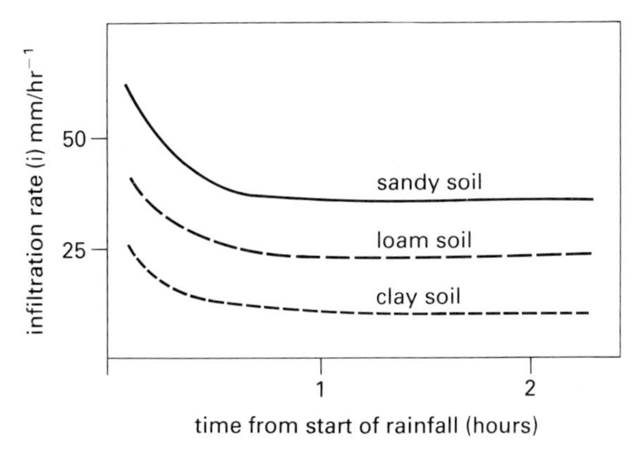

Figure 1.10 *Typical infiltration rates for different soils*

which restricts the downward passage of soil water. In both instances the water will be forced to drain laterally, in a downslope direction. This is known as *throughflow* (Fig. 1.4). Sometimes this water movement is concentrated along well defined sub-surface lines of seepage, referred to as *percolines*; these may even comprise small tunnels, or *pipes*, where the soil particles have been washed away by the sub-surface flow. Water transported by throughflow emerges as small springs and seepages, either on the lower parts of slopes or in the banks of stream channels, thus contributing to surface run-off.

Following the cessation of rainfall, water flow through the soil, either vertically or laterally, will continue for a time, thus gradually reducing the soil moisture content. Initially the soil may be saturated, or at *saturation capacity*. However, as gravity drains water from the soil, leaving behind only capillary water, the soil attains the state referred to as *field capacity*. Any further loss of soil water will reduce soil moisture below field capacity, giving rise to a *soil moisture deficit*. This deficit is stated in terms of the amount of water needed to restore the soil to field capacity. During late winter in Britain, after a period of considerable rainfall and little or no evapotranspiration, the soil moisture deficit is nil. However, as summer proceeds and the rate of evapotranspiration increases, so the soil moisture deficit will increase. It is estimated that, by the end of the summer in south-east England, this will be as high as 14 cm (see also the discussion on p. 7).

Percolation and groundwater

Rainwater which infiltrates the soil, and is not subsequently removed by throughflow or utilised by growing plants, will continue to migrate downwards under the pull of gravity, to pass into and through the underlying rock, providing this is permeable. This process of *percolation* results in the formation of *groundwater*. At depth within the rock the pores, joints, fractures and bedding planes become filled by this groundwater, forming a *zone of saturation*. The uppermost surface of this zone, dividing saturated rock below from unsaturated rock above, is known as the *water table* (this term is also sometimes used more loosely to describe the zone of saturation as a whole). Between the ground surface and the water table the spaces within the rock are aerated, but also contain some water which is in transit to the saturated zone (Fig. 1.11a). A rock stratum which contains an abundant supply of underground water, which may be tapped by wells and bore holes, or escape to the surface by way of springs, is known as an *aquifer*; this means that the stratum is 'water bearing'.

Two types of permeability in rocks, relating to the formation of groundwater, have been recognised: these are *primary permeability* and *secondary permeability*. The former relates to the passage of water through the rock pores, as in porous sands and sandstones, for example, the Bunter Sandstone in Nottinghamshire, Cheshire and west Lancashire, from which much of the region's water supply is derived.

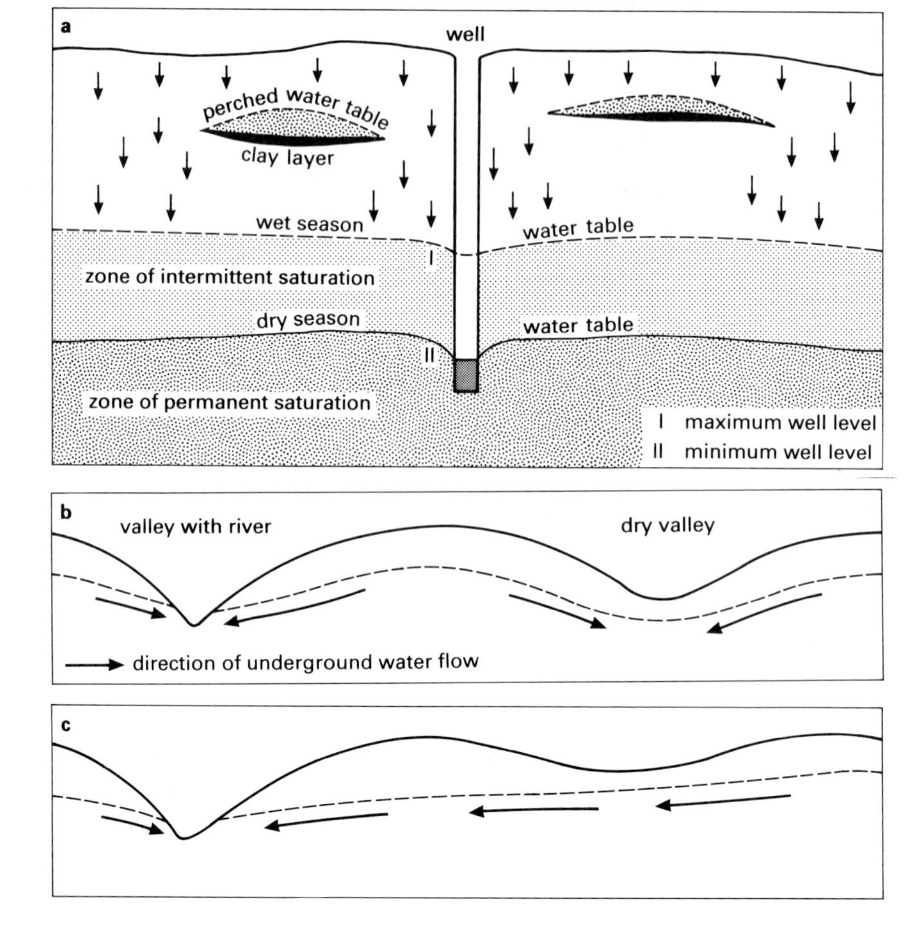

Figure 1.11 *The form of the water table (see pp. 19–21)*

The latter is due to the presence of cracks, such as joints and fissures, which develop in the rock subsequent to its formation and give rise to more concentrated lines of flow. Secondary permeability is characteristic of well-jointed rocks such as the Carboniferous Limestone and the various Jurassic limestones of Britain. Indeed, but for the presence of joints, many limestones would not be permeable. The permeability of limestones may actually increase with time, as solution by percolating rainwater, containing dissolved carbon dioxide, widens joints, fissures and bedding planes into broad clefts and tunnels capable of conducting large quantities of groundwater very effectively. Even in the Chalk, generally a less well-jointed rock than most limestones yet by far the most important aquifer in southern England, fissures play a vital role. Indeed, wells sunk into the Chalk may tap surprisingly little water, until horizontal adits are constructed and as many water bearing fissures as possible are intercepted.

The form of the water table

Within an aquifer, the water table is rarely horizontal, but possesses gentle gradients that are in effect a subdued replica of the surface relief. In other words, the elevation of the water table is usually greatest beneath high ground, and lowest beneath valleys (Fig. 1.11b). However, there is not always an exact coincidence between surface and underground drainage divides; in some instances the springs within one drainage basin may be tapping groundwater ('under-draining') from an adjoining drainage basin (Fig. 1.11c). This process is liable to occur where geological structure favours the lateral migration of groundwater on a regional scale (see below). The surface slope, or *hydraulic gradient*, of the water table causes groundwater to flow laterally, at a rate determined by Darcy's Law:

$$V = P\frac{h}{I}$$

where V is velocity of flow, h is head, I is length of distance of flow between two points, and P is a coefficient of permeability (Fig. 1.12). The ratio between h and I defines the water table gradient. The value of P will be higher, and thus flow more rapid, for a rock with large pores and/or numerous fissures, than for a rock with small pores and/or few fissures. In many aquifers pockets of groundwater are stored above the main water table; these are termed *perched water tables*, and occur where downward percolation is impeded by a relatively impermeable stratum (Fig. 1.11). It is often assumed that the Chalk forms one large aquifer; in reality, perched water tables are quite common, and appear to be due to thin layers of clay (*marl*) which are found at various levels within the formation. Another type of perched water table is found in deserts, for example that of central Saudi Arabia. Here major aquifers, mainly limestones and sandstones, contain large reservoirs of groundwater lying at considerable depths. These are not being recharged by present day rainfall, but represent 'fossil groundwater' which accumu-

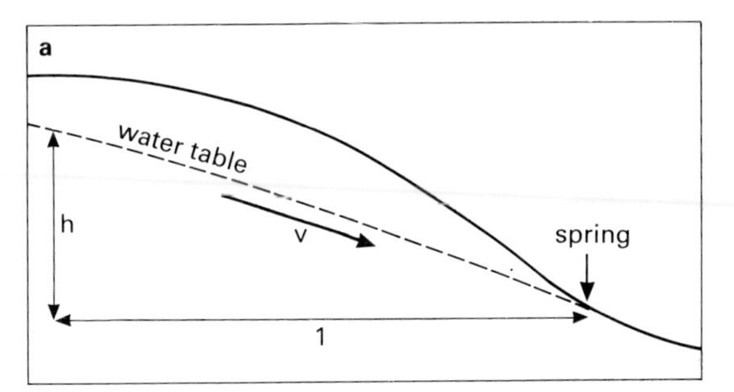

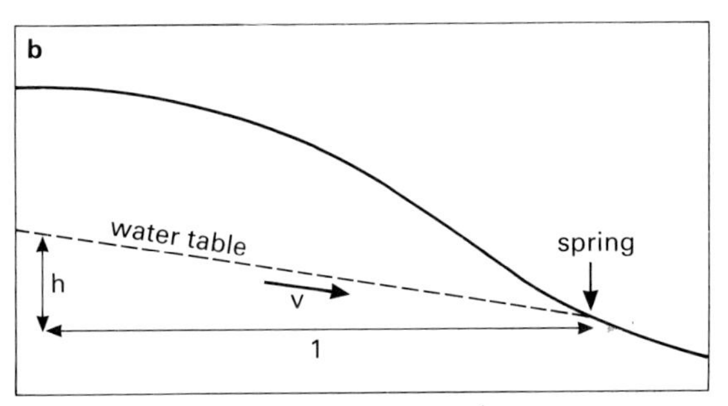

Figure 1.12 *Darcy's Law and spring discharge. The head of the water in **a** will be twice that in **b**, and the water table gradient is correspondingly steeper. The discharge of the spring in **a** will be twice that of **b***

Figure 1.13 *A desert well in granite country, Wadi Al-Khanagah, Saudi Arabia. This is a shallow well, tapping groundwater trapped only 4–5 m below the surface in the alluvium occupying the wadi floor*

lated during the wetter climates of the Quaternary. In addition, groundwater is found within the alluvial infillings of desert wadis, themselves the product of Quaternary fluvial erosion (p. 126). The water table here lies at a depth of a few metres, and is being recharged by current rainstorms giving rise to flash floods which, in turn, are rapidly depleted by percolation into the coarse alluvial sands of the wadi floors (Fig. 1.13).

Fluctuations in the water table

The water table is by no means unchanging in its level, but actually experiences substantial changes over time. Fluctuations are naturally most pronounced in areas with seasonal climatic contrasts, particularly of precipitation, but also occur under less contrasted climatic regimes. In southern and eastern England, where the annual rainfall is mainly within the range of 600–800 mm/annum^{-1}, approximately 120–180 mm (about 20%) finds its way by percolation to the saturated zone in the Chalk. However, there are variations in rainfall amounts from year to year which are sufficient to cause large changes in the height of the water table. For example, at Chilgrove in the South Downs of West Sussex, the water level in a well, measured over a period of 73 years, varied in height from 76.6 m OD to 34.8 m OD, thus giving a total range of 41.8 m. Seasonal fluctuations in chalk wells are also important; thus at Chilgrove, the average *annual* change in level, during the study period, was 15.4 m. These arise not simply from the fact that, in Britain, there is rather more rainfall in winter than in summer. Except in very wet summers, virtually all the rain falling between April and October is consumed by evapotranspiration, although in areas of impermeable rock such as clay and granite, summer downpours can result in some surface run-off. In aquifers such as the Chalk, percolation during this period virtually ceases, with the result that, throughout the summer, the water table is steadily lowered, as underground water stores are depleted by spring flow. However, from October onwards, as precipitation exceeds evapotranspiration, percolation is resumed and the level of the water table steadily rises to a maximum in March/April. In many chalk valleys, this is sufficient to bring the zone of saturation to the surface, and temporary streams, termed *winterbournes* and *lavants* in southern England and *gypseys* in east Yorkshire, begin to flow on valley floors which, throughout the summer, remain dry.

In some situations, for example where the water table is at a relatively shallow depth, depletion of groundwater during the dry season is the result of evapotranspiration, as trees and other plants, such as tamarisk bushes in desert wadis, are able to tap the water table by way of extended root systems. This process operates in many savanna and semi-arid regions of tropical Africa, where the water table is developed in permeable regolith overlying impermeable granite or gneiss (p. 115). Here the water table is also lowered by the extraction of water from wells and bore holes for human use. The latter process can lead also to long term reductions in the level of the water table. Even in southern England, there is evidence to show that the water table has fallen by some 20 m since Roman times, for example in the Cranborne Chase area of Dorset, probably as a result of factors such as excessive withdrawal and modifications in the natural vegetation cover rather than any climatic changes resulting in reduced annual percolation. More recently, the disastrous decline of well levels in the Sahel region of Africa has resulted from a combination of over use, climatic desiccation (associated with reduced and unreliable annual rainfall) and greater losses of rainwater to accelerated run-off and evaporation from bare soil surfaces, the combined result of over grazing, over cultivation and destruction of the natural vegetation cover.

Geological structure and underground water

The accumulation and flow of groundwater is influenced to a large extent by rock type, angle of dip, and the presence of fault and fold structures. For example, the most productive aquifers develop where the permeable stratum (limestone, chalk, sandstone, gravel) is underlain and 'sealed' by impermeable clay, which prevents further downward percolation.

Groundwater supplies are especially plentiful in areas of gently dipping sedimentary strata, comprising alternate layers of permeable and impermeable rock, as in the scarpland regions of lowland England. The dip slopes of individual cuestas afford large catchments where rainwater can percolate into the rock. The resultant water table assumes the form shown in Fig. 1.14. The hydraulic gradient towards the base of the scarp slope results, in accordance with Darcy's Law, in the flow of some underground water against the dip of the rock, and the formation of a line of springs, termed *scarp-foot springs*, usually of restricted discharge.

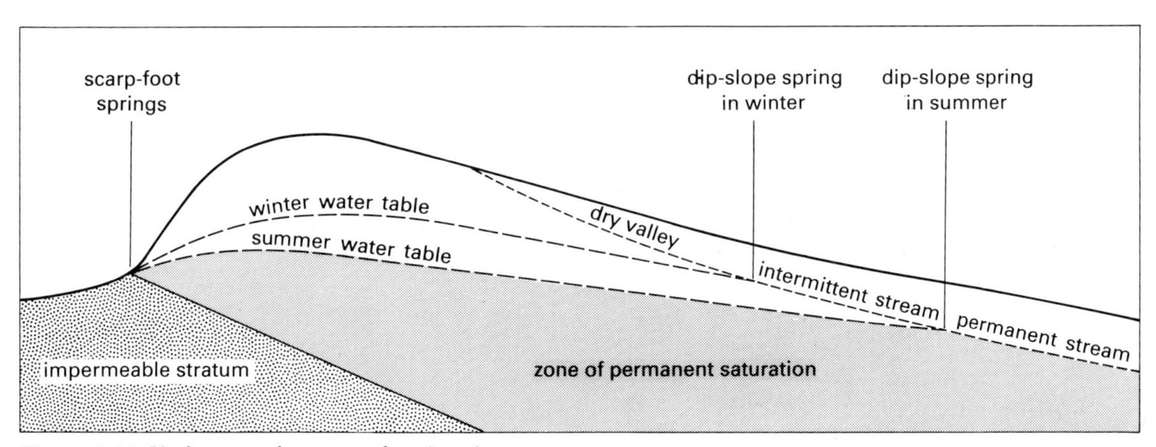

Figure 1.14 *Underground water and springs in cuestas*

These springs display geological control in two ways: first, they emerge at the line of junction between a permeable stratum above and an impermeable stratum below; secondly, their spacing, usually at intervals of 1–2 km, suggests the flow of underground water along concentrated lines, as determined by major joints or fractures in the rock.

However, in cuestas the greater proportion of the underground water flows in the opposite direction, to emerge eventually by way of springs on the floors of dip-slope valleys, termed *dip-slope springs*. This movement reflects hydraulic gradient, and the natural tendency for the water to flow 'down' the dip, along partings within the rock (bedding planes) or strongly fissured layers. Dip-slope springs tend to flow more strongly than scarp-foot springs, owing to their extended underground catchments. Moreover, they do not as a rule remain fixed at a particular geological horizon but migrate up-dip in winter (or the wet season) and down-dip in summer (or the dry season). In limestone and chalk areas, sub-surface solution beneath dry valley floors opens up joints, thus aiding the transmission of sub-surface water and increasing further the discharge of springs situated in valley bottoms.

In addition to the scarp-foot and dip-slope springs of scarpland landscapes, there are *fault-guided* and *Vauclusian springs* (Fig. 1.15). The former occur either where faults, often associated with zones of crushed rock along which water movement is facilitated, intersect the ground surface, or where, as a result of a permeable stratum being faulted against an impermeable stratum, water emerges at a line of springs sited along the fault. Vauclusian springs, named after the Fontaine de Vaucluse in south-eastern France, mark the *resurgences* of underground rivers. These usually occur in limestone terrains, as in the Mendips, where the River Axe emerges at Wookey Hole.

The influence of geological structure on underground water is best displayed by *artesian basins* (Fig. 1.16). These involve large synclinal structures in which an aquifer is sandwiched between overlying and underlying impermeable layers. Rainwater sinks into the ground at the margins of the basin, where the permeable rocks are exposed, and migrates down-dip towards the synclinal axis. The ground water

Figure 1.15 *The resurgence of the River Fergus, in limestone at An Clab, the Burren, western Ireland*

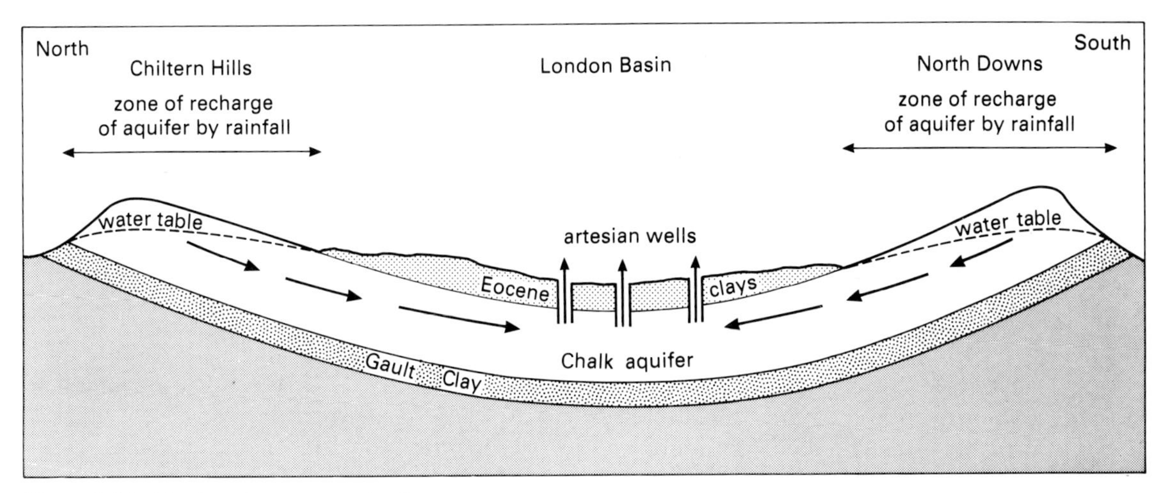

Figure 1.16 *The London artesian basin*

accumulating here, at depths of hundreds or even thousands of metres beneath the surface, is under great hydrostatic pressure. When wells are sunk through the overlying stratum, the water will rise spontaneously to the surface; hence the term *artesian well* (Fig. 1.17). A well known example in Britain is the London Basin, in which the principal aquifer, the Chalk, is sealed by Gault Clay below and Eocene clays above, but is continually replenished by rain falling on the dip slopes of the Chiltern Hills and North Downs. However, owing to long term continued and excessive extraction of water for domestic and industrial use, the water table in the Chalk has fallen to the extent that pumping is now necessary. The term 'artesian' is derived from an equivalent structure of this type in the Artois region of northern France.

Figure 1.17 *A borehole tapping artesian water, near the Algerian-Tunisian border north-east of El Oued*

CONCLUSION

As has been shown, the hydrological system comprises many components which interact in a complex and tightly inter-connected way. In one sense, therefore, it is unrealistic to separate out one of these components, surface water flow in the form of rivers, for much more detailed consideration. However, rivers have played – and continue to play – such a major part in the geomorphological evolution of the earth's surface landforms, that their separate study in the next chapter requires little justification.

ASSIGNMENTS

1 a. Suggest as many reasons as you can to explain why the water balance in the uplands of northern and western Britain differs from that in the lowlands of eastern and south-eastern England.

b. Why may the water balance also vary from place to place within these regions?

2 a. In which parts of the world, and for what reasons, is *overland flow* most likely to occur?

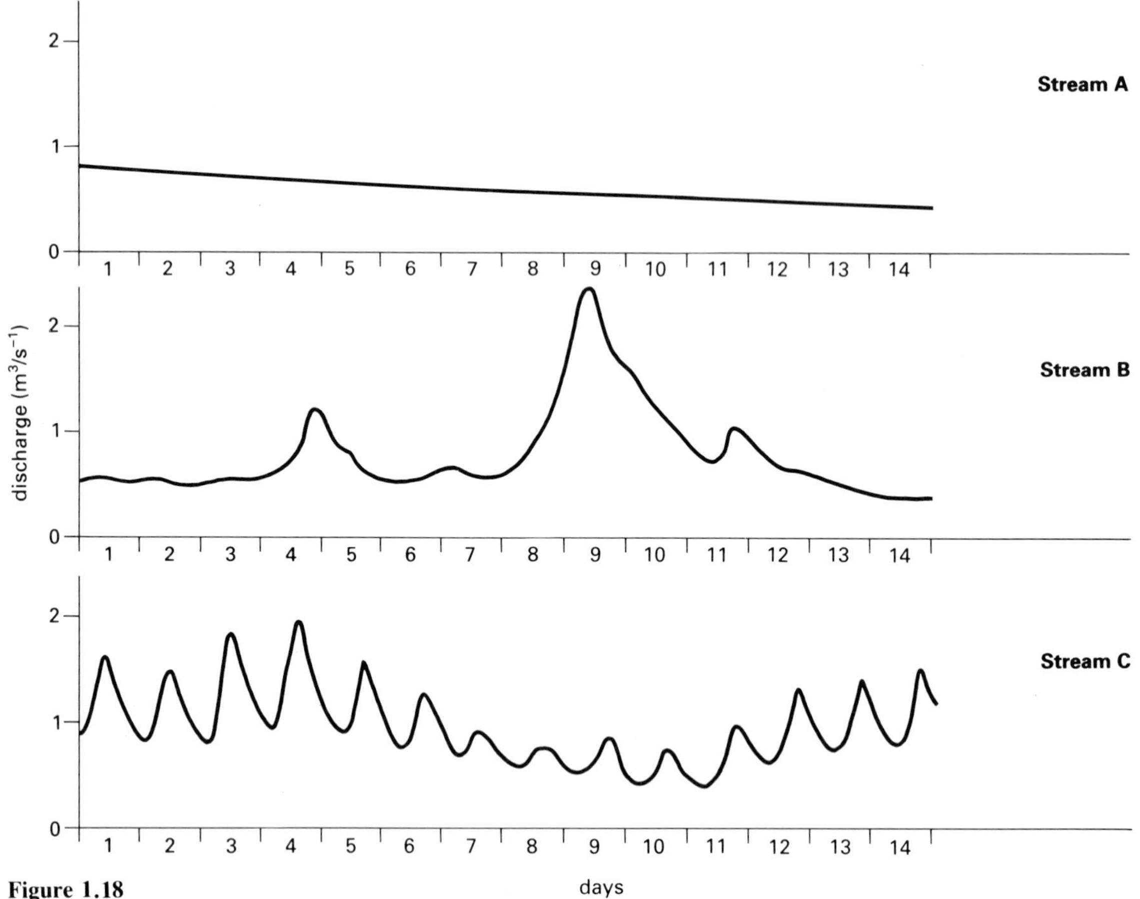

Figure 1.18

b. Explain the ways in which:
   i. the afforestation of upland areas in Britain,
   ii. the cultivation of steep slopes in a tropical humid country such as Malaysia,
   iii. the increase of cattle herding in an area on the southern fringes of the Sahara desert,
   iv. the building of large housing estates,

   will influence the nature and amount of overland flow.

3 Figure 1.18 shows hydrographs for three streams over a 14-day period in summer.
   a. Describe the features of the three hydrographs.
   b. What physical/geological/climatic conditions influence the discharges of these three streams?
   c. What factors, other than those you have referred to in b, influence the discharge of streams?

4 If you had to make a study of problems of flooding by a local river:
   a. What features would you look for in the field which would indicate the river's liability to flood?
   b. What long term discharge data would you need to obtain from the appropriate authority?
   c. How would you analyse this data, and interpret the results of this analysis?
   d. What other sources of information might you consult to assist your study?

5 a. Discover where your own domestic water supply comes from.
   b. Explain the reasons why your water supply is derived *either* from local sources *or* distant sources.
   c. If there were to be a severe summer drought, how might this affect your water supply and why?

2

Fluvial Processes and Landforms

The study of the processes and landforms associated with rivers, known as *fluvial geomorphology*, has rightly been regarded as a cornerstone of physical geography. All the earth's landscapes, no matter what the prevailing climate may be, bear the imprint of running water. This is true where rivers flow effectively for only part of the year, as in periglacial climates when the spring thaw of the winter snows occurs, or even only for a day or two at a time, for example the stream floods of hot deserts. Moreover, the vast majority of all valleys, the fundamental landform of most parts of the earth's surface, are initiated by fluvial action, though other processes contribute subsequently to their modification and development.

During the twentieth century, the study of fluvial geomorphology has undergone a radical change. Up until the 1950s, the emphasis was on the qualitative description of processes of erosion, transport and deposition by rivers; little attempt was made to measure, or quantify, and understand these processes in detail. In the concept of a *cycle of erosion*, propounded by the American geographer W M Davis, river valleys were classified mainly according to their form, into three main types. In the *youthful stage of development*, the valleys are marked by steep and irregular slopes, rising above a rapidly incising river. In the *mature stage*, the valleys possess less steep, more rounded and smoothed slopes, and the rivers lose their powers to erode vertically. In the *stage of old age*, the valleys are shallow and are bordered by very gentle slopes, masked by a thick and continuous regolith resulting from a long period of weathering and contain sluggish, meandering rivers with little power to erode. However, such a *stage approach* is now regarded as far too simple a way of studying valley form and development; and the implication that valleys actually evolve through the three stages in sequence, a process referred to as *sequential landform development*, is no longer acceptable.

Since the 1950s, the emphasis in fluvial geomorphology has switched to a detailed study of fluvial processes, using precise measurement and observation in the field, and scientific and laboratory analysis of the data obtained. This study of processes is not only useful in itself, in giving us a truer understanding of fluvial landforms, but is particularly valuable in helping to solve the problems that rivers pose for people. As such it forms the basis of *applied fluvial geomorphology*. Where a dam is to be built across a river valley, as part of a hydro-electric or irrigation scheme, it is essential to know precisely how much sediment the river is transporting, so that the life of the artificial lake can be calculated. Where a river is liable to cause dangerous flooding, and is thus a hazard to nearby settlements, it is necessary to understand the benefits of channelisation. This involves the artificial straightening of the river channel, and stabilisation of the river banks, and can help to reduce the problem by speeding up the escape of the floodwater. Such knowledge cannot come from the stage approach to fluvial geomorphology, but rests on an understanding of discharge variations in rivers, the nature and amount of the sediment load, and the forms of river channels and the changes they undergo.

RIVER ENERGY AND FLOW

A river's ability to perform geomorphological

work, in particular the eroding of its channel and the transporting of its sediment load, is determined by the amount of energy it possesses. The water in a river has *potential energy*, which is derived from the fact that the water is temporarily situated above its natural rest level, the lake or sea into which the river will eventually flow. Potential energy is increased according to both the amount of water present (volume), and the head of the water (the vertical distance above sea-level). *Kinetic energy*, or the energy of movement, is that generated by the flow of the river, which is actually using up the supply of potential energy. In simple terms, the amount of kinetic energy is determined by the volume of the flowing water and its mean velocity, or in other words its discharge (p. 26). Thus, an increase in volume and/or velocity leads to an increase in river energy. However, the relationship is not a simple one, in the sense that a doubling of velocity is likely to result in a four times increase in energy. This is the reason why large rivers or rivers in flood are, in terms of their geomorphological activity, very much more powerful than small streams.

A river's energy is used up as heat friction. This is generated either within the body of the river, where friction develops between adjacent threads of water flowing at different speeds, notably in turbulent flow, or at the boundary between the moving water and the channel sides and floor (the *wetted perimeter*). The latter losses of energy are especially important in rough channels, which (a) contain rocky projections and large boulders, (b) have numerous bushes growing along the channel banks and weeds on the channel floor, and (c) display irregular bed forms, such as sand ripples, resulting from the temporary deposition of sediment. The role of channel roughness, in resisting water flow, and thus reducing river velocity, is expressed quantitatively by the Manning flow equation:

$$V = 1.49 \frac{(R^{\frac{2}{3}} S^{\frac{1}{2}})}{n}$$

This states that velocity (V) is a function of channel slope (S), hydraulic radius (R) – which is the ratio between the cross-sectional area of the river and the wetted perimeter – and a 'coefficient of roughness' (n), often referred to as the Manning 'n'. Thus, an increase in either slope or hydraulic radius will cause an increase in river velocity; an increase in roughness will reduce velocity.

Rivers display considerable variations in energy, both from place to place (spatial) and from time to time (temporal). For example, there is normally a tendency for kinetic energy to increase in a downstream direction, in line with the increase in discharge resulting from the entry of numerous tributary streams into the main river. *Discharge* (Q) is defined as the volume of water passing a particular point of river in a unit of time, usually expressed as m^3/s^{-1}, or cumecs. It is calculated by the formula:

$$Q = AV$$

where A is the cross-sectional area of the river in m^2, and V is the mean velocity in m/s^{-1}. It was once widely believed that, as a result of decreasing slope from source to mouth, river velocity is reduced in a downstream direction. Thus, contrasts were drawn between the rapid currents observable in mountain torrents, and the apparently sluggish flow of large rivers as they approach the sea. However, measurement of *mean* velocity, as opposed to the most rapid single thread of flow, has revealed an increase downstream. This phenomenon arises both from the increase in channel depth and width, which normally leads to an increase of R in the Manning equation, and from the relatively smaller effect, in a larger channel, of a particular channel roughness value (n).

EROSION, TRANSPORT AND DEPOSITION BY RIVERS

River erosion

The most common type of river erosion involves mechanical *abrasion*, or *corrasion*, whereby coarse and angular fragments of hard rock are released, rolled and dragged along the channel floor, thus slowly wearing away exposed rock outcrops. A spectacular form of corrasion involves the development in solid rock of *pot holes*, especially in fast flowing rivers with strong eddy motions. The latter will, by localised erosion, create a shallow bowl; this may then become occupied by a large stone which is continually swirled rapidly around the bowl, deepening it into a pot hole by the process referred to as *pot-hole drilling*. The sheer hydraulic power exerted by rapid river flow may also lead to the fragmentation of bedrock in the channel, or *hydraulic erosion*, particularly where joints and bedding planes are present and have been opened up by localised corrasion or chemical attack. The latter process, *chemical erosion*, is especially operative in rocks such as limestone and chalk, which are prone to solution by acidulated water in the river.

In considering processes of river erosion, it is helpful to distinguish between erosion of bedrock, and the removal of loosely compacted sediments which have been laid down temporarily. Some rivers flow in *rock-cut channels* (Fig. 2.1), where processes such as corrasion and pot-hole drilling are dominant, but many occupy channels cut into alluvial deposits and are referred to as *alluvial channels* (Fig. 2.2). In the latter, erosion involves the washing away of incoherent sediments, comprising the channel floor and banks, by the hydraulic force of the flowing water. In the case of river banks, erosion concentrated at and below the water surface will cause undercutting and collapse of the upper face of the bank, particularly if this has been weakened by wetting during a previous high flow. Bank erosion also performs the important function of entraining within the river material which has been released by weathering of the valley slopes and transported down to the river by rainwash and mass movements.

River erosion is commonly seen to have three

Figure 2.1 *The rock-cut channel of the Galana River, in Tsavo East National Park, eastern Kenya. Note the effects of intense pot-holing, in hard gneiss, on the far bank of the channel*

Figure 2.2 *The alluvial channel of the Lymington River, at Brockenhurst, Hampshire. The channel is wide and shallow, and shows clear evidence of bank erosion of sand-gravel deposits*

main components: vertical downcutting, lateral erosion and headward erosion.

1 ***Vertical downcutting*** is characteristic of fast flowing rivers which transport a large bed load comprising coarse, hard particles. These are used to abrade and pot hole the channel floor, which is thus lowered relatively rapidly. Under certain conditions, where recession of slopes above the channel is restricted by the presence of hard rock which resists weathering, or by a dry climate, vertical downcutting will lead to the formation of deep narrow gorges. In the Swiss Alps slit-like gorges, such as that of the Aar at Meiringen and the Gorges du Trient at Martigny, were formed by sub-glacial rivers during the Quaternary glaciations (Fig. 2.3). Under great thicknesses of ice, meltwater flows under great hydrostatic pressure and at exceptional velocities, sometimes in excess of 10 m/s^{-1}. In these circumstances, the process of *cavitation* may occur. This involves the formation and collapse of bubbles within the water, causing shock waves against the channel walls. In glacial streams with a large sediment load, a sand blasting effect has been observed, leading to the formation of polished and striated surfaces as well as spectacular pot holes.

2 ***Lateral erosion*** occurs where a river swings to one side, thus causing bank erosion. Also, where the channel impinges on the base of the valley-side slope, erosion of the solid rock may be caused, giving rise to *meander cliffs*. However, it must be emphasised that, as a general rule, valley widening is due more to weathering and slope transport than to lateral undercutting by the river. It is widely believed that lateral erosion is most active either where the river is transporting a large sediment load, or when short-lived floods occur under desert conditions.

3 ***Headward erosion*** is active either at the head of the river, or at points where the river long-profile is locally steep. For example, rivers in limestone terrains may emerge from underground as springs, which are eating back into the hill slope and extending the valley head-

Figure 2.3 *The narrow, steep sided gorge of the River Aar, at Innitkirchen, Switzerland. The gorge was cut by subglacial meltwaters, flowing at very high velocities, during the Pleistocene ice age. Insufficient time has elapsed for the gorge walls to experience significant slope retreat and development*

wards; an associated process may be the collapse of the roofs of subterranean passages. On steepened valley sections, the rapidly flowing water causes accelerated erosion, with the result that the steepened section migrates upstream. In its most spectacular form, headward erosion is associated with waterfalls, particularly where these are formed by a hard cap rock overlying weaker strata. Erosion is concentrated in the plunge pool at the base of the fall, and may involve cavitation (p. 28); this leads to undermining of the fall and periodic collapse of the hard rock. A good example of headward recession of a waterfall is provided by the Victoria Falls, on the Zambezi River between Zambia and Zimbabwe (Fig. 2.4). Up to 100 m in height, and 1.7 km across, the falls occupy one side of a narrow chasm eroded from a major joint in the Karoo Basalt. A narrow exit from this chasm leads into a series of gorges, forming a very striking zig-zag pattern. This is developed where the Zambezi has eroded headwards for several kilometres, taking advantage of intersecting joint lines. Each limb of the zig-zag represents a former position of the falls; and, at the western end of the present falls, erosion has just begun to work back along the next exposed joint, so that in due course the existing falls will be abandoned.

River transport

This is the downstream movement of sediment either along the channel bed (*bed load* or *traction load*) by the processes of dragging, rolling and saltation (jumping) of particles, or within the body of flowing water (*suspended load*). Additionally, in some situations, particularly those involving catchments underlain by limestone, humid climates that favour chemical weathering, or hydrological regimes in which base flow is important, rivers transport large quantities of dissolved sediments (*solute load*). Measurements taken in rivers in the USA have shown that the proportion of solute load to

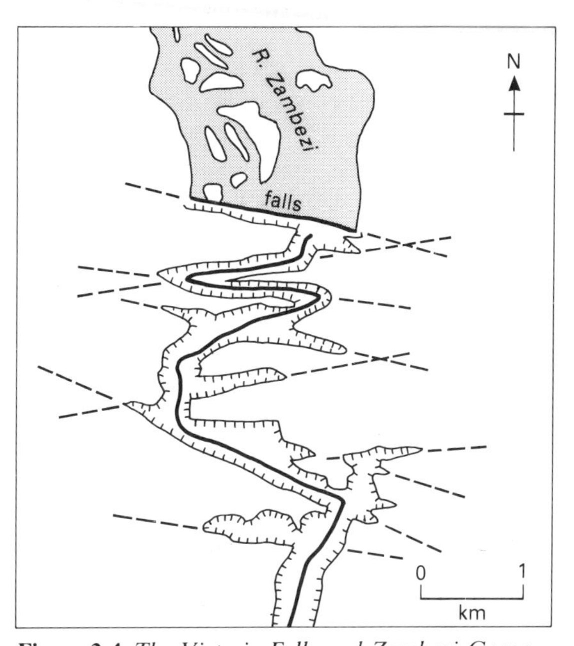

Figure 2.4 *The Victoria Falls and Zambezi Gorge*

suspended load increases from west to east, as the climate becomes gradually wetter.

To understand the way in which a river entrains sediment, consideration must be given to what happens to a particle at rest within the channel. As the water flows over the particle, it is subjected to *drag*, a force affecting the upstream face and top of the particle. If the drag is sufficiently powerful, the inertia of the particle will be overcome, and it will begin to roll or slide. The drag needed to initiate movement is known as the *critical tractive force* or, since the force is a function of stream velocity, as the *erosion velocity*. Another factor is the size of the particle; as this increases, so the erosion velocity must also be increased if movement is to occur. *Competent velocity* is the lowest velocity of flow at which particles of a particular size, resting loosely on the channel floor, are set in motion. It follows from this that, as river velocity increases, both the *total load* and the *size* of the particles being moved will, providing sediment is readily available, increase. Moreover, whilst the coarser fragments (boulders and gravel) will, except under extreme conditions of flow, constitute the bed load, many smaller particles (sand and silt) which at low velocities are subjected to traction will begin to saltate or even become temporarily part of the suspended load, along with fine clay particles. Conversely, as river velocity declines, for example, during the later stages of a flood, first the coarser and then the finer sediment will be deposited, as the competent velocity will no longer be attained. This explains the very important role of floods in erosion, transport and deposition by rivers.

However, there are complications in the process of sediment transport, as revealed by the so called Hjulstrom Curve (Fig. 2.5). Two characteristics have been determined by experiment: first, for particles of greater than 0.5 mm diameter, competent velocity increases, as expected, with grain size; secondly, for particles of less than 0.5 mm diameter, competent velocity increases with decreasing grain size. In simple terms, this means that sand particles can be picked up at relatively low velocities, whereas gravel and also fine silt and clay particles are more difficult to entrain. However, once the fine particles are picked up, they can be transported relatively easily as suspended load because of their low *fall velocity* (their rate of settling out in flowing water). All this has implications for alluvial channel form and development; thus a channel cut into sand is easily eroded further, whereas a channel in clay is more resistant.

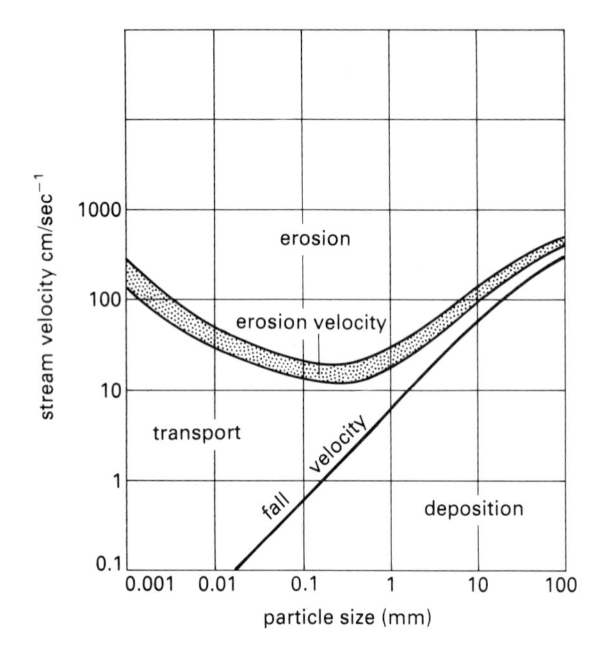

Figure 2.5 *The Hjulstrom Curve*

Other aspects of river transport are the changes in amount and nature of the load in a downstream direction. Three factors operate here: the addition of load both by river erosion in the strict sense, and the continued feeding in of weathered material from the valley sides; the selective transport of particles at different rates, since finer sediment is moved at lower velocities, over longer periods of time, whilst the coarser fragments tend to be left behind; and progressive *comminution*, whereby particles are reduced in size as they impact each other and the channel margins (this is the process of attrition).

Clearly, in detail the pattern of these down stream changes will be affected by several factors, such as the entry of tributary streams, passage of the river through areas of different rock type yielding different sizes of sediment, or the occurrence of steeper slopes providing greater inputs of weathered material. However, studies of actual sediment loads of rivers have revealed two major trends. First, the total sediment load increases downstream in most rivers, more or less in line with increases in volume and velocity. Secondly, individual sediment particles tend to become more rounded, and of finer calibre, in a downstream direction. For example, in the Mississippi the median particle diameter on the channel floor is 270 mm at 25 km from the source, 80 mm at 120 km from the source, and 0.16 mm at 5600 km from the source.

River deposition

Deposition of sediment takes place when the river becomes incompetent, either because there is a sudden input which in effect overloads the river, or where there is a loss of energy. The latter may occur where the river volume is reduced by percolation, a common phenomenon in deserts; or where velocity is reduced, owing to a sharp change in gradient. Such deposition may, in the long run, result in the development of large scale, semi-permanent landforms. However, much deposition is confined to the actual channel, is small scale, and merely temporary.

A common feature of river channels, especially those in which the load is heterogeneous but comprises a significant proportion of gravel sized particles, is the *pool and riffle sequence*. In this, the channel bed is undulating in long-profile, with alternate bars of gravel over which the water flows rapidly with a riffled surface and deep pools through which the river flows sluggishly. Field measurements have shown that these features do not occur randomly; rather, riffles are spaced regularly, at a distance usually 5–7 times the mean width of the channel. Each individual bar appears to be in a steady state, with the arrival of gravel from upstream being matched by the departure of gravel in a downstream direction. A bar is, in effect, a localised concentration of sediment which has been deposited temporarily from the bed load. It has even been suggested that bars are akin to traffic jams on a busy road. When the number of cars on the road exceeds a critical value, as during the rush hour, they become so close to each other that speeds have to be reduced, with the result that queues of slowly moving vehicles form at certain points. Likewise in stream beds, where there are 'jams' among the numerous bed load particles in motion, riffles are created.

The deposition of sediment bars also occurs in other situations (see the discussion of braided and meandering rivers on pp. 35–38). These are formed either on the floors of very wide channels, where they are elongated in a downstream direction, or at the inner margins of channel bends, as *point bars*, which may comprise a ridge of shingle separated from the river bank by a narrow depression (Fig. 2.6).

Figure 2.6 *Point bars, River Lune, at Brookhouse near Lancaster*

Figure 2.7 *An alluvial fan in the upper Rhône valley, Switzerland (see p. 33)*

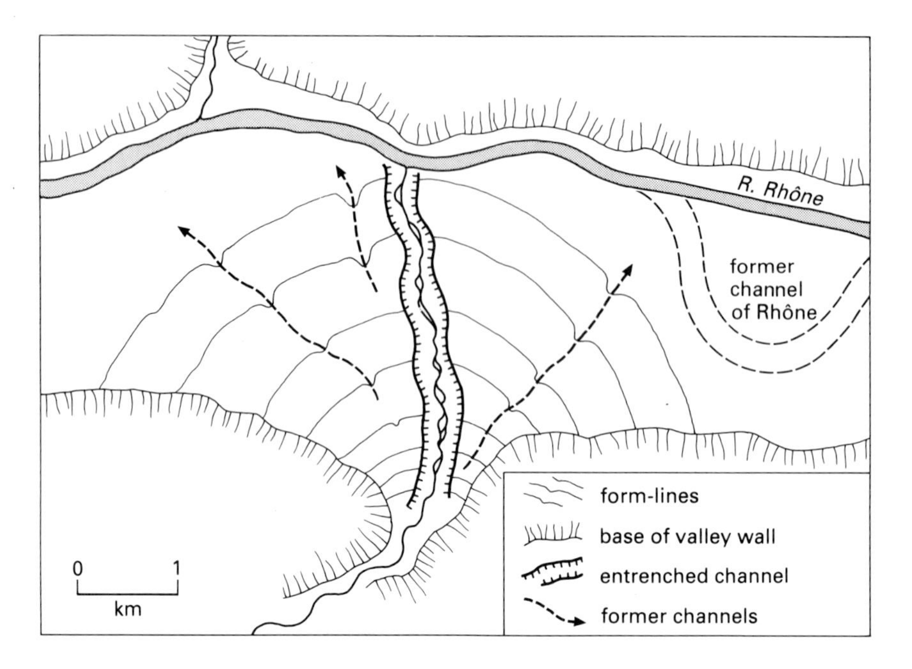

Figure 2.8 *The meanders and flood plain of the River Cuckmere, East Sussex*

In the former instance, deposition is related both to excessive transport of bed load during periods of high discharge, and to a loss of competence during ensuing periods of low discharge; in the latter, competence is very much less on the inside of the river bend, because the thread of maximum velocity is diverted to the outside of the curve by centrifugal force.

Most permanent river deposition takes place where conditions are such that incompetence persists over a long period of time. *Alluvial fans*, for instance, are characteristic of deeply glaciated valleys, such as that of the Rhône in Switzerland. Streams draining from the mountains experience a sudden loss of velocity at the break of slope between the oversteepened valley wall and the flat valley floor (Fig. 2.7). A cone-shaped mass of coarse alluvium, with the apex at the point where the stream leaves the mountain slope, gradually accumulates. Similar deposition occurs at the base of the mountain front in arid regions (p. 133). Fans are usually occupied by braided streams which continually shift their courses; these are very inefficient (p. 38), a factor which encourages deposition of sediment load over the entire fan surface. However, older fans become entrenched by one main stream channel, suggesting that after a long period of accumulation conditions have changed to the extent that formation of the fan has now ceased.

Flood plains are the most extensive landforms resulting from river deposition (Fig. 2.8). In simple terms, they develop during periods when the river experiences overbank flow (p. 34). As the flood water, highly charged with sediment, extends over the adjacent plain, silt in suspension settles out, leading to *vertical accretion*. Sometimes deposition, especially of the coarser particles, is greatest along the margins of the river channel, giving rise to natural *levées*. However, the widespread occurrence of gravels in flood plain deposits shows that other processes are involved in their formation. In particular, their frequent occupation by meandering rivers is associated with the formation of numerous point bars; these may become stabilised by vegetation, which then helps to entrap additional sediment in times of flood. Over a long period, the migration of river meanders will lead both to the development of extensive point bar deposits, and to the continual reworking of the flood plain alluvium as a whole. The former positions

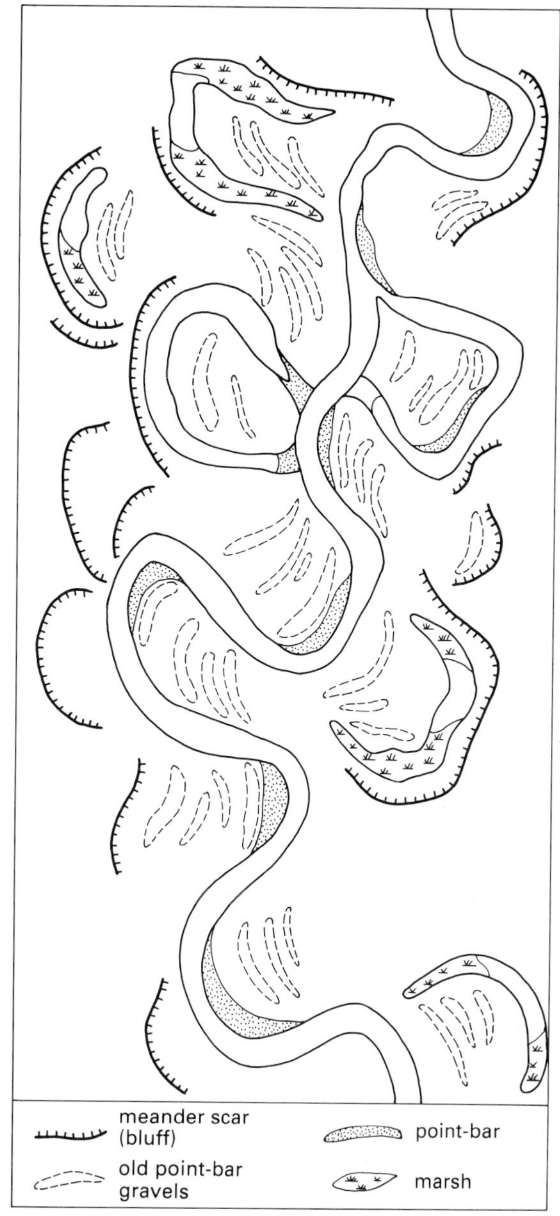

Figure 2.9 *The features of an alluvial flood plain*

of meanders are indicated by curvilinear *meander scars* marking former erosion on the outside of bends, a series of crescentic 'ridges' of gravel which mark successive point bars, and marshy depressions and *ox-bow lakes* on the sites of former river channels (Fig. 2.9).

THE FORM OF RIVER CHANNELS

The shape and dimension of channel cross-sections (Fig. 2.10)

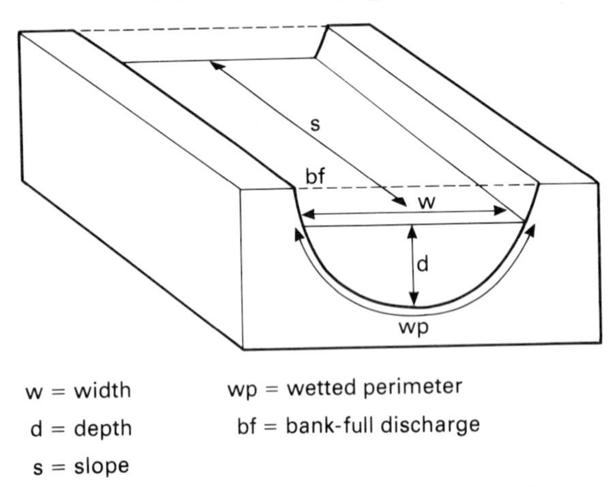

Figure 2.10 *The dimensions of a river channel*

These are influenced by a number of variables: the volume and velocity of the water flowing through the channel; the quantity and calibre of the sediment load; and the materials of which the channel floor and banks are composed. It is said that the ideal shape of a river channel is semi-circular, since this is the form giving the least wetted perimeter for a given discharge, and thus minimum losses due to friction at the channel boundary. However, where erosion of both banks is active, channels tend to be near rectangular or trapezoidal, or where one bank is eroded, as in a meander, asymmetrical (Fig. 2.11). The shape of the channel can also be expressed in terms of the *form ratio*:

$$FR = \frac{d}{w}$$

where d is channel depth, and w channel width.

There is a tendency for form ratio to decrease in a downstream direction, as width increases more rapidly than depth (p. 35).

The relationships between river discharge and its variations, both seasonal and short term (p. 14), and channel cross-section are complex. What is immediately clear, however, is that as a general rule channels must have the *capacity* to handle a wide range of discharges. It is only rarely that river flows exceed this channel capacity, resulting in *overbank flow* and the inundation of adjacent land on the flood plain. For most of the time, rivers flow at well below *bank-full stage*, at which the channel is filled from the top of one bank to the other. Measurement of the channel of the Seneca Creek, Maryland, USA showed a maximum capacity of 43 m^3/s^{-1}. Compare this with the channel capacity of the river Itchen at Eastleigh, which is only 13 m^3/s^{-1}. During the period 1931–61, the actual river discharge of the Seneca Creek exceeded channel capacity 61 times, an average of twice a year. Clearly, variation is to be expected from one river to another (the Itchen floods very rarely), but several studies have indicated a *recurrence interval* of bank-full discharge of approximately 1.5 years; in other words, floods are likely to occur twice in every three years.

The adjustment of river channels to vari-

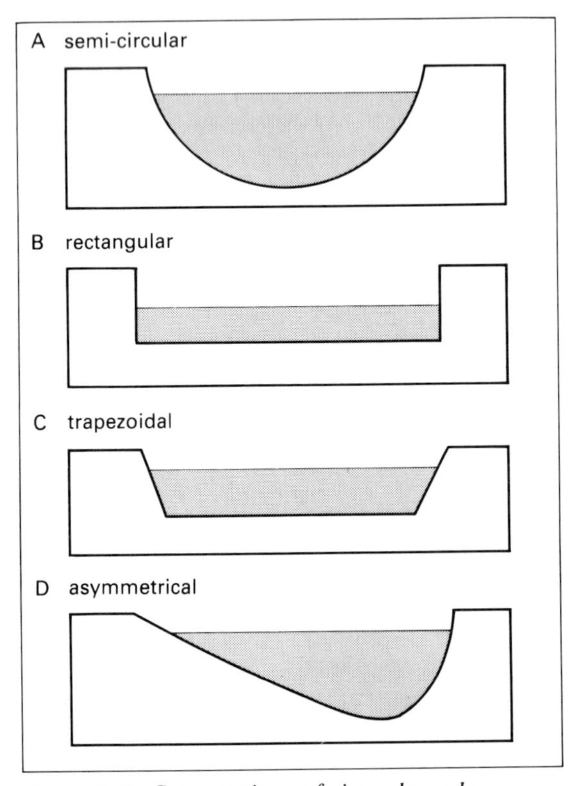

Figure 2.11 *Cross-sections of river channels*

ations in discharge can be expressed in two ways:

(i) At a particular cross-section of the channel, *at-a-station changes* occur. With each change of discharge, the channel as a morphological feature cannot, of course, undergo a perfect adjustment, since a particular rate of flow may be maintained for only an hour or two, whereas changes in the channel due to erosion and deposition are longer term processes. Rather, the channel itself must be viewed as semi-permanent, and only the length of the wetted perimeter can respond to day-to-day variations in discharge. The at-a-station changes that do take place can be expressed by three simple equations, which relate width of water surface (w), depth of water (d) and mean velocity (v) to discharge (Q):

$$w = aQ^b$$
$$d = cQ^f$$
$$v = kQ^m$$

a,b,c,f,k,m are constants, to be derived empirically for individual rivers.

Of course, factors other than total discharge (Q) also affect the shape and size of the river channel at any particular point. The type of discharge is important, as in a glacial meltwater stream with an unstable, or constantly changing, flow regime; this will cause severe bank erosion and the formation of a wide, shallow channel. Conversely, where the flow regime is more steady, river channels tend to be narrower and deeper. Bed load is also influential, in that where rivers transport considerable amounts of coarse sediment, channels are normally wide in relation to depth. Again, channel bank and bed resistance, determined mainly by the particle size of the channel constituents, exert a very strong influence on channel form. For example, a channel eroded into alluvial sediments with a high clay/silt content, which leads to increased coherence, will remain relatively deep because the banks are resistant. However, a channel cut into sand or gravel, with low coherence, will be shallow, because bank erosion and collapse occur frequently, so that width increases at the expense of depth; indeed the latter will be actually reduced by the deposition of some of the sediment derived from bank erosion.

(ii) Adjustments of channels to discharge are also expressed in terms of changes along the length of the river. These *downstream changes* can be stated by the same three equations used to describe at-a-station changes (see part(i)). Characteristic values for the exponents b,f and m in this context are 0.5, 0.4 and 0.1. The first two of these indicate that rivers become adjusted to downstream increase in discharge by an increase in width (in the order of from 10 m to 300 m) rather than an increase in depth (in the order of from 0.3 to 3 m). Changes of this magnitude can be accommodated only by a large increase downstream in the size of the river channel as a morphological feature. The value of the exponent m shows that there is a relatively modest increase in mean velocity of river flow in a downstream direction.

Channel plan forms

River channels display great variability in plan: a few are nearly straight in some reaches, others are gently sinuous, and some are fully meandering. The tendency of rivers to deviate from a straight course is expressed by the *sinuosity ratio*, which is the ratio between distance along the centre line of the *valley*, and the distance along the channel. A 1:1 ratio indicates a straight course; a 1:4 ratio denotes a well developed meandering course. Many channels are also characterised by sub-division of the flow, to give *anastomosing* or *braided* patterns. This may comprise a series of individual channels, or *anabranches*, separated by islands, or may become apparent within a large channel only when the water level falls and sediment bars are exposed.

River meanders characteristically display the features shown in Fig. 2.12a. The actual mechanisms by which meanders develop are understood in general terms, but in detail they pose difficult problems. The basic process is that of the erosion of the outer bank on the meander

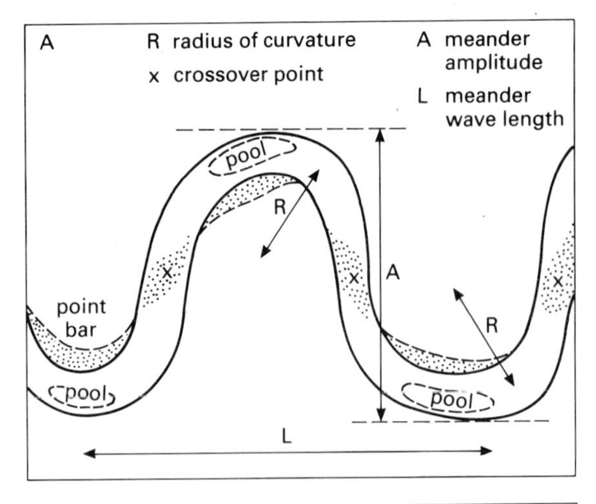

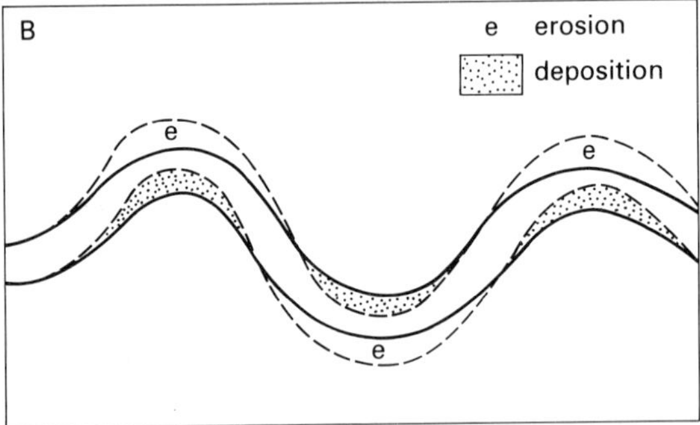

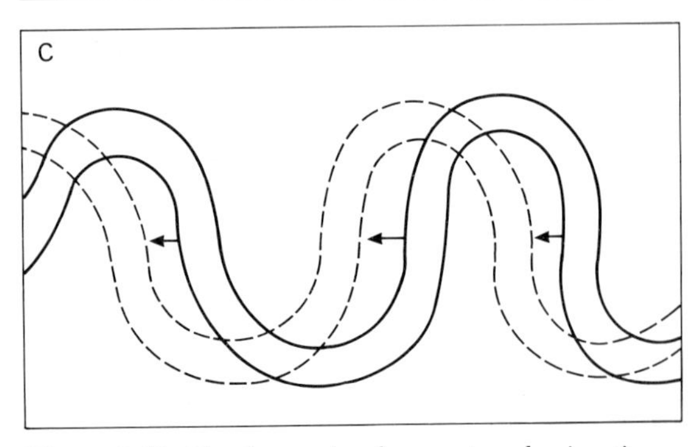

Figure 2.12 *The form, development and migration of meandering channels (see pp. 35–37)*

bend, where the thread of maximum velocity is diverted against the bank, and the transference of sediment to the inner bank, where it is deposited as a point bar. In this way meander amplitude, and hence sinuosity, can be greatly increased over a period of time (Fig. 2.12b). However, it is apparent that this pattern of erosion and deposition is modified at times, because meanders also appear to migrate downvalley, as a result of erosion and deposition between the meander bends (Fig. 2.12c).

It was once thought that the initial sinuosity of the channel, from which meanders are developed, was due to chance irregularities which deflected the stream from one side of the channel to the other. Alternate deflections would initiate, by way of bank erosion, a slightly winding channel which would then develop into a meandering channel by the processes described above. However, study of the *geometry* of meanders, as expressed by dimensions such as meander wave length (L), meander amplitude (A) and radius of curvature (R) (Fig. 2.12a), has revealed two things: first, that on a particular river meanders are very *regular* forms, and as such are not likely to be the outcome of random causes; and secondly, that these dimensions show a clear relationship to river discharge (Q). For example, meander wave length (L) has been found to be normally 6–11 times mean channel width (w), which is at least partly a function of discharge. Clearly, the size of meanders is directly related to the size of the river on which they are developed.

Another interesting point is that meandering rivers appear to contain the equivalent of pool and riffle sequences (p. 31), with the pools occurring where erosion is concentrated at the bends, and the riffles located at crossover points. The latter tend to occur at intervals of 5.5–8 times channel width, which is remarkably similar to the 5–7 times channel width spacing of riffles in straight channels. This observation had led to an interesting if rather complex explanation of meander formation. It has been argued that rivers develop in such a way that their energy is expended at a uniform rate along the channel, known as the *uniform energy grade line*. In a meandering river, there is a high expenditure of energy at crossover points, where the water is shallow and more heat friction is generated, and relatively little loss at the bends, where deep pools occur. However, when channel *curvature* is considered, the position is reversed. There is minimum energy loss at crossover points, where the river

Figure 2.13 *The braided channel of the East Fork River, McKinley National Park, Alaska*

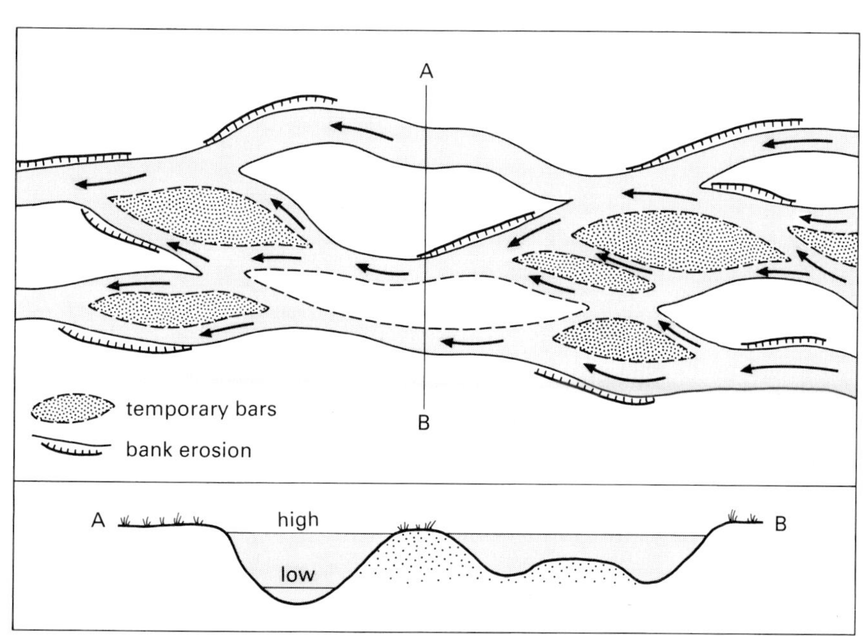

Figure 2.14 *The features of a braided river*

flow is straight ahead, and maximum expenditure at bends, where the river flow undergoes its greatest deflection. Because the effects of channel *profile* and *plan* effectively cancel each other out, meanders provide an ideal form for the development of a uniform energy grade line.

Braided rivers are usually associated with three conditions: unstable flow regimes, as in glacial meltwater streams, or in climates where flow is markedly seasonal; the transport of large bed loads, as in periglacial regions where large amounts of coarse debris are produced by active freeze-thaw weathering on slopes; and channels with banks composed of incoherent sands and gravels, which are easily eroded during periods of high discharge, thus adding further to the sediment load (Fig. 2.13). The three main features of a braided channel (Fig. 2.14) are: strong but localised bank erosion, which tends to widen the channel as a whole;

low elongated unvegetated bars of sand and gravel; and vegetated islands which normally stand above water level.

The development of a braided channel seems to proceed as follows. During periods when discharge is high, large amounts of sediment are entrained as bed load. This will accumulate at certain points within the channel, particularly when the discharge begins to recede again, to give sand and gravel banks. Some of these accumulations will be washed away during subsequent floods, but others will grow and become colonised by vegetation. They will then become more stable, the plants will assist the trapping of more sediment, and the bars will eventually become islands that are rarely inundated. However, the islands can rarely survive for long, since they are themselves composed of loose sediments and can suffer bank erosion by flowing water in the anabranches on either side.

An inevitable result of the formation of a braided channel is that, as depth decreases, width increases. This means that the wetted perimeter must increase, for a given discharge, the frictional losses become greater, and the velocity of flow is reduced. However, since high velocities are needed to transport the bed loads of braided rivers, some of the sediment load must be deposited. In the process, the channel *slope* becomes steepened, this causing an acceleration of flow! This is an interesting example of how a river achieves self regulation (see below), and in doing so eventually becomes efficient in transporting its sediment load, however large that may be.

THE FORM OF RIVER VALLEYS

Valley long-profiles

Although some individual valleys are characterised by irregularities, such as channel steepenings, rapids or even waterfalls, it has been widely observed that many develop a smooth concave-up profile. Some authorities have attempted to show that these long-profiles approximate to mathematical curves in which the decrease of gradient down valley is even and progressive. W M Davis proposed that in the early stages of development (p. 25) valley profiles are irregular, reflecting the influence of factors such as variations in the initial slope over which the river begins to flow, differences in rock type, and the occurrence of structural features such as faults. However, such irregularities are smoothed away by river erosion, to give a smooth *graded profile* over a long period of time; this is also referred to as the *profile of equilibrium*. An associated concept is that of the *graded river*; this has been defined in different ways, but one view is that the condition of grade is attained when the energy of the river is used up in the movement of the water and sediment load, so that none is available for erosion. Thus, the graded profile represents a *slope of transportation*. It is clear that such a balance between energy and work cannot exist at an instant of time, but is an average condition, existing over a period of time. For example, a river channel may be scoured during a brief flood; but following the flood the scoured areas may again be infilled by channel deposits. In order to demonstrate the reality of grade, it is therefore necessary to find channels which, over a period of perhaps several decades, have experienced only temporary and minor changes.

In modern terminology, rivers are regarded as *open systems* (Fig. 2.15). They are sustained by inputs of water, from precipitation, slope run-off and springs, and inputs of sediment, from slope weathering and channel erosion, but also experience outputs of water, where the river flows into a lake or the sea, and outputs of sediments, by channel deposition and the formation of deltas. Such systems have the capability to achieve a steady state when the inputs and outputs are balanced. If one variable changes, as when the sediment input into the river increases, or the discharge is decreased as a result of climatic change, the river will adjust its form in order to restore and maintain the steady state; in other words it will undergo *self regulation*. It has been widely assumed that the adjustment of river form most commonly

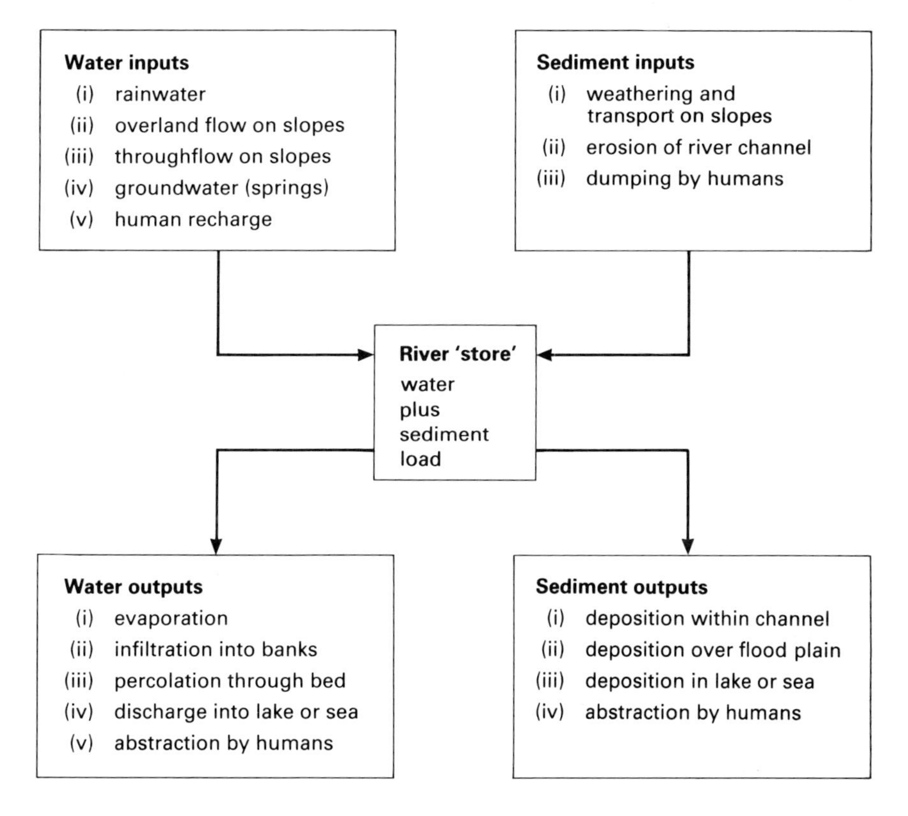

Figure 2.15 *The river as a geomorphological system*

involves a change in the channel slope. For example, with an increased sediment input, the river will need to flow at a greater mean velocity in order to transport the increased load. It can do so most readily by initially depositing part of the load; this will lead to an increase of slope downstream from the site of the deposition, and thus the required increase in velocity will occur. One piece of evidence supporting the channel slope adjustment hypothesis is that former valley profiles, as indicated by the longitudinal gradients of river terraces, have virtually the same angle as the present channel. This cannot be coincidence. After the uplift which led to the incision of the channel and the abandonment of the terrace, the river was able to restore its former gradient, which is that required to handle the discharge and sediment load of the river. However, it is now recognised that adjustments can occur in other ways, notably by changes in the width and depth of the river channel. Thus, an increase in stream energy can be offset by bank erosion, and the development of a wide, shallow channel of low efficiency.

Modern research has also shown that even irregular long-profiles may be graded. They comprise individual reaches, in each of which the steady state exists; but, overall, there is not a progressive reduction in gradient downvalley. Even so, the concave-up form is very common; and its formation can be explained as a response to the following controlling factors:
(i) the normal increase in mean velocity downstream enables the sediment load to be carried over a progressively gentler slope;
(ii) the reduced median grain size of the sediment load in a downstream direction has a similar effect;
(iii) the increased efficiency of the river channel (larger hydraulic radius, and reduced influence of roughness) also enables the river to transport sediment more easily in a downstream direction. Nevertheless, there are exceptions as in desert rivers where discharge is decreased downstream by percolation and

evaporation, thus requiring an increase in channel gradient; hence, a convex long-profile will be formed.

Geological structure also influences valley long-profiles. For example, faulting at the margins of a rift valley can result in spectacular waterfalls, as at the Kabalega Falls, Uganda, where the River Nile enters the East African rift valley (Fig. 2.16). Alternatively, falls commonly develop at ancient fault lines where weak rock downstream has been brought against hard rock upstream. Such falls are the product either of differential downcutting, or mark the point where a knickpoint (see below), receding upvalley, has been held up at the fault line. Waterfalls and rapids also form at the outcrops of layers of hard rock, as in upper Teesdale, northern England, where the quartz-dolerite of the Whin Sill gives rise to High Force and Cauldron Snout. However, the influence of geological factors on valley long-profiles may be more subtle. A particular rock type will tend to release sediment of a certain calibre, depending on its mineral composition and the spacing of joints and bedding planes. Other things being equal, where the sediment is coarse, the channel gradient will need to be steep for transport to occur; but where the sediment is finer the long-profile can be more gentle. This is one reason why graded profiles, developed across a series of different rock types, do not necessarily show a progressive decrease in slope downvalley.

Figure 2.16 *The Kabalega Falls (formerly Murchison Falls), Uganda. The falls are developed where the River Nile crosses the eastern faulted margin of the East African rift valley. At one point the flow of the river is confined to a narrow cleft only 6 m across*

Changes of sea-level exert a profound effect on the form and evolution of valley long-profiles. A rise in sea-level, such as that which occurred between 10 000 and 6000 years ago following the last Quaternary glaciation, when large quantities of meltwater were returned to the oceans, effectively reduces the gradient of the lower reaches of a river. The resulting decrease in velocity will lead to extensive alluviation of lower valley courses. A fall in sea-level, by contrast, increases gradient and velocity, and thus causes erosion. Oversteepened reaches, known as *knickpoints*, experience headward erosion, and ultimately migrate to the head of the valley. A succession of sea-level falls will produce a series of knickpoints, separated by gentler graded reaches related to former high sea-levels. In practice, it is difficult to differentiate true knickpoints from structurally determined breaks of river gradient, simply because the former, as they experience headward erosion, often encounter hard rock barriers or fault lines.

Valley cross-profiles

River valleys are said to be characteristically V-shaped in cross-section, by contrast with the U-shaped profiles produced by valley glaciers in upland regions (p. 93). However, this is a somewhat crude generalisation, for many river valleys are trench like, with steep sides and a flat floor, or are markedly asymmetrical, with one slope much steeper than that opposite it. Where there is a nice balance between the rates of river downcutting and slope recession, V-profiles do tend to be formed, though even in these the valley side slopes are usually convex in their upper parts. In humid climates where mass wasting is active, valley slopes are often convexo-concave, or convexo-rectilinear-concave, in profile (pp. 72–73).

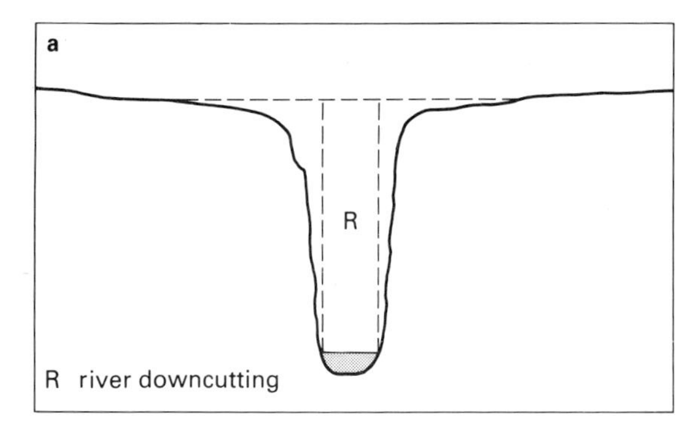

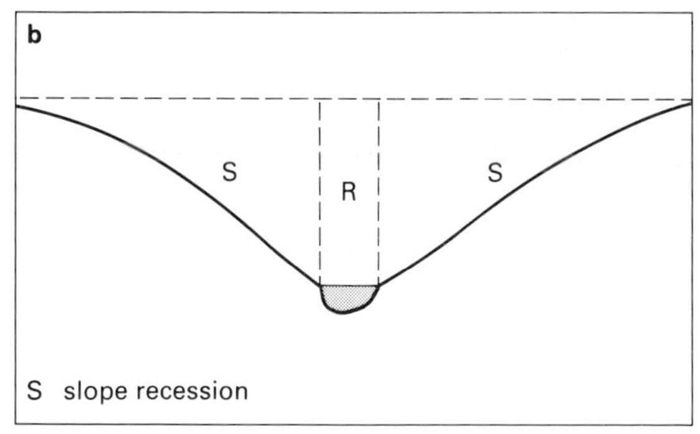

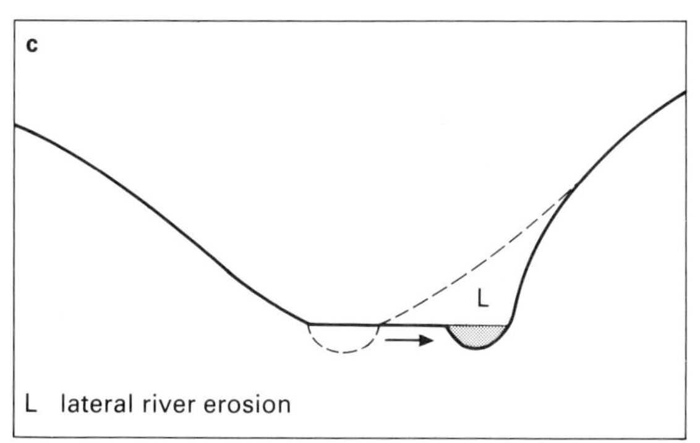

Figure 2.17 *The cross-profile of a river valley in relation to river erosion and slope retreat*

Another widely held belief is that, over time, valley side slopes decline in steepness, so that the narrow V of the early stages of development later gives way to a much more open V. Such a change is likely to occur where the river cannot cut downwards, owing to proximity to the *base-level of erosion*, the sea or lake-level into which the river is flowing and below which it cannot erode. However, a more realistic approach is to relate valley cross-profiles to the relative rates of river downcutting and slope retreat (Fig. 2.17). Thus, where a river occupies a deep and narrow V-shaped valley, this means that conditions have favoured downcutting, but worked against slope recession – which has therefore lagged behind. Conversely, a broad and open V-shaped valley occurs where valley widening processes such as weathering, slope transport and even lateral erosion by the river, have been more effective than vertical incision.

Five main factors influence the balance between river downcutting and slope retreat.

1 ***Vertical uplift of the land*** causes active river incision, as long-profiles are steepened, flow velocities increased, and extra energy is generated for processes such as corrasion. The resultant fluvial downcutting may also be increased by high discharges in mountain areas, and by the presence of coarse bed material fed into the rivers by steep valley slopes.

2 ***Rock type*** may modify the local development of valley cross-sections, in that hard coherent rocks are able to support steep valley sides, whereas incoherent rocks undergo collapse, thus resulting in lower slope angles. Also, mechanically strong rocks can sometimes be deeply incised by rivers, yet are able to resist slope recession successfully (Fig. 2.18).

3 ***Geological structure*** affects valley shape in

Figure 2.18 *The Jonte gorge, incised into Jurassic limestones, near Millau, southern France*

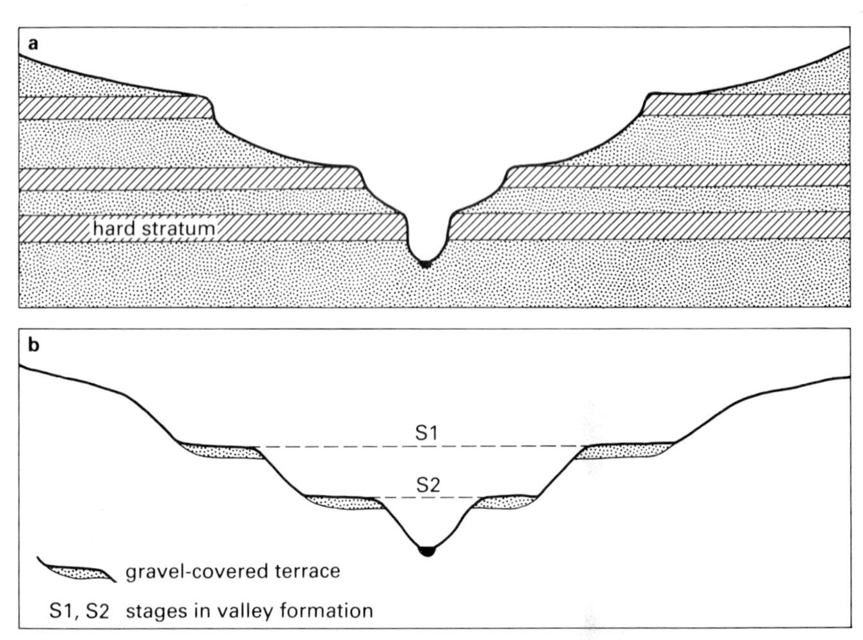

Figure 2.19 *Structural benches (**a**) and river terraces (**b**)*

several ways. Lines of geological weakness, such as joints or shatter-belts allied to powerful faults, assist river downcutting and the formation of gorge-like valleys. Where the river has taken advantage of a weak stratum, like a layer of clay or sand, in a sequence of sedimentary rocks dipping gently in one direction (a *uniclinal* structure), it will migrate laterally, undercutting one valley side to produce an *asymmetrical valley* by the process of *uniclinal shifting*. Where the river has cut down into a *horizontal* structure, comprising hard and soft layers, selective weathering and transport on the valley sides will produce a stepped profile, with *structural benches* or *terraces* associated with each hard stratum (Fig. 2.19a).

4 Climate is believed to exert a major influence on the form and development of valley cross-sections. For instance, where conditions are favourable to weathering and mass transport, as in periglacial environments, where freeze-thaw weathering is dominant and large amounts of debris are moved by solifluction, not only will the valleys tend to be widened but incision by the river will be hampered as a result of being overloaded with sediment. Indeed, the valleys may become partially infilled to give a characteristic flat-floored profile. Climate also operates on a more local scale, by way of aspect. Thus, one valley side may decline more rapidly in angle than that opposite it, resulting again in the formation of an asymmetrical valley. This may be due to more active freezing and thawing of the ground on the slope facing south or south-west (p. 109). Other possible mechanisms are differences in vegetation cover, which in general exerts a stabilising influence on slopes, reducing the effect of transport processes such as creep, or the drying out of the slope facing the prevailing winds, again rendering slope transport less effective.

5 Falls of sea-level lead to *rejuvenation*, or the renewal of vertical downcutting by rivers, and the development of valley-in-valley forms. Sequences of *river terraces* result where, at each stage of stable sea-level between successive falls, the valley floor becomes flat and covered by a layer of gravel (Figs. 2.19b and 20). However, some river terraces are of *climatic* origin. Thus a valley floor is built up by rivers heavily laden with sediment, such as the outwash streams from a large glacier or ice-sheet, and then eroded when the supply of sediment is drastically reduced and the rivers possess surplus energy, as during interglacial conditions. Such terraces, related to the advance and retreat of the Quaternary glaciers, have been widely identified in Alpine valleys; indeed, these terrace gravels were interpreted, early in this century, as the product of four distinct glacial periods, termed the Gunz, Mindel, Riss and Würm.

Figure 2.20 *River terraces on the Snake River, Wyoming*

THE FORM AND DEVELOPMENT OF DRAINAGE PATTERNS

The term *drainage pattern* refers to the actual arrangement, in plan form, of the main rivers and their tributaries draining a land area. Drainage patterns reflect a wide range of influences, including morphology, geological structure, climate and the history of drainage development. It is not surprising, therefore, to find great variability; many individual types of drainage pattern, such as *dendritic* (like the branches of a tree), *radial* (like the spokes of a wheel), *rectangular, trellised, centripetal* and *deranged* (characterised by a lack of organisation into a clear pattern) have been identified.

In considering the development of drainage patterns, it must be emphasised that most rivers, at the time of their initiation, are mainly influenced by the slope of the land surface. Thus, on a small scale, sub-parallel gullies form on a valley side slope, following the line of maximum gradient; whilst on a larger scale dip-slope rivers are guided by such factors as the direction of dip of sedimentary strata, the tilted surfaces of fault blocks, the slopes of large volcanoes, and the occurrence of structural depressions, as in rift valleys and synclines. Such *consequent rivers* are, from the time of their initiation, *accordant to geological structure*; they contrast with *discordant* rivers which cut right across important geological features such an anticlines and synclines.

However, with the passage of time, river systems undergo change. For instance, an initial river will gradually entrench its valley. On the slopes that are created smaller tributary streams will begin to flow; and in time even smaller streams will form on the slopes between these tributaries. In this way, a complex drainage network will come into being (Fig. 2.21). There are reasons to believe that chance is an important element in the growth of such a network. The method of generating *random walks* has been used to investigate drainage development, in the following manner. On a sheet of squared paper river sources are located at equal intervals. The flow of the rivers down

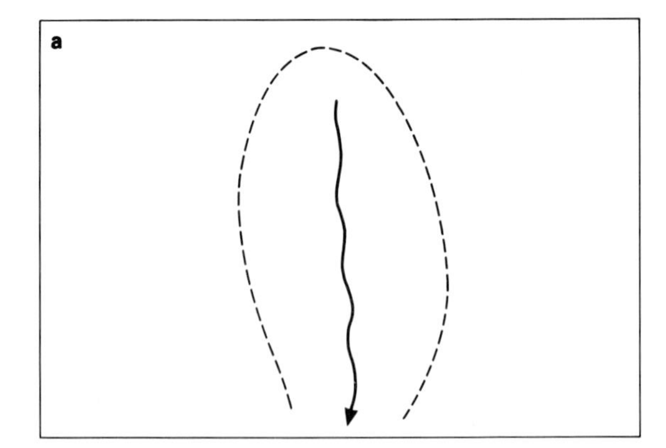

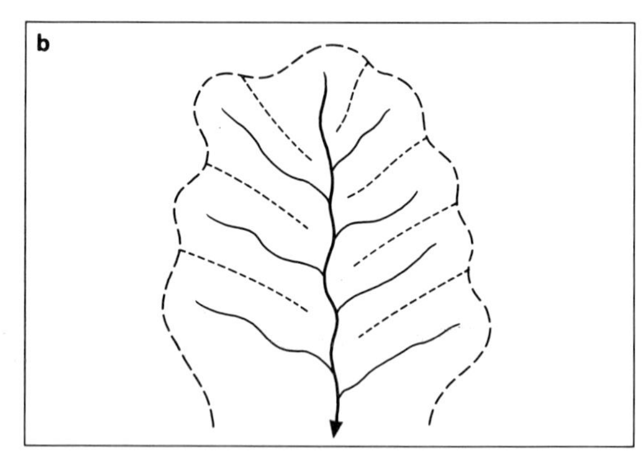

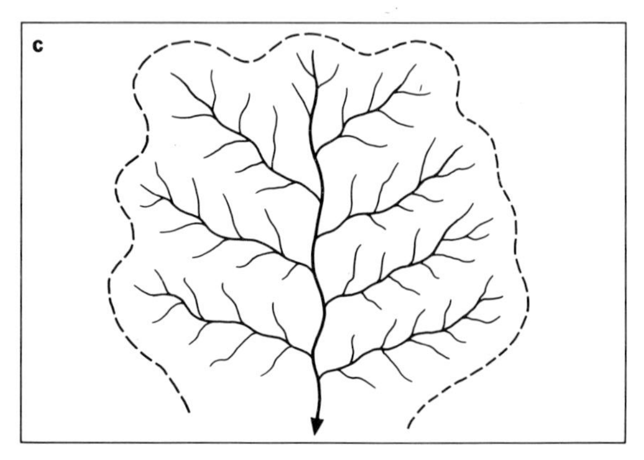

Figure 2.21 *The idealised development of a drainage network*

the paper is then simulated by throwing a die. Throws of one and four indicate flow directly down the paper for one unit square; throws of two and five a movement at 45° to the right for one unit square; and throws of three and six a movement of 45° to the left for one unit square (Fig. 2.22). Where streams diverge from each other beyond a certain distance, new stream sources must be located. Patterns generated in this way are often remarkably similar to those of actual river systems, particularly the dendritic types characteristic of areas of uniform slope and rock type.

Figure 2.22 *The generation of a stream pattern by the random walk method*

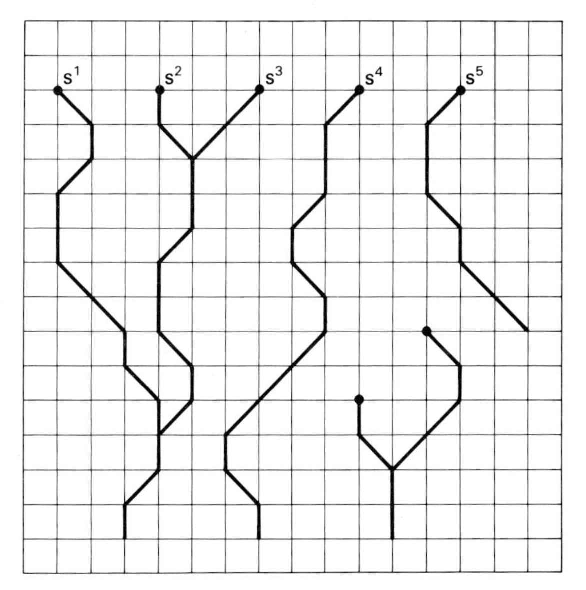

Other changes affecting drainage patterns include the addition of tributaries which pick out, usually by headward erosion, the lines of geological weakness; in the process, the river network becomes increasingly adjusted to structure. Thus, in granite terrains with well developed joints intersecting at right angles, the drainage will assume a *rectangular pattern*. Again, in areas of tilted sedimentary strata, comprising soft clay and hard sandstone, limestone or chalk, *subsequent rivers* will erode along the weak clay outcrops, forming strike vales and leaving the harder outcrops standing up as cuestas. In this way, a scarp and vale landscape, with a *trellised drainage pattern*, will come into existence (Fig. 2.23).

One process associated with the growth of subsequent streams is *river capture*. This is widely assumed to be a common phenomenon,

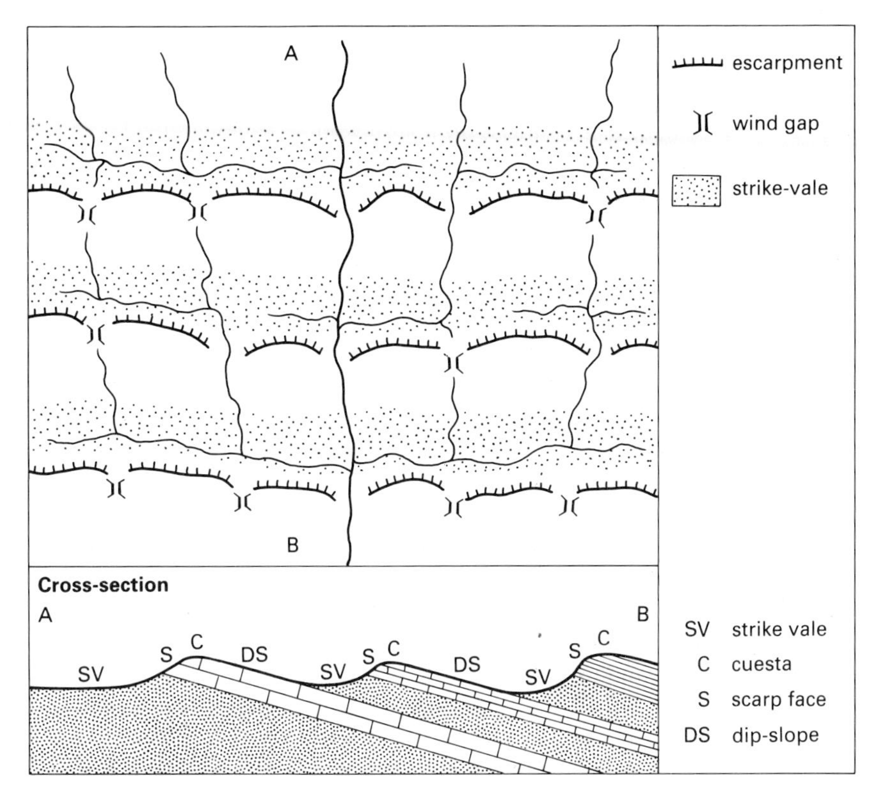

Figure 2.23 *Trellised drainage and scarp and vale scenery (see p. 164)*

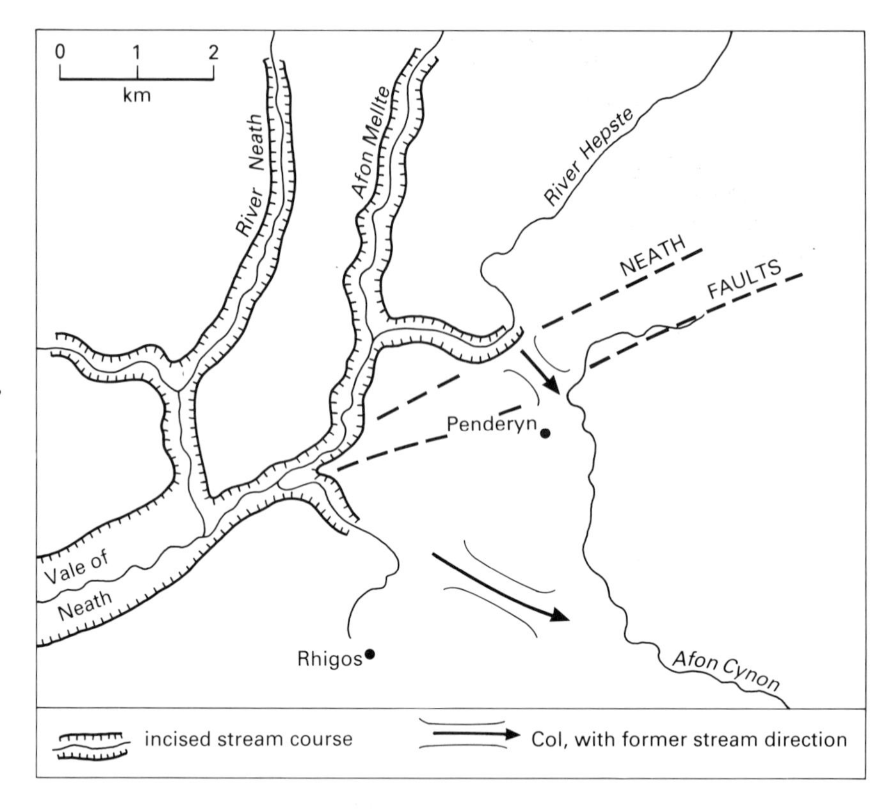

Figure 2.24 *River captures at the head of the Neath valley, south Wales. The River Hepste formerly flowed south-eastwards across the col at Penderyn into the Afon Cynon, whilst the Afon Mellte and the upper Neath flowed across the col east of Rhigos. The River Neath, working headwards along the Neath faults, has diverted the three streams to the south-west, to give the present pattern of drainage*

though it needs to be emphasised that conditions must be highly favourable to the capturing stream, if it is to incise to a sufficient depth and experience the necessary headward erosion for the captured stream to be diverted. The process is thus rather unlikely in areas of homogeneous rock, but is more likely to occur where zones of weakened rock can be selectively and rapidly eroded, as in the case of the shatter belt followed by the River Neath in south Wales (Fig. 2.24). Diagnostic features of river capture include: the sharp change of river course at the site of the diversion (*elbow of capture*); the presence of a *col* (*wind gap*) marking the course of the diverted stream prior to its capture; and the misfit character of the beheaded stream, which is now clearly too large for the valley it occupies. However, caution is needed, for all these features can be formed in other ways. A right angled bend in the river course can reflect structural influences such as joints and faults; a col can result from the retreat of a scarp face and the truncation of a dip-slope valley head, to give a *recession col*; and a misfit stream can result from climatic changes leading to reduced discharge.

Drainage basin analysis

For purposes of more detailed study, the drainage systems of a large area can be divided into their component parts. These are, both for reasons of easy definition and because they reflect the manner in which drainage is organised, usually individual *drainage basins*. Such basins are identified on a variety of scales, but always display two main characteristics: a well defined basin perimeter, known as the *watershed* or *divide*; and a network of tributaries, fed by overland flow, throughflow and seepage within the basin, which eventually join together to create one main river. The various elements of the drainage net within the basin can be measured and analysed, in the context of *drainage basin morphometry*. Not only can basin area contained within the watershed and basin relief, or the height difference between the highest and lowest points, be determined, but also the number and lengths of individual segments of the drainage network.

1 Stream order analysis is one commonly used method of quantifying the drainage net. A N Strahler has proposed a system in which the very smallest headwater tributaries are identified and designated as first order streams. Where two such streams join a second order stream is formed; and so on (Fig. 2.25a). The order of the basin itself is defined by the highest order stream contained within it, hence fourth order basin, fifth order basin, and so on. There is a systematic decrease in the numbers of streams in a given order, with increasing order number, when plotted on a graph (Fig. 2.25c).

The method used by Strahler, though still widely followed, has come in for some criticism, and other methods of designating stream order have been derived, such as that of R L Shreve (Fig. 2.25b). The advantage of the latter is that the stream order number is more likely to show a relationship with channel size and capacity; for example, in the Strahler system a fourth order stream will have a capacity far in excess of four times that of a first order stream. The disadvantage of Shreve's method is that a much larger number of stream orders will be defined, and there will be gaps in the sequence. The latter make analysis involving the plotting of, say, stream numbers against stream order more complex.

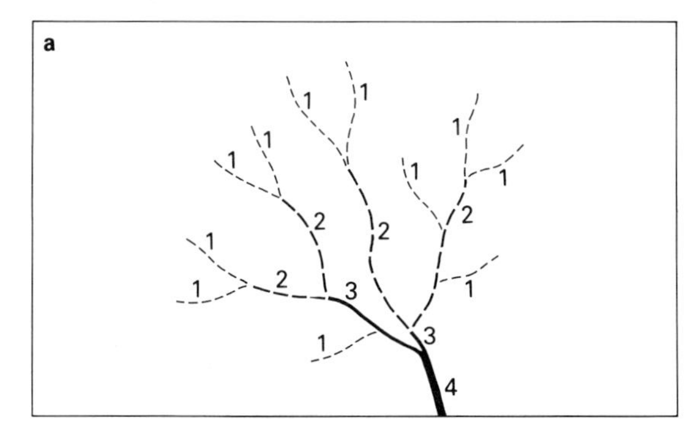

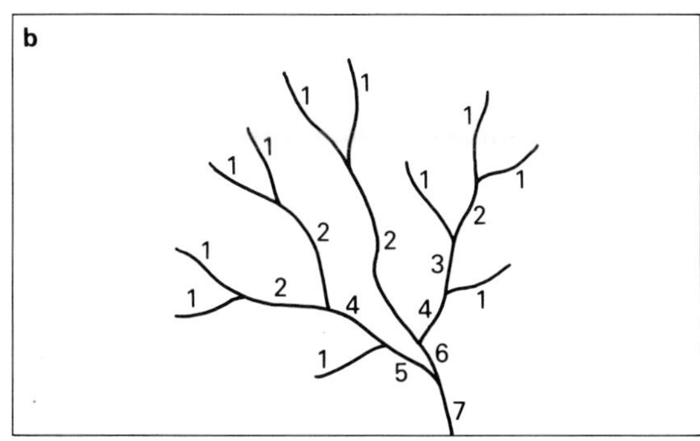

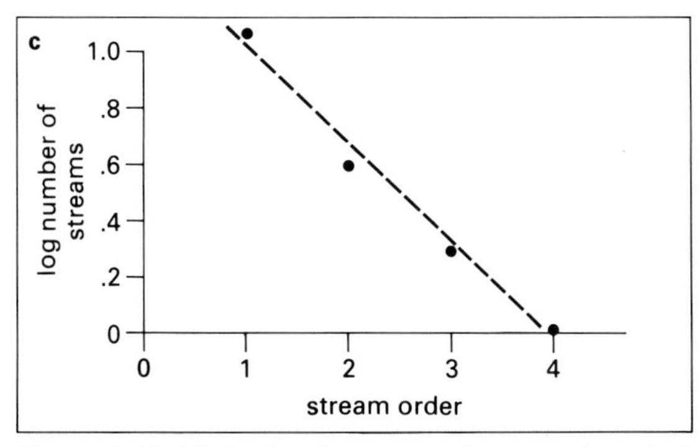

Figure 2.25 *Methods of stream ordering and analysis*

2 Drainage density is a useful measure of the frequency and spacing of streams within the drainage basin; it also helps to define the *texture of dissection*. This reflects the extent to which the landscape is cut into by valleys, and will in turn influence slope development. Drainage density, usefully abbreviated to Dd, is calculated by dividing the total stream length within a basin by the total basin area; it is then expressed in terms of km channel length per km^2 of basin area. There are, however, some practical difficulties in calculating Dd, for example in areas of seasonal rainfall where many headwater streams do not flow in the dry season; in other words, the wet season Dd will have a higher value than the dry season Dd. Since drainage density is usually measured from available topographic maps, it is important to know whether or not these show only the permanent rivers. A related problem arises in the study of Dd in limestone and chalk terrains. For example, Dd values in the English chalklands are at present very low, less than 1 km/km^2, even when the seasonal *bournes* are taken into account. However, the presence of

Figure 2.26 *Badlands at Millard Ridge, South Dakota*

numerous dry valleys, clearly occupied by streams in the recent geomorphological past, points to a former higher value for Dd. For such landscapes, it may be useful to calculate both Dd in the strict sense of the term and also the *valley density*.

Drainage density must reflect to some degree the amount of run-off that a basin generates, since the total channel capacity needs to be sufficient to cope with normal discharges, otherwise flooding will be frequent and widespread. Moreover, a high value for Dd will imply rapid and efficient run-off during rainstorms; at the exit from the basin there will be sharp peaks on the hydrograph (p. 16), and these will occur rapidly after the peak rainfall. However, it is possible that, over time, channels may enlarge and their capacity thus be increased, so that for a given amount of run-off Dd can be reduced by rationalisation of the drainage net.

Observed values for Dd range widely, from less than 2 km/km^2 in many limestone terrains, to 100–500 km/km^2 in areas of intensely dissected, unvegetated clay and shale known as *badland topography* (Fig. 2.26). It is tempting to suppose that Dd is essentially a function of *rock type* and *total annual precipitation*. Certainly rock type, and in particular its degree of permeability, can be an important factor. Clay, for instance, tends to produce rapid run-off and, as stated, can give rise to exceptional values of Dd. However, this is by no means always so; in the Weald Clay of south-east England, where rainfall amounts are moderate (750 $mm/annum^{-1}$) Dd values are less than 5. Moreover, in areas of high annual precipitation, for example, the highlands of peninsular Malaysia where precipitation exceeds 2500 $mm/annum^{-1}$, Dd values are not particularly high, except in areas where the rainforest has been cleared, leading to the generation of much greater quantities of surface run-off.

It is apparent that drainage density is determined by many factors, including: *relief*, with steep slope angles generating rapid run off and gentle slopes reduced run-off; *rainfall intensity*, which tends to be great in association with convectional rainfall and in tropical regions where absolute humidity is high; *infiltration capacity of the soil*, which reflects not only the parent rock but also climate, as in savanna regions where at the end of the dry season the soils are baked and impermeable; and the *vegetation cover*, a dense forest reducing by interception the impact of heavy rainfall, and a cover of grasses favouring high rates of infiltration. Not surprisingly, the highest values of Dd usually occur in semi-arid regions, or areas with a markedly seasonal precipitation regime, such as the savanna and Mediterranean type climates. In the humid mid-latitudes, associated with rainfall of generally low intensity, occurring throughout the year, Dd values are markedly lower than in semi-arid regions. In the humid tropics, Dd values are intermediate between temperate and semi-arid values; the heavy rainfall tends to generate run-off, but this is countered by the dense forest cover and the permeable deep regolith (p. 115).

A final factor influencing Dd may be *time*. In the early stages of development of the drainage network, the rivers may be widely spaced (low Dd), but as a result of the formation and growth of tributaries may become more dense (high Dd). Studies of glacial tills of different ages in the USA have revealed that Dd values rise from 25 km/km^2 on tills dating from 13 000 BP (Before Present) to 78–89 km/km^2 on tills dating from 40 000 BP. What is not clear is whether, when Dd reaches a certain critical value, it then remains constant, thus indicating a steady state condition; or whether, as a result of competition between tributary streams, there will be a rationalisation of the network and, therefore, a reduction in Dd.

CONCLUSION

The role of rivers in the formation and modification of landscapes, by erosion, transport and deposition of sediment, has been fully illustrated in this chapter. The commonest landform of the earth's surface, the river valley, is partly the result of a combination of vertical downcutting and lateral erosion by rivers. However, it is rare for such valleys to be created by rivers alone. Other processes, such as weathering, and slope transportation of weathering products, may be stimulated or rendered more effective by river action. But the part of these processes in shaping individual valleys, and also the landscape in its entirety, is so vital that they, and their effects, now need to be considered separately and in considerable detail in the following chapter.

ASSIGNMENTS

1 a. Make a field visit to a river in your home area. Walk along a stretch (1–2 km) of the river bank, making notes of ways in which the natural channel has been modified or affected by human activities.
   b. Suggest reasons why these modifications were made, and attempt to explain the effects they have had on river channel processes.

2 Make a field visit, with fellow members of your class, to a local river channel to which there is ready access, and which appears to be relatively unaltered by human activities.
   a. Set up a base line, comprising wooden poles inserted into the ground at intervals of 25 m. The poles should form an exactly straight line, running approximately parallel to the river channel. The base line should be at least 250 m in length.
   b. By measuring, with a tape, offsets at right angles from the base-line to the near and far banks of the channel, make an accurate map of the channel. (An appropriate scale would be between 1:100 and 1:500.)
   c. Mark on your map (i) sections of the channel bank which appear to be eroded, (ii) any accumulations of sediment within the channel, and (iii) the sites of deep pools.
   d. Attempt to explain the pattern of erosion and deposition you have observed.

3 Make a further field visit to the river channel studied in (2) above.

a. Measure five channel cross-sections, at appropriate intervals by stretching a tape measure from bank to bank. Using a graduated wooden pole, make vertical measurements at intervals along this tape down to (i) water level, and (ii) the stream bed. (Clearly this exercise can be carried out only in relatively shallow rivers, unless an inflatable boat is available.)
b. Use your data to draw, at an appropriate scale, five cross-sections of the river channel.
c. Calculate the *form ratio, cross-sectional area, wetted perimeter* and *hydraulic radius* of each of your channel sections.
d. Suggest possible reasons for the shapes of your channel sections.

4 Suggest, with full reasons, the effects that you think the following would have on the processes operating in a river channel:
a. a change in climate from humid temperate to periglacial (in which the dominant process becomes mass wasting, a combination of freeze-thaw weathering and solifluction);
b. the building of a dam which effectively cuts off sediment from upstream;
c. a change in land use within the river basin from arable farming to forestry.

5 a. Using the background information given on pp. 41–43, draw a simple systems diagram, similar to Fig. 2.15, to show the factors influencing the cross-profiles of river valleys.
b. Explain briefly how changes in each of these factors might lead to modifications of valley cross-profiles.

6 Identify from OS 1:50 000 or 1:25 000 maps available to you, *three* meandering rivers, one relatively large, one medium sized and one relatively small.
a. Trace an appropriate stretch of each river.
b. Calculate the sinuosity ratio for each river.
c. Choose one typical meander from each river, and measure its wave length (L) and amplitude (A). Comment briefly on the relative dimensions of these for each of the three rivers studied.
d. If it is possible to determine from the maps the approximate widths of the river channels, draw a simple graph showing the relationship between channel width and meander wave length.

7 a. Using graph paper and a die, 'construct' a fourth order stream pattern (Strahler definition) according to the method described on p. 44.
b. From an OS 1:50 000 or 1:25 000 map, identify and trace an *actual* fourth order stream pattern (Strahler definition).
c. Draw graphs (see Fig. 2.25c) for each pattern, showing the relationship between numbers of streams in a given order with increasing order number.
d. Comment briefly on the results of the exercise so far.
e. Re-order the stream numbers in both your river patterns according to the Shreve method, and draw additional graphs showing the relationship between numbers of streams in a given order with increasing order number.
f. Giving reasons, state which method of stream order analysis (Strahler or Shreve) you prefer.

8 Select *two* OS 1:50 000 maps, from those available to you, for different parts of the United Kingdom.
a. Choose an area on each map measuring 10 km by 10 km (the National Grid squares can be used for this purpose).
b. Trace the blue lines (rivers and streams) within each area. Artificial drainage lines, such as canals and dykes, should be ignored if possible.
c. Measure the total river length in kilometres for each area.
d. Calculate the drainage density (Dd) for each area, expressed as km channel length/km^2 basin area.
e. Suggest reasons for the degree of similarity or difference between the Dds of the two areas. (You will need to discover information about geology and climate from sources available to you.)

3

Weathering and Slope Recession

One of the most characteristic landforms in mountain areas is a steep and rugged cliff, at the base of which rock fragments have accumulated as a *scree* (*talus*) slope. In Britain such features are well displayed in Snowdonia, for example along the eastern flanks of the Llanberis Pass, and the Lake District, notably in the great screes fringing the southern margins of Wastwater. The cliffs themselves are mainly the result of *rock weathering*, by which fragments of rock become detached and fall away under the influence of gravity on to the basal scree slopes. Over a long period of time the cliff face will be worn back (this is a type of *slope retreat*), and the scree deposits will build up and eventually bury most or even all of the cliff (Fig. 3.1). Thus the initial cliff, in extreme cases vertical, but normally greater than 50–60° in angle, will be transformed into a gentler slope, at 30–40°, formed by the accumulating scree. This is a very simple model of slope development which serves as an introduction to the study of weathering and slopes and illustrates how *process* (weathering and slope retreat) exerts an important control over *form* (the shape and steepness of the slope). Of course, not all slopes evolve in this simple fashion, for the reason that weathering processes are greatly variable in their operation and effects; and the products of rock weathering do not simply fall by gravity but are transported, particularly where slopes are more gentle in angle, by a variety of processes, including running water and mass slippage of large amounts of weathered materials.

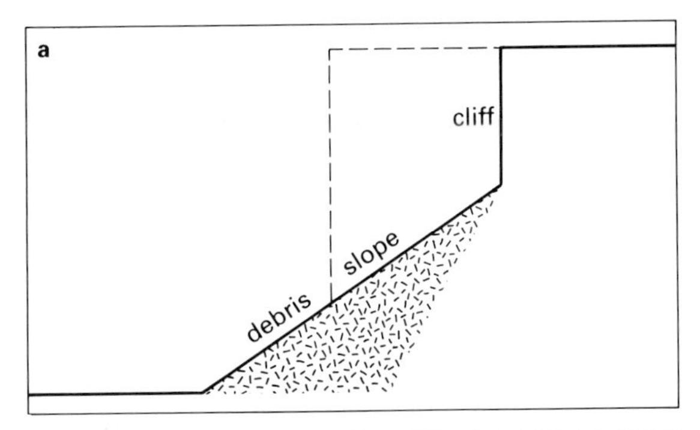

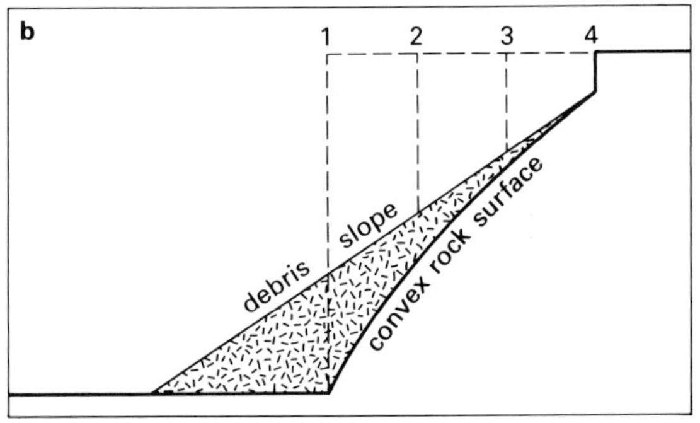

Figure 3.1 *The evolution of a free face and debris slope*

THE PROCESSES OF WEATHERING

Weathering has been defined simply as the breakdown of rock by physical and chemical processes; in the former the rock is broken down by entirely mechanical means such as expansion and contraction as the rock surface is heated and cooled, whereas in the latter the chemical composition of rock minerals is changed by agents such as water, oxygen and mild acids developing under natural conditions. Weathering is essentially a very slowly acting process, particularly in those types of rock which are classified as *resistant*, but its effects are usually evident on any exposed rock mass. Thus narrow cracks (*joints*) can be seen to have been widened out by weathering processes; and the rock surface is commonly pitted by selective weathering attack. Moreover the rock outcrop, particularly where it is near-horizontal, may be littered by fragments which have been completely detached by weathering processes. In some instances rock surfaces may become completely buried by a layer of weathered material, formed over a long period of time during which little or no transport of the material has occurred, known as *regolith*.

The products of rock weathering vary greatly, depending on the characteristics of the rock and the actual processes which are operating. At one extreme is the breakdown of the rock into large blocks (*block disintegration*); this results from the concentration of weathering along lines of weakness in the rock, such as joints and bedding planes, and leads to the detachment of large, frequently angular boulders. At the other extreme is the formation of clay, comprising very tiny particles, from the chemical breakdown of minerals such as feldspar, commonly found in igneous rocks. An intermediate form of weathering is *granular disintegration*, whereby the rock is broken down into numerous small fragments, usually a few mm in diameter. The process particularly affects crystalline rocks, which are made up of numerous small crystals of quartz, feldspar, mica and so on; if one type of mineral is weathered, the effect will be to loosen the structure of the rock as a whole, so that it will crumble into a mass of 'altered' and 'unaltered' minerals. Granular disintegration may also occur in rocks such as sandstone which comprise small fragments of quartz cemented together by substances such as iron oxide or calcium carbonate. If the cement is attacked by weathering, the sandstone will be disaggregated into loose sandy deposits.

Physical weathering processes

The physical, or *mechanical*, breakdown of rocks is mainly attributed to the effects of changes of temperature. However, it needs to be emphasised that rock disintegration may

Figure 3.2 *Sheet joints in granite, Haytor Rocks, Devon*

occur without the intervention of weather. For example, where rocks such as granite and gneiss, formed at considerable depth and under very great pressure within the earth's crust, are exposed at the earth's surface by the eroding away of overlying rocks, the process known as *pressure release*, or *dilatation*, takes place (Fig. 3.2). As the unloading occurs the formerly deep-seated rocks tend to expand upwards and outwards, resulting in tensional stresses at right angles to the surface and the formation of cracks parallel to the surface; this structure is commonly referred to as *sheet jointing*, and may be observed on many exposed granite masses, such as inselbergs (p. 121) and tors (p. 121). The sheet joints are lines of weakness that can subsequently be exploited by other weathering processes; alternatively it may be that the processes of dilatation can go much further, and by themselves lead to the break-up of the rock, giving detached surface layers (*exfoliation*) which in turn break up into numerous individual boulders (block disintegration).

1 ***Freeze-thaw weathering*** probably occurs most effectively when water penetrates joints in the rock, freezes and in the process expands by approximately 10 per cent. As a result the fis-

Figure 3.3 *Freeze-thaw weathering of schist boulders on a glacier surface in Switzerland*

sure will be widened and, in time, fragments of the rock will be prised away (Fig. 3.3). A long series of frost cycles can lead to the detachment of joint bounded blocks of rock. On very steep slopes these will fall or slide and accumulate as masses of scree at the slope foot. However, on flatter areas, the fragments will remain to give *blockfields* or *felsenmeer*. Freeze-thaw weathering can also operate on a smaller scale, when water penetrates the rock by way of its pores; on freezing, it will form ice crystals that, by expansion, are able to break the rock into flakes or granular particles. The immense potential of freeze-thaw action is shown by the fact that, theoretically, freezing water can exert a maximum pressure of over 2000 kg/cm^2 at a temperature of −22°C. However, this is rarely attained or indeed needed, since most rocks have been weakened already by processes such as pressure release or chemical action along joints, and a force of less than 100 kg/cm^2 is usually sufficient to cause disintegration.

2 Insolation weathering or thermal fracturing, is attributed to large temperature changes from day to night. For example, in hot deserts the daytime temperature of rock surfaces can be raised to 50°C or more by solar heating; during the ensuing night, the temperature may drop to 10°C or less by radiation heat loss. The resultant expansion and contraction of the rock sets up stresses which, over a long period, may weaken and disintegrate the rock. The process of thermal fracture may be particularly effective in crystalline rocks composed of dark and light coloured minerals which expand and contract at different rates.

One process that has been widely attributed to insolation weathering is exfoliation, or the detachment of layers of rock (Fig. 3.4). However, where thick sheets of rock up to 10 m in thickness are released, it is now accepted that these are primarily the product of dilatation (p. 52), and that thermal changes are of little significance. Most rocks are relatively bad conductors of heat with the result that, although the surface temperature can be raised to 50°C or more, this

Figure 3.4 *Small scale exfoliation of a granite surface in the desert of Saudi Arabia*

Figure 3.5 *Cavernous weathering of granite in the desert of Saudi Arabia*

heating penetrates only a few millimetres into the rock. The stresses set up by thermal expansion are thus confined to a very shallow layer, and can cause only small scale exfoliation and the breaking away of platy fragments. Indeed, there are doubts as to the real effectiveness of thermal fracture, even under the most favourable circumstances. Researchers have attempted to simulate such weathering in the laboratory, by heating and cooling rock samples many thousands of times, with little or no detectable break-up of the rocks. Of course, such experiments may be unnatural, in the sense that to heat and cool a rock for the equivalent of 200 years does not subject that rock to the same amount of stress as heating and cooling over an actual 200 year time period.

3 Salt weathering involves the presence of salt solutions within the rock. Where these are crystallised, the effects in terms of rock disintegration are similar to those resulting from ice crystal formation. Most commonly, salt crystals grow either just beneath the rock surface, as high temperatures cause evaporation, or in shady spots where moisture lingers as at the base of *pedestal rocks*. As a result of salt crystal formation stresses are applied, and rock fragments become detached; however, these are usually small, giving an effect of surface scaling. Where salt weathering is particularly concentrated *weathering pits* and *tafoni* (cavernous weathering) are formed (Fig. 3.5).

Chemical weathering processes

Chemical weathering includes a range of chemical reactions which alter the composition of rock minerals, the volume of the rock, and the strength and coherence of the rock. For the most part chemical processes act selectively, attacking some minerals but not others, especially in complex crystalline rocks. Chemical weathering is either concentrated at the rock surface, or along joints and bedding planes which allow the penetration of water and air (Figs. 3.6, 3.7). Both *block* and *granular disintegration*, although widely attri-

Figure 3.6 *Small scale solutional etching of Carboniferous Limestone near Tenby, Dyfed*

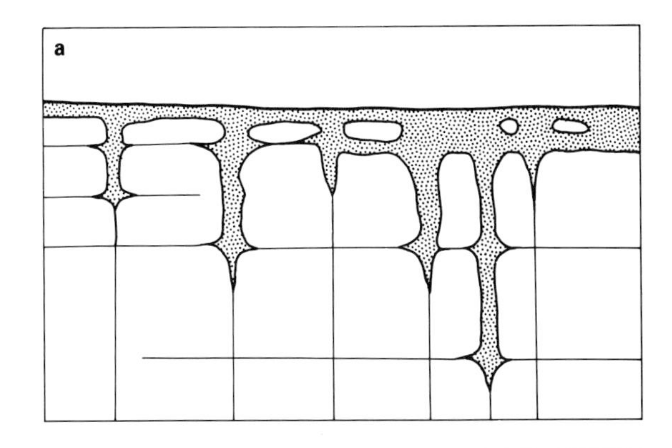

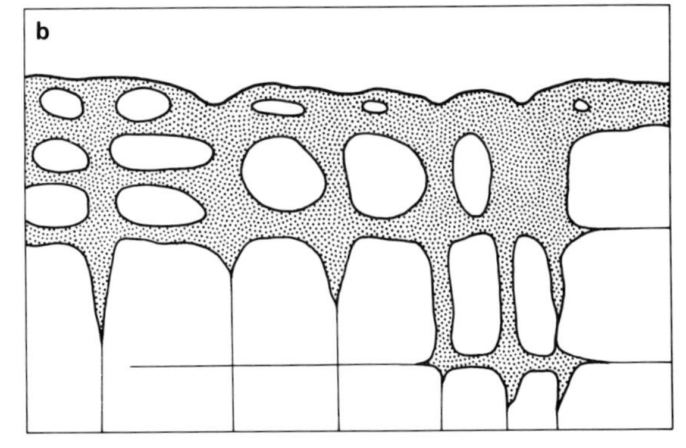

Figure 3.7 *Selective chemical weathering of a jointed rock. Note the breakdown of the rock into joint-bounded blocks, which are then further weathered into rounded corestones*

buted to physical weathering only, can result from chemical processes. Indeed it is important to realise that the distinction between physical and chemical weathering is a somewhat arbitrary one, in the sense that they frequently operate in conjunction and actually assist each other, as in the case of a joint which is initially opened up by chemical attack and then exploited by freeze-thaw weathering. Regoliths resulting mainly from chemical weathering may comprise unweathered and/or insoluble residues (*residual decomposition products*) such as quartz sand and pebbles. However, since certain chemical reactions produce mainly clay minerals, such regoliths may be predominantly fine grained, by comparison with physically weathered regoliths which are often coarser. For instance, there is an obvious contrast between the sand and clay regoliths of tropical humid regions, where chemical weathering is most active, and the spreads of broken angular rock in periglacial environments, where frost weathering is dominant.

Another distinctive feature of chemical weathering is its ability to penetrate more deeply into the rock than physical weathering, which is essentially a surface or near-surface phenomenon. However, it is essential for acidic water involved in sub-surface decomposition to be continually renewed, otherwise dissolved salts will build up to the extent that the water will be neutralised and thus inactive. Chemical weathering is particularly effective in rock which is alternately wetted and dried, as in the zone of seasonal fluctuation in the water table.

The following are common chemical reactions involved in weathering:

1 ***Solution*** by soil moisture and groundwater affects both original rock minerals such as rock salt and, more importantly, minerals which have themselves already been weathered, for example by carbonation or hydrolysis.

2 ***Carbonation*** is particularly associated with limestone, the principal constituent of which, calcium carbonate, is changed to calcium bicarbonate by rainwater containing carbon dioxide (carbonic acid). The bicarbonate is then removed in solution, though it may be re-precipitated as tufa at springs or as stalactites, stalagmites and helictites within caverns.

3 ***Hydration*** affects rock minerals which have the capacity to take up water. In the process, these undergo increases of volume which set up physical stresses within the rock, as in the conversion of iron oxides to iron hydroxides. Hydration commonly causes the surface flaking of rocks, as in salt weathering (p. 54).

4 ***Hydrolysis*** is a complex reaction affecting minerals in igneous and metamorphic rocks. For example, the process is active in the weathering of feldspar in granite. A chemical reaction between water and feldspar produces potassium hydroxide and alumino-silicic acid. The former is carbonated and removed in solution; the alumino-silicic acid breaks down into clay minerals, notably kaolinite, and silicic acid which is also removed in solution. The end product of hydrolysis is thus the formation of residual clay.

5 ***Oxidation*** involves rock minerals combining with oxygen, usually dissolved in water. Iron minerals are especially susceptible, as in the reduced form of iron FeO, which in free draining regoliths is changed to oxidised iron FeO_3. The latter is soluble only in highly acidic water and tends to accumulate in the regolith, giving it a striking reddish hue.

Biological or organic weathering

A separate category of weathering, distinct in some ways from physical and chemical weathering processes, is widely recognised by geomorphologists. One common example of what is termed biological weathering, is the penetration of rock joints by tree roots, which as they grow and thicken prise the rock apart and cause block disintegration, in a manner not unlike freeze-thaw weathering in its effects. However, of greater significance are the chemical changes, relating to such processes as animal bodily functions, and the decay of plants. Thus, on offshore islands occupied by large colonies of seabirds such as gannets and auks, chemical weathering by excreta causes some rock weathering. More importantly, the decomposition of plant materials, which is particularly active in humid tropical environments, forms *humic acids* which break down rock minerals by *chelation*. This complex process increases the solubility of iron compounds, and allows them to be leached from the regolith or absorbed by growing plants. Weathering by humic, or organic, acids is undoubtedly a factor aiding the formation of deep weathered layers in the tropics (p. 114). Other notable processes include respiration by plant roots; this increases the carbon dioxide content of the soil and assists the formation, with rainwater, of weak carbonic acids which attack rock minerals, notably carbonates.

THE PATTERNS OF WEATHERING

The processes of rock weathering by no means operate uniformly over the earth's surface, but vary considerably from one place to another, in terms of the actual type and the rate of operation of the weathering. Since weathering is an important determinant of slope form and evolution, frequently plays a direct role in shaping individual landforms, and conditions the nature and thickness of regoliths, it is clearly important for geomorphologists to identify the reasons for these spatial variations.

On the very broad scale weathering appears, not surprisingly, to be conditioned by the climate, and in particular climatic elements such as precipitation (type and amount) and temperature (absolute values, and seasonal and diurnal fluctuations, particularly on either side of 0°C). This has led geomorphologists to define *morphogenetic*, or *morphoclimatic, regions*; these are large sub-divisions of the earth's surface supposedly characterised by more or less uniform climatic conditions, and distinctive sets of weathering processes and phenomena. This approach, known as *climatic geomorphology*, has been developed considerably since 1950, when L C Peltier identified nine morphogenetic regions: glacial, periglacial, boreal, maritime, selva, moderate, savanna, semi-arid and arid. Each region is defined by parameters of annual rainfall and temperature, and by its association with particular geomorphological processes.

Nevertheless, whilst the concept of climatic geomorphology is clearly an attractive one, there has been much disagreement in detail between individual researchers as to the nature, extent and even number of morphogenetic regions. This is partly due to lack of data for some parts of the earth, but also reflects the complex pattern of actual weathering phenomena resulting from the climatic changes, both temporal and spatial, of the recent geological past. For example, in southern Britain there is evidence in the present landscape of weathering under warm and humid conditions, under periglacial conditions, and under the present humid temperate conditions.

To avoid the details of this controversy, it is appropriate here to undertake only a generalised survey of regional variations in weathering related to climate. This is, admittedly, over simplified but will aid the understanding of some important weathering phenomena.

1 Equatorial and humid tropical regions (see also pp. 114–116) The main controlling factors here are the abundance of soil moisture, related to the high annual rainfall, and the prevalence of high temperatures throughout the year speeding up chemical reactions. Both factors ensure that chemical weathering is overwhelmingly dominant: indeed they cause processes of rock decay to be four or more times as rapid in the humid tropics as in temperate regions. The large amounts of dead vegetable matter in the rainforests help to increase tropical weathering rates even further. Equatorial and humid tropical regions are, as a result, characterised by regoliths commonly reaching depths of 30–60 m and comprising a structureless mass of sand and clay with large unweathered boulders (*corestones*) (Fig. 3.8). Because of the masking effect of the regolith, and the lack of exposures of solid rock, physical weathering is by contrast reduced to a minimum. However, the climatic conditions do not, in any case, favour such weathering, even where rock outcrops occur.

Figure 3.8 *Deeply weathered rock exposed in a road cutting near Kuala Lumpur, Malaysia. Note the gullying by rainwash of the weathered material (mainly sand and clay) and the sharp transition from weathered to unweathered rock near the base of the exposed face*

2 Seasonally humid tropical regions (see also pp. 118–119) The climatic regime of high summer temperatures and quite heavy seasonal rainfall again favours chemical weathering. However, regoliths are generally less thick than in the humid tropics. Furthermore, with a less dense vegetation cover, surface wash erosion is more effective, so that in many areas the uppermost layers of the regolith are being removed quite rapidly. In some seasonally humid regions, such as the savanna of West Africa, this stripping of the regolith has partially exposed the fresh rock of the basal surface of weathering (p. 120) in the form of low domes and inselbergs. These are often much affected by physical disintegration, usually involving large scale exfoliation by dilatation.

3 Hot deserts (see also pp. 125–126) Although the very high diurnal temperatures are conducive to chemical weathering, the general lack of moisture is a hindrance. The widely accepted view is that the considerable range of temperature is the dominant factor in weathering, causing the break-up of surface rock layers by expansion and contraction. However, there has been a growing realisation that chemical processes are more active than was once thought. For example, hydration, operating just below the surface, leads to the flaking of rock exposures in deserts. It is, in fact, important to emphasise that hot deserts are by no means absolutely dry. Most experience infrequent rains, which can penetrate pores and joints and cause internal weakening of the rock by chemical action. Surface water also results from heavy dews and mists because, although the humidity of the desert air is low, chilling of the ground at night is so intense that the dewpoint is frequently reached. Such dews and mists can produce quite effective decay of rock surfaces. Also, the more humid periods of the recent past (p. 113) may have led to more chemical weathering than at present.

However, it is probably true to say that hot deserts today are characterised by low rates of weathering. The processes are, in the main, acting superficially, forming shallow mantles of broken rock, at the opposite extreme from humid tropical regions; moreover, they are highly selective, concentrating on structurally weak zones or on shaded locations where moisture from rain and dew can persist. It has been suggested that, in the most arid regions, weathering is so weak that rock faces retreat at an annual rate of less than 0.5 mm/1000 years, by contrast with the 1–2 mm/year of some mountain slopes in the Alps.

4 Temperate regions Although there is much regional variation, temperate climates are, as a whole, marked by moderate temperatures, mainly within the range 10–20°C, and moderate amounts of rainfall, within the range of 500–1000 mm/year. During winter and especially at high altitudes, snow is common and temperatures may drop below freezing point. Freeze-thaw weathering is thus active particularly in susceptible rocks such as chalk and limestone. However, the freezing is rarely severe and does not penetrate to any great depth. The wedging away of large joint bounded blocks is rare under present conditions; where the results of this process are observable, as in many parts of upland Britain, these are mainly the product of the more severe climatic conditions of the Pleistocene.

Chemical processes are also active in temperate regions. Oxidation of iron minerals cementing sandstones can be commonly seen, measurements of the solution loads of limestone streams indicate that carbonation is effective, and granite surfaces are being pitted by the selective hydrolysis of feldspar crystals. However, owing to the moderate temperatures and relative lack of humic acids, these processes are less effective than in the humid tropics.

In fact, all weathering processes, both physical and chemical, seem to operate less rapidly today in temperate regions than in the past. This conclusion is based both on the occurrence of many deposits, such as *coombe rock* and *head* which are the result of periglacial freeze-thaw weathering, and on deeply weathered layers, such as those on granite in south-west England and northern Scotland, which appear to have been formed under wetter and warmer conditions during the late Tertiary era.

5 Glacial regions These are characterised by the presence of ice-sheets, ice-caps and valley glaciers, which may actually protect large areas of the land surface from weathering. The glacial ice acts in the manner of a cushion reducing the impact of atmospheric temperature changes. There is abundant snowfall, mainly in winter, and generally low temperatures, although these frequently rise above 0°C. Rock surfaces, especially in high altitude glacial regions, are heated up rapidly by the sun's rays. Freeze-thaw weathering is the dominant process, acting on rocks protruding above the ice (*arêtes* and *nunataks*) and on valley walls above glaciers. There is much meltwater, released from snow and ice during the day, which enters joints in the rock, and freezes at night. Shattered rock fragments fall readily from the steep faces, so that there is constant renewal of exposure of the rock to further weathering. Some of the highest recorded rates of rock wall retreat, up to 2 mm/year, are recorded in these circumstances. The extensive scree deposits, and much of the debris transported on the surfaces of glaciers as lateral and medial moraines (p. 89), are the result of slope retreat by frost action (Fig. 3.9). Pressure release is a major contributory mechanism, as is the preliminary widening of joints by chemical weathering. In summer, rain falling in glaciated mountains contains dissolved carbon dioxide and oxygen, thus providing weak acids which can attack rock minerals, though the rates of reaction are slowed by the relatively low temperatures. Additionally, water derived from the thawing of snow contains high proportions of dissolved carbon dioxide, largely because the solubility of carbon dioxide is actually increased at low temperatures; this increases the effectiveness of reactions involving carbonation.

Figure 3.9 *Freeze-thaw weathering of exposed rock faces adjacent to Glacier de Tsidjiore Nouve, Switzerland. Note the accumulation of weathered material which has fallen on to the glacier surface*

6 Periglacial regions (see also pp. 100–110) Annual totals of precipitation, occurring both as snow and rain, are generally less here than in glacial regions. Nevertheless, surface water is abundant at certain times, such as during the spring thaw, and in many places as permafrost results in swamps and bogs. Temperatures are often extremely severe in winter, but rise above 0°C during the summer months. In the intermediate seasons of spring and autumn, there are fluctuations about 0°C, sometimes as many as 100 in a single year. In the absence of protective glacial ice, the ground surface is readily affected by these changes of temperature, so that freeze-thaw weathering is considerable, leading to the widespread occurrence in periglacial regions of block fields, felsenmeer (Fig. 3.10), tors resulting from frost attack on

Figure 3.10 *Felsenmeer at the summit of Pyhyatuntari, Finnish Lapland*

jointed rock, and extensive spreads of angular debris.

Nevertheless, the process of freeze-thaw weathering in periglacial environments is not fully understood. It was once thought to be most effective in areas where diurnal frost cycles are numerous. However, it has been shown that these involve penetration of freezing into the ground to a depth of 5 cm or less so that the weathering effects will probably be slight. It is therefore argued that the annual frost cycle is more important. The winter freezing goes much deeper into the ground, and exerts more protracted stress within the rock, thus increasing the likelihood of break-up.

Despite the low temperatures, periglacial environments also experience some chemical weathering. The poor drainage of low-lying and flat areas favours the formation of peat and acid soils, which provide organic acids to aid weathering. Moreover, the streams contain significant solution loads; for example, meltwater emerging from beneath snowpatches contains calcium bicarbonate, showing that carbonation is active under the snow.

The influence of rock type on weathering

Whilst the pattern of weathering on the broad scale reflects climatic variations from place to place, on a local scale it is influenced more by the diversity of rock type. For example, within Great Britain the weathering processes are in general terms typically those of a temperate region, as described on p. 58; yet there are important contrasts in the ways in which particular rocks, such as granite, schist, basalt, sandstone, limestone, and clay are broken down by weathering. These variations in the response of individual rock types to weathering are related to a number of rock properties, some of which aid weathering processes and others of which impede them.

1 Rock strength and hardness vary enormously, both in terms of the rock as a whole and of its individual constituents. An obvious contrast exists between a block of granite, which can be broken only by heavy hammer blows, and a weakly cemented sandstone, which can be crushed between the fingers. The hardness of the former is the result of two factors. First, it is an igneous rock composed of numerous crystals which gradually solidified and became closely bonded together during formation. Secondly, the individual crystals, such as quartz and feldspar, are themselves very hard. The weakness of the sandstone, on the other hand, reflects the fact that, although the rock may comprise hard quartz particles, there has been insufficient time for the precipitation of a cement, such as iron oxide, that will adequately bind them together.

Another factor that may influence the strength of a rock is its age; hence the common use of the phrase 'old hard rocks'. Tertiary sandstones in south-east England are usually weak and incoherent, whereas Palaeozoic sandstones, such as those in the uplands of Wales, are mostly well cemented and thus very coherent. Moreover, older rocks have often been deeply buried beneath younger formations, or affected by several episodes of crustal movement. The resultant compression will have helped to bind the rock constituents together and greatly increase rock strength.

Nevertheless, a rock's resistance to weathering is only partially determined by its strength. Most hard rocks possess weaknesses, either of structure or composition, that facilitate their break-up in the long term. For example, granite, already referred to as very hard, is a crystalline rock that is actually very prone to chemical weathering under humid tropical conditions.

2 Chemical composition influences rock resistance because rock minerals vary in their susceptibility to chemical change and breakdown. For example, calcium carbonate, the main constituent of chalk and limestone, and a cementing mineral in other types of sedimentary rock, is prone to carbonation by acidulated rainwater (p. 55). It is, in fact, convenient to classify common rock minerals according to their ability to withstand chemical alteration, otherwise referred to as their stability. Among the more stable minerals is quartz in its crystalline form; this is almost immune to change, with the result that when igneous rocks containing the mineral are broken down, a predominant component of the residual debris is quartz crystals. The more susceptible unstable minerals include olivine, augite and plagioclase feldspar; the latter is one of the first minerals to be decayed when granite is weathered under humid tropical conditions.

In general, the more stable minerals are light coloured, whilst the less stable are dark coloured. As a result a rock such as granite, with a high proportion of near white minerals such as quartz and feldspar, is relatively resistant to chemical decay under most climatic conditions, whereas rocks such as diorite, gabbro and andesite, which contain a greater proportion of darker coloured plagioclase feldspar, augite and hornblende, will be relatively prone to chemical attack. It is also possible that chemical composition has some effect on physical weathering. For example, dark coloured rocks such as basalt, gabbro and serpentine absorb solar heat more readily, heat up and expand quite rapidly, and thus experience stresses which may fracture them. Again, rocks containing an admixture of light and dark coloured minerals may experience differential expansion and contraction leading to granular disintegration.

3 Rock texture refers to the crystalline nature of a rock, and in particular whether it is *coarse grained* or *fine grained*. The effects of texture on weathering are highly complex, and differ from one rock type to another. In some instances, coarse textured rocks are resistant; in others, where some of the constituent minerals are unstable, selective chemical attack quickly reduces the rock's coherence. In finer grained rocks, the many crystals are tightly bonded and interlocked, thus increasing strength. However, the crystal boundaries also provide lines of potential weakness along which weathering agents can penetrate. As a result, fine grained igneous rocks often weather more rapidly than coarse grained rocks.

4 Rock joints and bedding planes are critical factors in controlling the nature and rate of weathering. For example, a well bedded and closely jointed rock allows the ready penetration of water, acids and oxygen, all agents of decomposition. In addition, the joints effectively increase the sub-surface area of the rock that can be attacked by chemical processes, as well as constituting lines of physical weakness that can be exploited by processes such as freeze-thaw (pp. 52–53). By contrast, massive rocks without bedding planes and with few or no joints, are inherently resistant. Only the surface of the rock can be attacked by weathering agents, and little or no chemical or physical break-down can occur internally. It is noticeable that in areas of limestone where massive layers are separated by thinly bedded layers, the former stand out as bold free faces, and the latter are weathered into relatively gentle debris covered slopes.

Bedding planes, the lines of junction separating individual layers of sedimentary rocks, are particularly apparent in most limestones, chalk and some types of sandstone, but are less evident in clays. They constitute lines along which the rock readily splits, and also provide routes for the underground movement of water; in limestone country underground passages frequently result from the opening up by solution of major bedding planes. *Joints* are very narrow, but often extensive, cracks. They result from the cooling and contraction of igneous rocks and the drying out of sedimentary rocks; they are also produced by the tensional forces which affect any type of rock subjected to earth movements. In many instances, rocks possess two sets of vertical joints which intersect at right angles when viewed in plan (Fig. 3.11). In very old rocks, the joints are aligned in a number of different directions, so that their pattern is complex or even confused, though some of the joint directions may still appear visibly more dominant than others. In some types of igneous and metamorphic rocks, notably granite and gneiss,

Figure 3.11 *Rectangular joint patterns exposed on a wave-cut platform in Lower Lias Limestone, Nash Point Lighthouse, South Glamorgan*

Figure 3.12 *Great Staple Tor, near Tavistock, Devon. Note the 'blocky' appearance of the tor, resulting from weathering of vertical and horizontal joints in the granite, and (to the right) fallen blocks which have been wedged away by ice formerly occupying the joints*

the vertical joints are intersected by near-horizontal or curving sheet joints, resulting from dilatation (p. 52); the effect is to divide the rock up into numerous cube-like blocks. As these joints are penetrated by weathering processes, piles of boulders are formed by block disintegration (Fig. 3.12). Tors, as on the granite of Dartmoor in Devon, have been formed in this way, both as a result of selective chemical weathering of joint lines and the prising apart of joints by ice formation (p. 53). On some individual tors, the sheet joints are overwhelmingly dominant, leading to a form of large scale exfoliation and the formation of more rounded 'lamellar' tors.

SLOPE RECESSION

Slopes, developed along the sides of valleys and at the margins of hills, are in many respects the most important of all landforms. Certainly they comprise the major part of the physical landscape over most of the earth; moreover, it is the variations in steepness and profile of slopes that give to most landscapes their essential character. Although often deceptively simple in appearance, with their smoothly curving outlines and absence of striking 'features', slopes are highly complex landforms. Many bear the imprint of a long history of development, preserve a record of past climatic changes, and reflect an intricate relationship between the rocks which underlie them and the processes of weathering and transport helping to shape them. Nevertheless, it is necessary to approach the study of these complex and often controversial landforms by way of simple initial assumptions, and then to build in the detail at a later stage of the discussion.

One way of explaining the basic features of some mountain slopes has been outlined in the introduction to this chapter (Fig. 3.1). However, one question which at that point was conveniently ignored was: how did the cliff, in time weathered back and modified in form, come into existence in the first place? Two possible answers are (a) that it was created along a valley margin by glacial erosion during the Quaternary period, and (b) that it was created by faulting. However, so far as slopes generally are concerned, it is clear that most were initiated by the erosion of rivers. Vertical corrasion results, in the absence of weathering and slope transportation processes, in steep sided, narrow gorges. Such valleys may be seen in the Swiss Alps, where rapid incision by meltwater streams beneath glaciers has created slit-like valleys. In the 10 000 or so years since these striking gorges were exposed by glacier retreat, there has been insufficient time for significant modification of the valley walls by weathering and transport. However, it seems reasonable to assume that, over a lengthy period of time in the future, these walls will experience slope retreat, the valleys will become opened out, and ultimately more gentle slopes will be formed.

Thus we have here the basis for another very simple model of slope development, in which it is assumed that the river completes its erosion before slope development begins to operate. Needless to say, for most actual valley side slopes this is too simple a view. Normally, as a river cuts downwards at a more moderate rate, initiating the valley slopes, so the latter immediately come under attack by weathering and thus experience retreat from an early stage. The actual shape of any river valley, and thus the steepness of its slopes, will in fact depend very much on the relative rates of river incision and slope wasting by weathering and transport. As Fig. 2.17 shows, where the former is dominant the valley shape will be that of a narrow V, with steep sided slopes; where the latter is more effective, the valley will assume a more open form, with much gentler slopes.

There are, of course, other ways in which this model is too simple. River erosion is not always vertical, but may be lateral, leading directly to the undercutting and steepening of valley side slopes. Additionally, factors other than river erosion and weathering influence the form and steepness of slopes. Among the many *slope controlling factors* are the following:

1 Rock type is a primary control of slope steepness, because the angle that a particular rock can support will depend on its *shear strength*. If the latter is exceeded by the *shear stress*, as determined by the pull of gravity on the rock mass, part of the rock will collapse and slide over a *failure plane*, the angle of which is itself related to the coherence of the rock. In simple terms, this means that hard, coherent rocks such as granite, gneiss and gabbro more readily support steep slopes than, say, weakly cemented sandstones which will tend to collapse over a much gentler failure plane. This does not mean, however, that granite slopes will *always* be steeper than sandstone slopes. For one thing, the sheer strength of granite, and indeed other rock types, will be greatly reduced if it possesses joints and fractures into which water can percolate. These *discontinuities* render the rock more prone to failure, as well as reducing the angle of the failure plane. For another, slopes in granite may be reduced in steepness by rapid and effective weathering, as in warm humid climates, giving rise to a thick regolith of little shear strength.

2 Structure influences slope development in several ways. For example in sedimentary rocks where the dip is inwards, that is towards the slope, individual strata, even when loosened by weathering, remain *in situ*; thus the slope is stable and tends to maintain its steepness. However, where the dip is downslope, detached masses of rock can readily slide over the bedding planes; such slopes tend therefore to recede rapidly and in the long term experience a decline in angle.

3 Earth movements can directly affect slope form, as in the formation of fault scarps, but also have indirect effects. For instance, in areas experiencing rapid uplift, as in young fold mountains such as the Himalayas, rivers cut rapidly downwards, initiating and maintaining steep slopes which are characterised by active weathering and transport. In structurally more stable areas, where rivers have long ago cut down to the base-level of erosion and thus experience little or no vertical incision, long continued slope wasting is likely to have reduced most slopes to a gentle angle.

4 Climate, as we have seen, influences greatly the type and rate of weathering, and thus the thickness of the slope regolith. It also affects slope transportational processes, including both rainwash and mass movements such as soil creep and solifluction. It is not surprising that some authorities claim that different climates produce different slope forms, pointing to the contrasts between the smoothly curving, mass-wasted profiles of many humid temperate slopes and the more angular, irregular and often steeper slopes of arid and semi-arid landscapes which have not been smoothed by mass movements.

5 Vegetation can also influence weathering and slope transport. A thick forest cover will, by its root systems, help to stabilise the regolith and maintain slope steepness. By contrast, where the vegetation cover is sparse, dislodgement and transport of soil particles by rainfall and run-off can be much more active. This is seen in semi-arid and seasonally arid climates, where low angled slopes such as pediments are often extensive, reflecting the ready transport of alluvium by rainwash during short lived desert storms.

The interrelationships between slope controlling factors, slope processes and slope form, constituting what may be termed the *slope system*, are shown in outline form in Fig. 3.13. From this it will be seen that a fundamental distinction can be drawn between those controlling factors arising from outside the earth (*exogenetic*), and those arising from within the earth (*endogenetic*). Of the former, climate is of the first importance, not only for its direct effects on slope weathering, but also because of its influence on other slope factors and processes. For example, considerable annual rainfall, and thus high surface run-off, may result in more active river incision and slope transportation; on the other hand, it will also tend to nourish a denser vegetation cover, which will reduce the effectiveness of both these processes. The principal endogenetic factors are rock type, structure and rate of land uplift by earth movements. These will in turn influence rates of river erosion, together with weathering and slope transport in the ways described above. They will also help to deter-

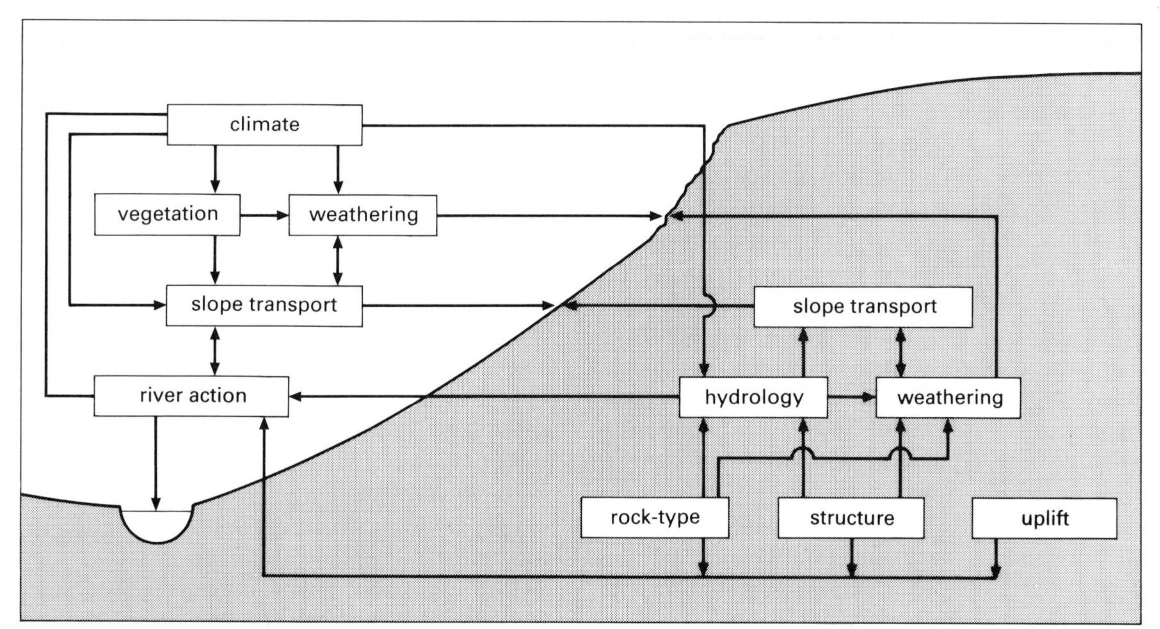

Figure 3.13 *The slope system*

mine hydrological conditions, for example surface run-off, throughflow, percolation, and the occurrence of springs and seepages on slopes – though these will, of course, also reflect to some degree the prevailing climatic conditions.

SLOPE TRANSPORTATIONAL PROCESSES

Once initiated, slopes owe their subsequent development both to a range of rock weathering processes, as described above, and to the transport away of the loosened rock debris, or weathering products. If this transport did not occur, the slope would become mantled by a thick layer of regolith, which at best would greatly impede further weathering, and at worst halt it altogether, thus bringing slope recession to a halt. In reality, a condition of balance, or *equilibrium*, tends to develop on many natural slopes between the rate of weathering and the rate of transport. One symptom of this equilibrium is the occurrence, usually on a smooth slope of moderate or low angle, of a soil or debris layer, up to a metre or so in depth, which appears to become neither thicker nor thinner with time. Although debris is added, by weathering of bedrock, at the base of this layer, material is removed at an equal rate from its surface. The development and maintenance of this condition of equilibrium is very much influenced by slope steepness. Where this is too great, the debris layer will slip rapidly away, to expose bedrock; where the angle is too gentle, the debris will accumulate to a considerable thickness and increasingly mask the bedrock. For this reason, slopes on which a balance between weathering and removal has been achieved are characterised by a *particular maximum angle*, and are commonly referred to as *equilibrium slopes*.

It is important also to emphasise that the rate of recession is very much influenced by the slope angle. On steep slopes, where transport is generally more rapid, the bedrock is also weathered more effectively because of continual *renewal of exposure*; as a result slope retreat is also rapid. However, on gentle slopes, where transport is generally slower and the resultant thicker regolith offers greater protection to the underlying rock, weathering becomes less effective and the rate of slope retreat is less. There are, inevitably, exceptions to this simple rule. For example, a steep slope in a very dry climate may experience little weathering (p. 58), so that the processes of transport will be largely redundant and slope recession will be negligible.

The action of running water on slopes

Rainwash transport, particularly of fine materials, has long been considered a contributory process in slope development. Some geomorphologists argue that concave slopes, because of their form and their frequent occupation by alluvial sediments, are wholly the product of running water; others have proposed that, under certain conditions, the whole of the slope profile is shaped by rainwash. Yet, as will be shown, there are difficulties in explaining effective rainwash erosion at the slope summit. Indeed, since running water, when it occurs at all on slopes, takes the form of a very thin layer, with relatively little competence to transport sediment particles, it can clearly have significant impacts only over long periods of time.

One theory of slope run-off is that proposed by R E Horton (see also p. 11), who argued that surface flow will occur when rainfall intensity exceeds the infiltration capacity of soils on the slope. When such infiltration-excess flow occurs, the layer of flowing water thickens downslope, as the excess water at any point is added to by water flowing from above (Fig. 3.14). It will also increase in velocity downslope, particularly if the gradient steepens, as on a convex slope. This gives the flow increased power towards the slope base, so that its transporting ability, which is limited towards the slope crest, becomes significant.

Horton proposed that slope profiles can be divided into three:

(i) On the upper part of the slope, where the

Figure 3.14 *The Horton model of overland flow and slope development (see p. 13 and pp. 66–67)*

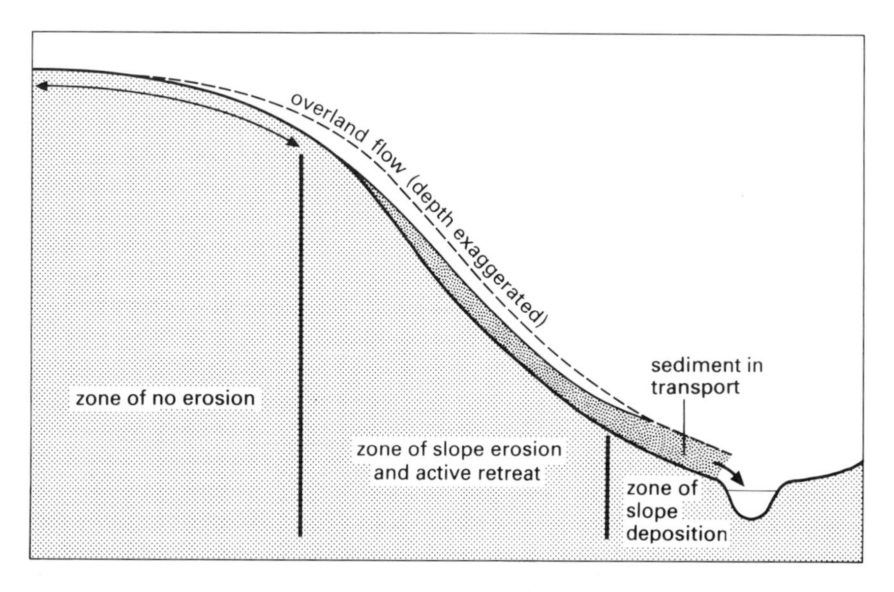

surface water layer is thin and slow flowing and the *eroding force* weak, there will be a *zone of no erosion* having a *critical length* (x_c) from the slope crest to the point at which transport of soil particles begins. This critical length varies from one slope to another, and from time to time on one slope, depending on factors such as soil type, vegetation cover and rainfall intensity.

(ii) On the middle part of the slope, as the eroding force increases, transport of soil particles will begin, and the slope will retreat actively.

(iii) On the lower part of the slope, the running water will be fully loaded with sediment and, providing a decrease of gradient reduces velocity, erosion will be replaced by deposition.

The implication of the Horton model is that running water is an important factor both in slope recession, in particular the wearing back of the steep middle sections of slopes, and in determining slope form. For instance, the broad summital convexities of limestone areas could be due to a greatly extended critical length (x_c), resulting from a permeable soil cover with a high infiltration capacity.

However, the Horton model is open to certain criticisms. First, it is now known that the surface erosion of slopes is not related to the depth and velocity of overland flow alone, but also to other factors such as *raindrop erosion*. When raindrops strike bare ground, small soil particles are dislodged and splashed upwards and outwards. On level ground, these particles are merely redistributed, but on a slope there is a net movement in a downslope direction; indeed, experiments have shown that, in cultivated land, 90 per cent of the erosion on slopes is caused by the rainsplash mechanism.

Secondly, for the reasons given on page 13, infiltration-excess flow is unlikely to occur in most mid and high latitude regions. Here, throughflow and saturation overland flow are more common. The latter can transport surface sediment particles, particularly towards the base of the slope, and thus influence the evolution of the slope profile. Throughflow may be slow and diffuse, or may be concentrated along certain paths (p. 17). It then becomes effective as a transporting agent, removing solutes and fine particles and carrying them towards the slope base; it is thus able to play some role in slope development, supplementing surface processes.

The action of mass movements on slopes

This varies in type of movement, rate of operation and scale. Three basic mechanisms are involved: *flowing, sliding* and *heaving* (the raising of particles at right angles to the slope). Flows are most effective in thick weathered mantles which contain much soil water. They are characterised by maximum velocity near the surface and reduced velocity at depth, and slow but continuous movement. Slides develop at the base of the regolith, where there is a well defined *slide plane* over which there is bodily movement of the debris. The actual slide is often rapid as the accumulation of stress above the slide plane is suddenly released.

1 Soil creep is probably the most widespread of all mass movements, and occurs in a wide variety of climates. It has been defined as the slow movement of particles down a slope as a result of the net effect of individual displacement. Creep is normally so slow as to be imperceptible, so that great precision is needed to measure it. In temperate regions, movement is greatest in the uppermost 50 cm of the soil layer, but even here amounts to only 1–2 mm/year. Nevertheless, in terms of volume of material moved down the slope, soil creep may be up to six times as important as rainwash. The evidence of active soil creep in the field is plentiful, and includes: accumulation of soil on the up-slope side of fences, walls and hedges; curved tree trunks where, as soil movement pushes the trunk from the vertical, the tree responds by attempting to restore vertical growth; and the downhill bending over of strata loosened by weathering.

Soil creep includes *gravity creep* and *soil heave*. The former takes place when soil particles are set in motion by some disturbing factor. The particles then come under the pull of gravity, which operates vertically. However, because of the presence of bedrock and other soil particles, this vertical component will be transformed into a component of movement parallel to the slope surface. As one particle moves, it will dislodge other particles, and so on, until the initial disturbance is absorbed. The series of movements constitutes gravity creep. Soil heave involves the raising of particles at right angles to the slope, followed by vertical settling under the influence of gravity. A sequence of up and down movements leads to the transport of individual particles considerable distances.

There are several processes which lead to gravity creep and heave, among them: expansion and contraction of the soil from day to night; wetting and drying, important in certain clay minerals which expand when wet; frost action, involving the formation of ground ice; the growth of plant and tree roots; the activity of soil fauna, including earthworms and termites; volume changes resulting from weathering processes such as solution. These individual processes vary in effectiveness in different climates. In periglacial regions, frost disturbance is easily the most dominant; in humid temperate areas, both wetting and drying and frost action are powerful; and in the humid tropics, wetting and drying are dominant, with disturbance by roots and soil fauna, and removal of solutes by weathering, of secondary significance.

The main effect of soil creep is to smooth and round the slope. The convex slopes of humid regions have been attributed to creep acting on the upper slope where rainwash is at a minimum. It is suggested that, as there is a natural downslope increment of soil because the soil formed at any point is added to by soil creeping from above, the slope will need to become steeper downslope, so that the increasing amount of soil can be evacuated.

2 Solifluction is in some ways a more specialised, complex and rapid form of soil creep, with rates of movement as high as 5–10 cm/year. The process is dominant in periglacial regions (pp. 105–106).

3 Rock slides and land slides are most active in areas of high relief and unstable slopes, such as the Alps, Himalayas and Andes. In rock slides the effects of bedding and joint planes are important, not only in allowing the rock to fragment but also in providing ready made slide planes, as with downward dipping bedding planes over which the detached masses can slip (Fig. 3.15). Slopes affected by rock slides show,

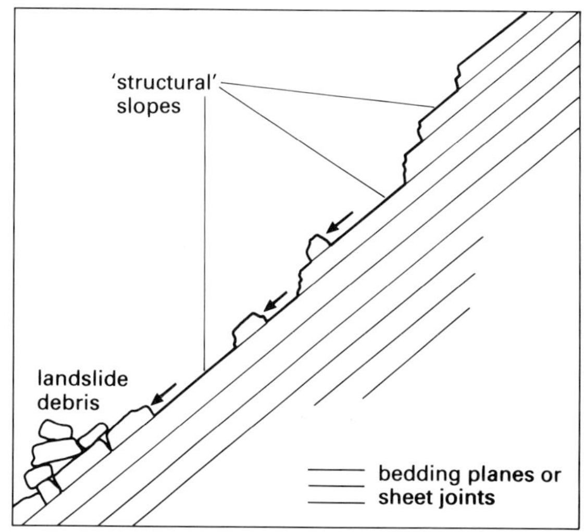

Figure 3.15 *Rock slides and the slope profile (see p. 68)*

in detail, the strong control exerted by geological structure. Land slips usually occur in the less strong rocks such as sands and clays, or in weathered material resting on solid rock, in which case the land slip is superficial as opposed to deep seated. In either case, the prolonged build-up of ground water may load the slope. This will have the double effect of increasing the stress on the slope, and reducing friction along slide planes (p. 68). By increasing *pore water pressure* large quantities of water may also force the particles in the sliding mass apart, promoting flowage. When slumps of rock and/or debris take place, after heavy rain, often across arcuate slide planes by the process known as *rotational slip*, the lower part or toe of the slipped mass often becomes highly mobile, and forms *earth flows* or *mud flows* (Fig. 3.16).

4 Catastrophic mass movements occur when slopes are affected by sudden and massive failure, particularly where they have been oversteepened by glaciation and where special trigger mechanisms such as earthquakes occur. The resultant *debris avalanches* can have appalling consequences, as in the Huascaran avalanche in the Peruvian Andes, in May 1970. An 800 m-thick mass of rock and ice, disturbed by an earth tremor, slid from the mountain summit of Huascaran and fell 1000 m before spreading rapidly over the valley floor beneath. This released sufficient energy to send a mass of rubble, partly floating on a cushion of air and travelling at a maximum speed of 480 km/hour, a distance of 16 km to the Rio Santa valley, where the town of Yungay was overwhelmed and 10 000 people killed instantly. A smaller scale but nevertheless tragic disaster occurred at Aberfan, in south Wales, in 1966. An old coal waste tip had been constructed above the village, unwittingly on a spring line. The mass of waste gradually became impregnated with

Figure 3.16 *A typical land slip*

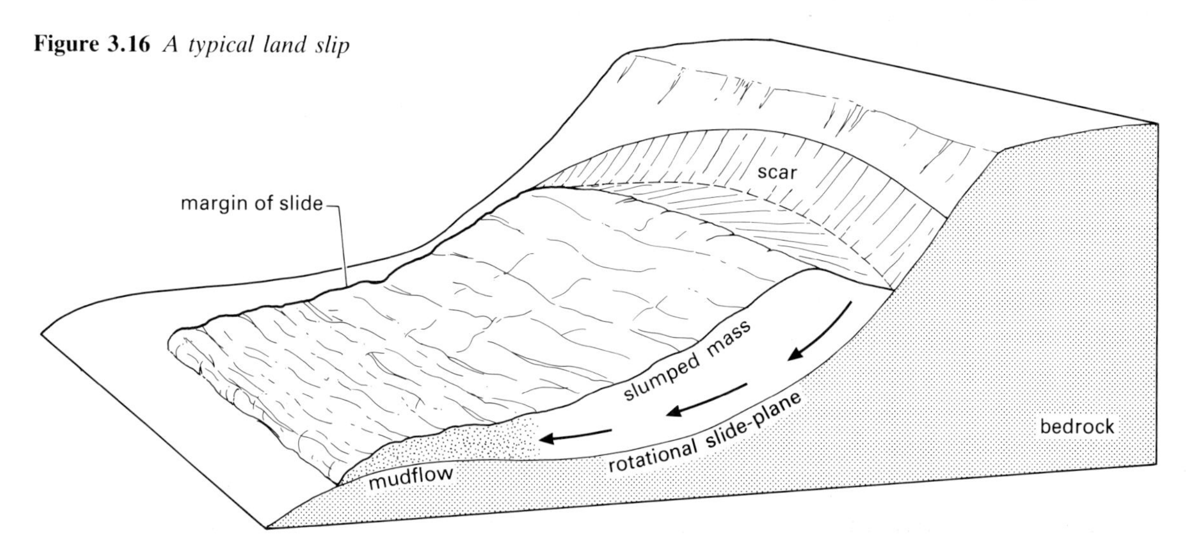

water; the resultant increase in weight of the tip, allied to the high pore-water pressures, produced extreme instability and triggered a catastrophic mud slide. This engulfed part of the village, including the village school, and claimed the lives of 116 children.

Many other similar tragedies, resulting from catastrophic slope failure, could be described from various parts of the world. Fortunately, however, mass movements of this type are relatively rare, though showing a tendency to increase owing to human interference with natural slopes by excavation, construction, deforestation, impeding drainage, and so on. It is still more usual for slope processes, and resultant changes in slope form, to be very slow acting and, indeed, almost imperceptible to the human eye.

SLOPE PROFILE ANALYSIS

Owing to the complex interactions of factors and processes within the slope system, slopes display a wide range of *profiles*, some relatively simple and some, in areas of complex geology or a long erosional history, much more irregular. Nevertheless, study of slopes in a wide range of environments reveals that particular slope profiles occur commonly.

Basic slope forms

1 The cliff is a vertical or very steep, largely bare rock face from which weathered debris falls or is washed as quickly as it is released from bedrock; hence a cliff is also referred to by geomorphologists as a *free face* (Fig. 3.17). Cliffs are frequently developed on coasts and in glaciated valleys; *river cliffs* are found in river valleys where lateral corrasion undercuts the slope base or where hard bands of rock outcrop on the valley side. In the latter instance, slope recession in underlying weak strata often has the effect of undermining the hard layer and maintaining its steepness. Over a period of time, cliffs undergo parallel retreat (p. 78), as a result of the unimpeded weathering of the whole rock surface. However, unless removed by basal transport, for example, by a cliff foot stream, the weathered debris eventually accumulates to mask the base of the cliff (Fig. 3.1).

Figure 3.17 *A limestone free face, developed in massive dolomitic limestone, near Meryrueis, southern France*

2 The debris slope is usually more or less straight in profile, or *rectilinear*. It consists of weathered material, which builds up at the base of the cliff as a deposit of talus or scree, at an angle which is controlled by the size and shape of the talus fragments (Fig. 3.18). Where these are large and angular, the angle of rest may exceed 35° to the horizontal and even approach the angle of the free face (above 40°). Where the debris slope grows upwards to mask the cliff, the amount of weathered debris shed from the cliff will be reduced; and at each stage of development, this smaller amount of debris will be spread over an increasing area of talus. This will mean that, beneath the talus, a protected convex rock slope will form (Fig. 3.1b).

Figure 3.18 *A scree slope (debris slope) above the Arolla valley, Switzerland*

3 Repose slopes, which are also rectilinear in profile, resemble debris slopes in the field. However, they are actually underlain by solid bedrock, which is covered by a thin layer of debris being transported slowly down the slope; in other words, these are *erosional* slopes. There is often confusion between repose slopes and debris slopes; this is understandable, since the upper part of a debris slope, where talus overlying bedrock is thin, is close to being a repose slope. Indeed, some repose slopes may represent the upward extension of the convex rock slope where removal of talus prevents the latter from keeping pace with the retreat of the cliff above.

Repose slopes develop approximately at the angle of rest of overlying debris, frequently at 30–35° to the horizontal. Sometimes they are referred to as *debris controlled slopes* or, where occupied by large fragments, as *boulder controlled slopes* (Fig. 3.19). Providing weathering of the bedrock continues to release particles of the same size and shape, the angle of rest of the debris cover, and thus the angle of the slope itself, will not change significantly. In other words, the slope will undergo *parallel retreat*. In nature, the steepness of repose slopes may slightly exceed the angle of rest of fragments, so that a very slow but steady evacuation of weathered particles can occur. Alternatively, the repose slope angle may equal

Figure 3.19 *A boulder controlled slope near Voi, Kenya. Note the contrast in angle between the steep slope above (occupied mainly by large boulders of gneiss) and the gentle slope in the foreground (occupied mainly by fine sand and gravel transported from the steep slope by rainwash processes)*

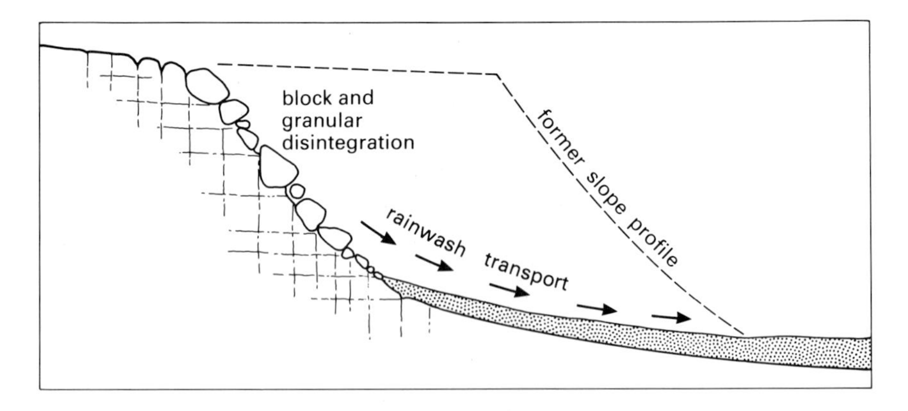

Figure 3.20 *The retreat of a boulder-controlled slope (see p. 71)*

the angle of rest of the larger fragments, with the finer particles resulting from *in situ* weathering of these fragments being transported readily downslope (Fig. 3.20). Whichever mechanism applies, the sum total of debris released by further weathering is equalled by that leaving the slope at its base. The debris layer thus maintains a constant thickness, and more or less equal weathering over the whole of the slope surface is assured. Repose slopes are, therefore, characterised by a balance between debris production and removal, and are thus good examples of equilibrium slopes (p. 66).

4 ***Convex slopes*** are usually found on the upper part of the slope profile, hence the use of the term *summital convexity* (Fig. 3.21). They are sometimes structurally determined, as on granite hills with curving sheet joints subjected to massive exfoliation, but are more usually the result of transportational processes. Like repose slopes, they are underlain by solid rock, on which rests a layer of weathered material which is being moved downslope by processes such as rainwash and soil creep. Convex slopes are believed to be most typical of rock types and climates which favour slowly acting mass movements.

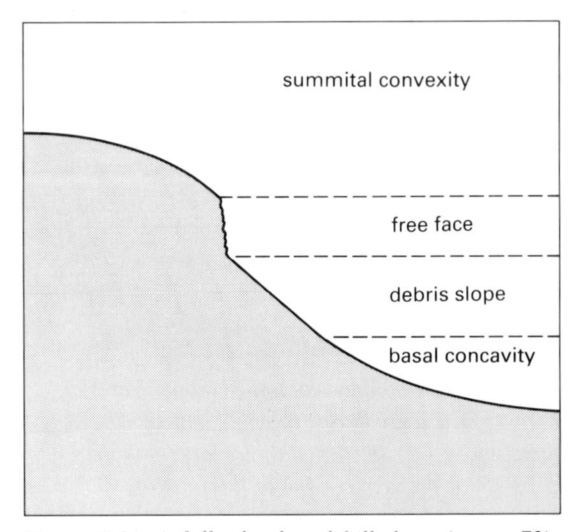

Figure 3.21 *A fully developed hill slope (see p. 73)*

5 ***Concave slopes*** are usually found on the lower part of the slope profile, hence use of the term *basal concavity* (Fig. 3.21). They are sometimes the result of deposition, as on alluvial fans, but are commonly of erosional origin. Basal concavities are very characteristic of arid regions, where they comprise gently sloping rock surfaces with a thin cover of alluvium known as *rock pediments* (p. 132). However, concavities also occur in humid tropical and savanna regions, in humid temperate lands, and even under periglacial conditions. Over time, basal concavities appear to be extended headwards, at the expense of steeper slopes from which they may be separated by a sharp break of gradient. Essentially, concave slopes are *slopes of transport*, over which the products of weathering from the steeper slopes above are evacuated.

6 ***Complex slopes*** result from the combination of some or all of the individual forms described above, as in *convexo-concave, convexo-*

rectilinear-concave or *free face debris slope pediment* sequences. One suggestion is that, when fully developed, slopes comprise a four-unit profile, including summital convexity, free face, debris slope and basal concavity (Fig. 3.21). However, this is potentially misleading, since such profiles are rarely found in areas of soft rock, which are unable to support free faces, or under climatic conditions in which mass movements are very active and lead to rounding of slope profiles. Fully developed slopes seem most likely to be developed in areas of high relief and hard massive rocks in a semi-arid climate, but have been observed in other environments, including periglacial regions (p. 110).

The analysis of slope form

Modern geomorphologists are no longer satisfied with the subjective description of slope form, in terms that lack objectivity and precision, but have increasingly focused their attentions on the *quantification* of slopes. This involves slope *morphometry*, or the measurement of slope form and steepness. The morphometric approach is regarded as essential for at least two reasons. First, there is a need to base general theories or models of slope development, as described in the final section of this chapter, on firm and clear evidence. Secondly, comparisons of slope form and evolution from one climate to another, or from one rock type to another, must be related to the facts rather than to visual, and sometimes very imprecise, impressions of slopes gained from cursory field study.

The usual way of approaching slope study of this kind is by *slope profile measurement* in the field. The sites of profiles to be surveyed are first selected; for example, in a particular valley profiles may be taken at equal distances of, say, 100 m along the valley from the head downwards. At each site the profile of each valley side is then surveyed using a tape and level. For practical purposes it is usually sufficient to measure, along the line of the profile, the slope angle over successive 10 m lengths. The profile can then be readily plotted to scale and, together with the other profiles surveyed, can be subjected to analysis along the following lines:

i. The basic dimensions of the slope as a whole, and in particular its height, length and horizontal equivalent length, can be determined (Fig. 3.22).
ii. The mean and maximum slope angles on each profile can be identified.
iii. The slope profile can be divided up into its component units. These are of two types: a *slope segment* is a portion of the slope over which the gradient remains constant

Figure 3.22 *The principal dimensions of slopes*

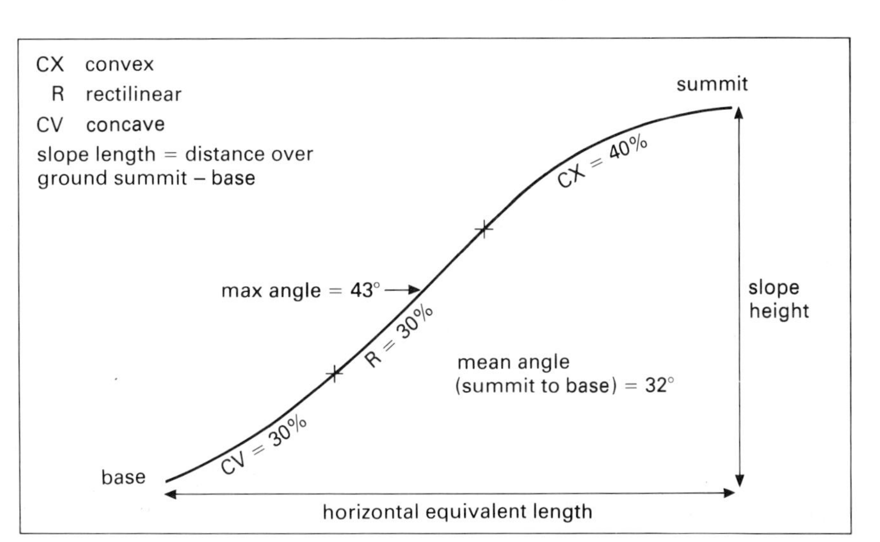

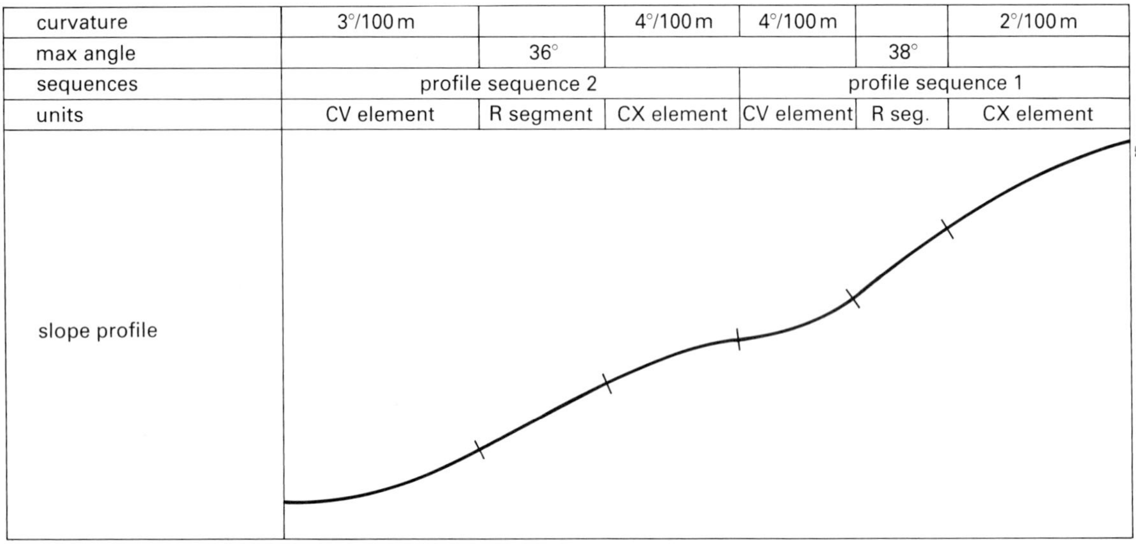

curvature	3°/100 m		4°/100 m	4°/100 m		2°/100 m
max angle		36°			38°	
sequences	profile sequence 2			profile sequence 1		
units	CV element	R segment	CX element	CV element	R seg.	CX element
slope profile						

Figure 3.23 *The analysis of slope profile sequences*

(a rectilinear slope); a *slope element* is a part of the profile on which there is consistent curvature (as on a convex or concave slope).

iv. *Slope sequences*, of convexity, rectilinearity and concavity, can then be recognised, and information relating to each profile tabulated as on Fig. 3.23.

v. The relative importance of each unit on a slope profile can be expressed as a percentage of total slope length. For example, the summital convexity may occupy 40 per cent of the slope length, the rectilinearity 30 per cent, and the basal concavity 30 per cent.

The information derived in this way can be used for the comparison of individual slope profiles. Thus, successive profiles measured across a valley, to give a *downvalley profile sequence*, may reveal systematic changes in slope form and steepness related to the increasing depth of the valley. Alternatively, the information from the individual profiles measured in an area of uniform rock type or relief might be used in the construction of an *average slope profile*. In other words, combining the data from, say, 100 profiles surveyed in an area of limestone could reveal that, on average, 70 per cent of the profile length is convex, 20 per cent rectilinear and 10 per cent concave; or the mean maximum slope might be calculated as 32°. Yet again, the plotting of a histogram showing the distribution of all 100 maximum slope angles might reveal a very limited dispersion, thus indicating the probability that most of these limestone slopes had attained an equilibrium angle (p. 66).

SLOPE EVOLUTION

Over a short period of time, except in circumstances such as those described on p. 66, slopes may change very little either in profile or steepness of angle. However, this does not mean that slopes should be regarded as unchanging, or *time independent* landforms. In the long run the action of weathering and transport may, in fact, produce some very significant changes. Not only will the slope be worn back, or experience retreat, as the underlying rock is continually loosened and removed, but some units may grow at the expense of others, and the slope as a whole may be experiencing a slow steepening or decline in angle. When a slope, over a time period of perhaps 100 000 years or even longer, undergoes a progressive change of form, this is referred to as *slope evolution*.

Geomorphologists have, in fact, devoted much time and effort to the study of slope evolution, even though it may seem a very theoretical matter. Whether or not at some time in the past a slope has declined progressively in angle, or experienced parallel retreat, hardly seems of much relevance to people living in a house on that slope. Whether or not a massive and catastrophic slope failure is imminent is, by contrast, a highly relevant matter! Even so, one task of the geomorphologist is to explain variations in landforms from one part of the earth's surface to another, and to show how these reflect not only climate or rock type but also the past *erosional history*; and it may well be that these spatial variations, observable today, are the outcome of past changes, just as much as of the present day processes which are operating on the slopes.

Nevertheless, there are some very real problems confronting the study of slope evolution. It is rarely possible, from an examination of existing slopes, to know what they were like, say, 20 000 or 40 000 years ago, since those slopes have been destroyed for ever in the formation of more recent slopes. Ideally, however, one needs to know the form of the slope at every stage of its development, since the time of its initiation, if slope evolution is to be understood fully. As we shall see, geomorphologists have devised possible methods of overcoming the problem of reconstructing the *sequential development* of slopes over time, though it would be misleading to pretend that these are entirely satisfactory.

1 The theoretical approach to slope evolution

One way of approaching the difficult task of reconstructing slope development in the past is not to seek direct evidence, but to suggest the sequence of slope forms that should, logically, be formed from an assumed initial slope. The resultant model of slope evolution can then be tested by comparing the deduced slope forms with those actually observable in the field today.

A good example of this approach is the model proposed by A Wood (Fig. 3.24). Wood conveniently assumed that slopes are developed from the protracted weathering of a vertical cliff. We have already seen (p. 51) that such a cliff will retreat, and that, at its base, a rectilinear debris slope will form. If no debris is removed from this slope, for example by river action at its foot, the cliff face must eventually be buried by the accumulation of weathered material falling from the cliff. However, if debris is removed from the debris slope as rapidly as it is added, the debris slope will cease to grow upwards. Nevertheless, the recession of the exposed cliff will continue, with the result that an intermediate slope, rectilinear in form, underlain by rock, and occupied by debris in transit from the cliff to the debris slope, necessarily develops. Eventually, this slope, referred to by Wood as the *constant slope*, will grow upwards to consume the cliff.

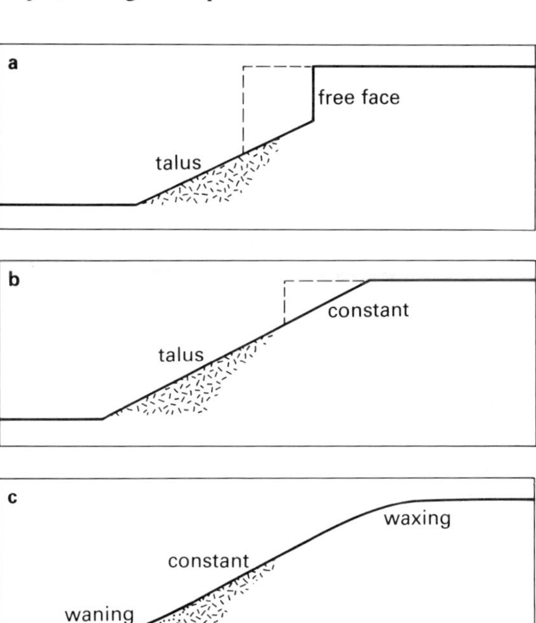

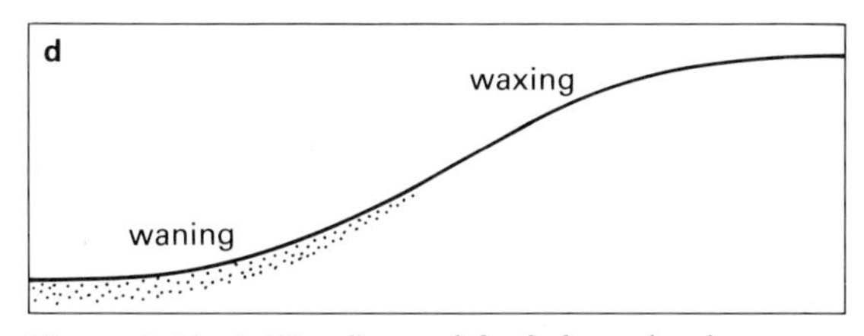

Figure 3.24 *A Wood's model of slope development*

Later still, the crest of the constant slope will become rounded by weathering, to give a convex slope, referred to by Wood as the *waxing slope*; whilst at the base of the constant slope, the accumulation of finer material, weathered from the debris slope and washed to its foot, will give rise to a concave slope, or *waning slope*. In the very final stages of slope evolution, the waxing slope will extend downwards, and the waning slope upwards, to give a convexo-concave slope profile overall.

Quite clearly, the various slope forms postulated by Wood actually exist, and in that sense the field evidence supports the model. However, it would be far too rigid to assume that all slopes have experienced, or will experience, precisely the sequence of development as outlined by Wood. For example, it is quite conceivable that some actual convexo-concave slopes, developed in weak rocks along the margins of shallow river valleys, have always been convexo-concave, though over time the convex slope may have extended at the expense of the concave slope, or vice-versa. This does not totally invalidate the Wood model, but merely emphasises that it is a very idealised way of looking at slope evolution!

2 Slope models based on direct observation

The method employed most successfully here is that of *space-time transformation*. The aim of this is to arrange a number of individual slope profiles surveyed in the field, either within one valley or over a wider area, in a *time sequence*. Consider the case of a valley that has been formed by the process of headward erosion over a period of several thousands of years. The slope profiles near the valley head will, in real terms, be *younger* than those in the middle part of the valley; in turn, the latter will be younger than those in the lower part of the valley. In other words, as we move in space down the valley, we in effect pass back in time, in terms of slope development. Thus we have, from our survey, the data to construct an *evolutionary sequence* of slope profiles.

A pioneer study based on space-time transformation, and using old sea cliffs rather than valley side slopes, was carried out by R A Savigear in Carmarthen Bay, south Wales, where a stretch of hard sandstone cliffs has been progressively cut off from the sea by an extending salt marsh. Marine erosion of the cliff base was halted earlier in the west than in the east, so that the abandoned cliff, now modified by subaerial weathering and slope transport, can be interpreted as an evolving slope. Survey of profiles shows that in the east, where wave erosion ceased recently and the slopes are therefore young, rectilinear segments at 32° are characteristic, though there is also some summital convexity present. On the older western slopes, rectilinear segments are more limited in extent and gentler in angle (28°); moreover, there are broad summital convexities, together with basal concavities formed of material weathered from the old cliff. From this evidence, one might assume that in the absence of basal undercutting, whether by the sea (as in this case) or a river (as is common in valleys) slopes will decline in angle over a period of time, and undergo a change in form involving a change from rectilinear to convexo-concave.

Another study, employing a rather different approach, was undertaken by A N Strahler in the Verdugo Hills, California. Maximum slope angles were measured at selected points in a large number of deeply incised valleys. The assembled data were then divided according to whether the slopes had an active stream at the base, or had accumulations of debris at the base. It was found that, in the former, maximum slope angles averaged 44.8° and in the latter 38.2°. This was taken to mean that basally eroded slopes were able to maintain a steep angle, but that if, at a later stage, stream erosion ceases and basal protection occurs, the slopes will decline in steepness. Clearly this conclusion is in line with that drawn by Savigear from his study of the Carmarthen cliffs. Strahler also found, in the Verdugo Hills, a close correlation between the steepness of the valley side or *ground slopes*, and that of the river in the valley floor, or the *channel slopes*. He argued that, since it has been widely accepted that channel slopes decrease over time, it follows logically that, in the long run, slopes also decline in steepness. However, it has subsequently been shown that, under certain conditions, channel slopes may become steeper over time, so that the probability of slope steepening must also be accepted.

Models of slope evolution

One model of slope evolution, that of A Wood, has been described in outline above; the following are the best known, and arguably the most fundamental, models.

1 The slope decline model This can largely be attributed to the American geographer, W M Davis, writing early in the twentieth century. Davis proposed that, although at an early stage of development (*youth*) valley side slopes are steep, in time they will necessarily become gentler, until at the final (*old age*) stage they will constitute a subdued undulating plain (*peneplain*) (Fig. 3.25). The model is based on two main arguments. First, where downcutting by rivers ceases as they approach the base-level of erosion, continued weathering and transport on the interfluves must reduce their cross-sectional areas and thus inevitably cause a gradual reduction in mean slope angle. Secondly, because weathered debris is transported downslope, there will be a tendency for the lower part of the slope to be more protected from weathering and the upper part to be more exposed to weathering. Thus, the upper slope will recede more rapidly, and again an overall decline of slope angle must result. The slope decline model also envisages that with time slopes become smoothed or *graded*. In youth, slope profiles will be irregular, with the hardest rock bands forming free faces and the weaker rocks debris covered slopes. However, in time the free faces, which are unprotected by a debris mantle, will weather back and eventually be destroyed, so that by maturity the slope will be smooth, with a continuous layer of soil being transported by rainwash and creep.

The slope decline model can be tested by field observations. For instance, where it is found that, within an area of uniform geology and relief, maximum slope angles vary considerably, the probability is that decline is operating. But where, in the same conditions, maximum slope angles show very little variation, the likelihood is that slopes are in a state of equilibrium (p. 66) and are maintaining their steepness. The evidence suggests that, in different situations, both types of evolution can occur. Where rivers are cutting downwards very rapidly, slope decline is improbable, but where vertical river erosion is restricted, allowing slope deposits to accumulate, decline is more probable.

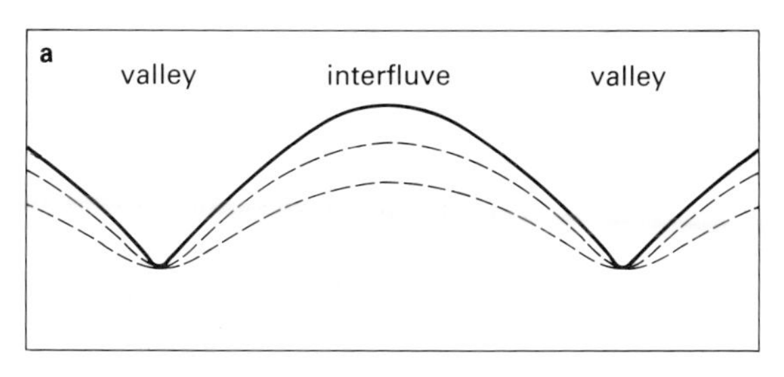

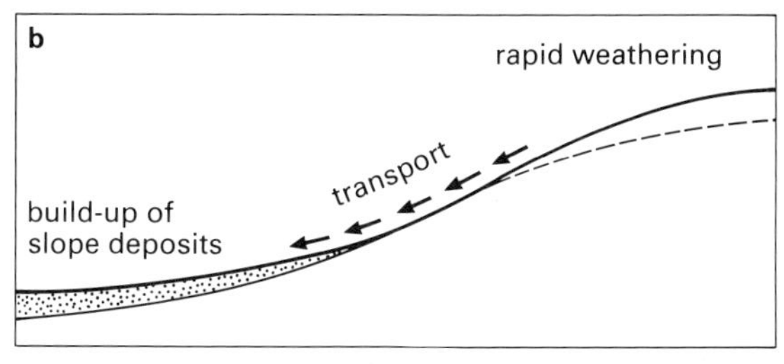

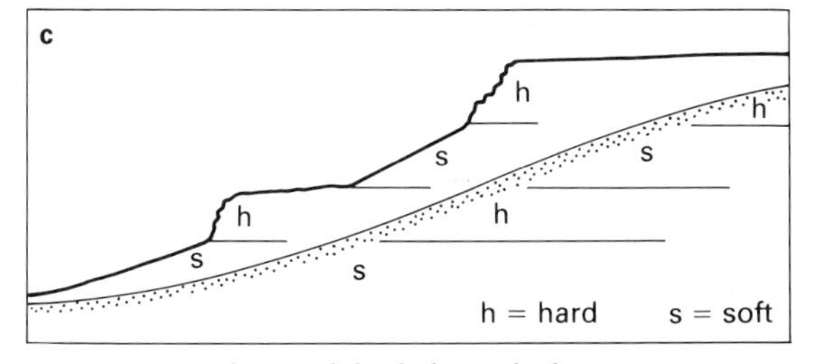

Figure 3.25 *The model of slope decline*

2 The slope replacement model This stems from the work of the German geomorphologist, W Penck. Penck argued that slope form and steepness are largely controlled by the rate of erosion of rivers. Where these cut down at a constant rate, slopes are rectilinear; but with accelerating and decelerating rates of erosion, slopes are convex and concave respectively. One important concept proposed by Penck was that when river downcutting ceases, the recession of the main slope unit parallel to itself, because of uniform weathering over its face, will inevitably lead to the formation of a gentler basal slope unit across which debris is transported into the river. Penck showed that eventually this basal slope would extend itself and replace the main slope unit (Fig. 3.26). Penck also believed that slope replacement could occur in other ways. For example, where a steep slope unit exists below an upper gentler slope unit, the more rapid retreat of the former, related to more effective transport processes and thus exposure and weathering of the underlying rock, will result in time in the destruction of the latter.

Penck's model is highly theoretical, yet some of its main features have been successfully incorporated by L C King in his *cycle of pediplanation*, which appears to be particularly applicable to slope evolution in semi-arid and savanna regions. Perhaps the main flaw in the model lies in the emphasis Penck places on the rate of river downcutting. As shown on p. 65, the slope system embraces many controlling factors, notably climate and rock type, which are likely to influence the ways in which a slope evolves. Moreover, some geomorphologists believe that slope processes may change over time, as in the case of a slope which is declining in angle. On this, soil creep will become less active, and the action of rainwash relatively more important. If the former process produces rounding, or convexity, and the latter results in concavity, the form of the slope overall will necessarily change.

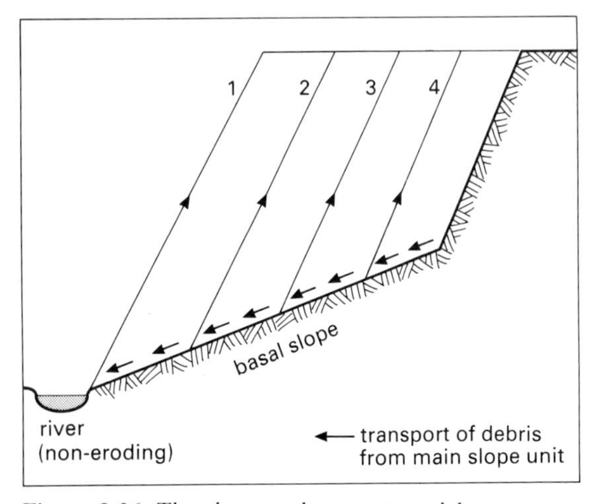

Figure 3.26 *The slope replacement model*

3 The parallel retreat model. It is commonly stated that Penck was responsible for the view that slopes undergo parallel retreat. In reality, Penck regarded only individual units as retreating without loss of steepness, and argued that, as a result of different rates of recession of individual units depending on their angle, replacement of some units by others was inevitable. Indeed, he showed that unless river downcutting occurs all slopes must decline in steepness.

However, there is evidence that parallel retreat of slopes, in a more general sense, does occur. Thus, scarp faces, valley slopes and buttes and mesas in desert areas may display similar profiles and maximum slope angles. It is unlikely that all these slopes, in different situations, are at exactly the same stage of development, and it is therefore reasonable to assume that the present slope forms have been maintained over long periods of time, involving substantial slope recession. One factor that may contribute to parallel retreat in deserts is that rock weathering rates are often low (p. 58), but that slope transport, by running water generated during desert rainstorms, is highly effective. Steep rock surfaces tend to remain bare, experience uniform weathering, and thus undergo uniform slope retreat. It follows that, under conditions where weathering is more rapid, transport less effective, and build up of regolith occurs, parallel retreat of slopes is unlikely.

Geomorphologists have for many years sought the correct model of slope evolution. Some have believed in slope decline, some in parallel retreat, and some in slope replacement; few have believed in all three! However, it has become increasingly apparent that the three models are not mutually exclusive, but each may be applicable in particular circumstances. These circumstances depend very much on (a) the prevailing climate, (b) geological structure, (c) rate of land uplift, (d) river activity, (e) nature and rate of weathering, and (f) efficiency of slope transport. Since there are almost innumerable ways in which these factors can combine, it is hardly logical to expect slopes in every part of the world to behave in precisely the same way.

ASSIGNMENTS

1 Visit available rock exposures in your home area (such as as road cuttings and old quarries).
  a. Make notes on the rock characteristics likely to influence weathering processes, such as mineral and chemical composition, grain size, bedding planes and joints.
  b. What evidence is there that the rock is being weathered by physical, chemical and biological processes?
  c. Is there any evidence, in your view, of weathering under past conditions, when the climate was warmer or colder than at present?

2 The figure below is a type of graph (*climograph*) often used to depict the climatic conditions which favour particular types of weathering and erosion.

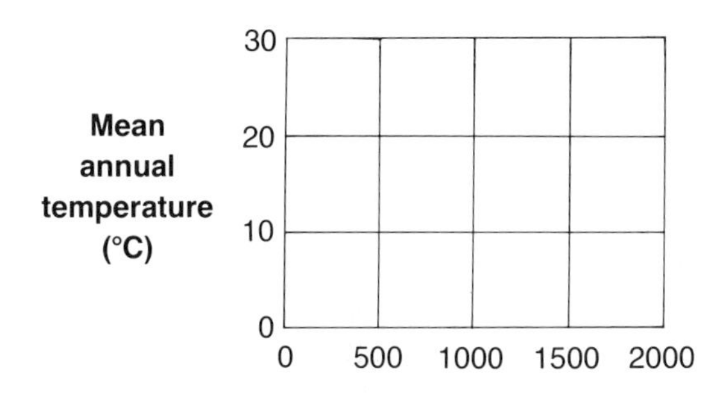

Figure 3.27

  a. Use the graph to indicate the climatic conditions favouring:
    i. rapid chemical weathering (RCW)
    ii. weak chemical weathering (WCW)
    iii. rapid physical weathering (RPW)
    iv. weak physical weathering (WPW).
  b. Describe and explain briefly the main weathering processes you would expect to occur under the climatic conditions (i), (ii), (iii) and (iv).
  c. What are the factors (other than climate) that will influence the type and rate of weathering at a particular locality?

3 Make a field visit to study slopes in your local area.
  a. Sketch as accurately as you can the profiles of a number of slopes and estimate the heights of these slopes, the maximum angle of steepness, and the direction in which the slope faces (aspect). If you have simple survey equipment, such as a clinometer and a tape measure, you can survey these slope profiles, and draw them accurately on graph paper.
  b. Estimate the proportion (as a percentage) of each slope profile that is convex, concave or rectilinear in form.
  c. Make notes of any evidence indicating the processes (such as soil creep or rainwash) that are modifying these slopes.
  d. Suggest possible reasons (such as the processes you have noted, slope height, rock type, aspect, vegetation cover) why the slope profiles you have studied differ from each other in form and steepness.

4 The figure overleaf shows graphs (histograms) of the frequency of occurrence of maximum slope angles in two areas, A and B, experiencing similar climatic conditions.
  a. What is the significance of the fact that the range of maximum slope angles in each is low?
  b. Give four possible reasons why the maximum slope angles in the two areas are different.
  c. If the two sets of slopes were in fact in the same area, with the steeper slopes having actively eroding streams at their base, and the gentler slopes not having streams at their base, what conclusion would you draw about slope evolution in the area?

5 The following table shows data obtained by field survey of five slope profiles (equally spaced in a downvalley direction) in two valleys, one in lime-

stone (A) and the other in clay (B).

a. Describe and explain briefly the changes in slope height and maximum slope angle in a downvalley direction for each valley.
b. With the aid of sketch profiles, describe the changes in slope form in a downvalley direction for each valley.
c. Suggest reasons why the slopes in valley A show some important differences from those in valley B. You should pay particular attention to:
   i. the greater steepness of the slopes in valley A;
   ii. the dominance of convexo-rectilinear slopes in valley A;
   iii. the dominance of concave slopes in valley B.

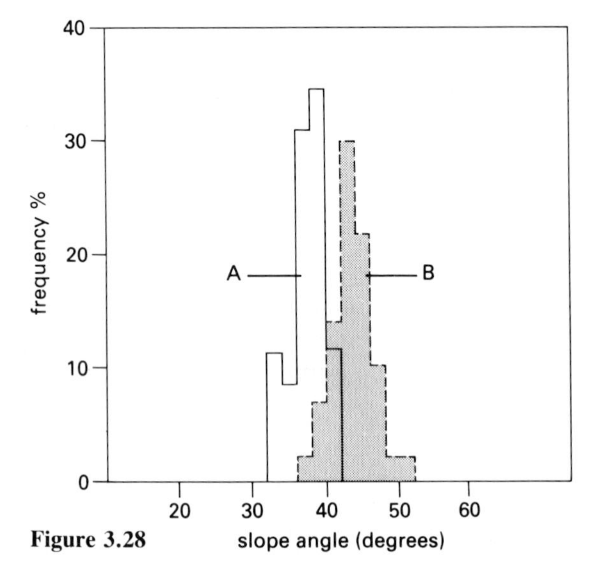

Figure 3.28

		Profile	Slope height (m)	Max. slope angle (°)	Percentage of profile convex	Percentage of profile rectilinear	Percentage of profile concave
A	Limestone	1	15	17	100	0	0
		2	24	25	80	20	0
		3	57	32	58	42	0
		4	87	31	52	48	0
		5	120	32	48	52	0
B	Clay	1	8	2	32	0	68
		2	20	3	28	0	72
		3	30	5	26	0	74
		4	44	7	24	0	76
		5	55	9	20	0	80

4

The Landforms of Cold Environments

Figure 4.1 *The snout of Glacier du Mont Miné, Switzerland. Note the large amounts of debris on the ice which are sliding down the steep glacier face to accumulate as moraine, and the faults (thrust planes) resulting from glacier advance in the middle distance*

One of the most memorable experiences any geomorphologist can have is to visit a glacier in the field for the first time (Fig. 4.1). An immediate impression will be gained of a great force at work, as the glacier, comprising many millions of tonnes of ice, moves inexorably downvalley under the influence of gravity. The actual glacier velocity may be low, except on steep sections, or ice-falls, where masses of ice frequently break away to create dangerous avalanches; yet the vast quantities of broken rock debris carried on the glacier surface, the blocks of rock sliding continuously and noisily from the glacier margins on to rapidly growing morainic ridges, and the thunder of meltwater streams, containing so much sediment that the water has a milky appearance, all testify to the amount of rapid geomorphological work that is being carried out. It is not surprising that many geomorphologists regard glaciers as the most powerful of all erosional agents, capable of transforming the physical landscape at an unparalleled rate, and with very striking results.

The importance of ice, in erosion, transport and deposition, is further underlined by the present day extent of glaciers, ice-caps and ice-sheets, occupying some 15 million km^2 of the earth's surface. Most of this ice is included in the Antarctic ice-sheet (11.5 million km^2) and the Greenland ice-cap (1.7 million km^2). Smaller ice-caps and valley glaciers are found in high mountain ranges, such as the Alps, Himalayas, Rockies and Andes, or in high latitude areas, notably Iceland, Baffin Island and Spitzbergen. During the Quaternary era, lasting approximately for 2 million years, the ice cover became much more extensive. For example, the Laurentide ice-sheet, expanding over much of Canada and the north-east USA, had a maximum extent of nearly 14 million km^2, whilst the Scandinavian ice-sheet, which affected much of north-western Europe, grew to 6.7 million km^2. Over the earth as a whole the Quaternary ice at its maximum covered 47 million km^2. Bearing in mind the thickness of these great ice-sheets, of up to 2000 m or more, and their great capacity for erosion and the transport and deposition of vast amounts of sediment, it is inevitable that the Quaternary glaciation was perhaps the most important event in the shaping of physical landscapes over some 30 per cent of the earth's surface.

However, the Quaternary era did not simply embrace one episode of glacial advance. Until quite recently it was believed that there were four or five distinct glacial periods, separated by warmer interglacial periods when the climate was broadly similar to that of today and major glacial retreats occurred. Current research is revealing a more complex history. It now seems possible that there were as many as 20 glaciations, each lasting up to 100 000 years, and that the interglacials were quite short (approximately 10 000 years each). The last major retreat of the ice took place some 10 000 years ago. Following the so called post-glacial 'climatic optimum', when temperatures were warmer than at any time since, the climate has cooled slightly over the past 500 years, giving rise to fears that the earth is on the threshold of another major glacial advance.

In addition to the areas actually covered by ice, there are extensive tracts of land, particularly in North America, northern Europe and over much of Siberia, which experience a very cold climate, with severe winter freezing and a relatively brief summer thaw. Although snow may fall in appreciable quantities, it is removed by melting each year, and thus the build-up of glacier ice is prevented. Such *periglacial* environments extend today over some 20 per cent of the earth's land surface, and up to 50 per cent of the total area of the USSR alone. Moreover, it must be remembered that, with the advance of the Quaternary ice-sheets, the periglacial zone was shifted towards the Equator, so that the landscapes of many present day temperate regions were greatly modified by past periglacial weathering, erosion, transport and deposition. In our discussion of the landforms of cold environments it is therefore convenient to make a division between *glacial environments* and *periglacial environments*.

GLACIAL ENVIRONMENTS

Glaciers as geomorphological systems

Glaciers and ice-sheets form where the amount of winter snowfall exceeds that lost by melting, or *ablation*, during summer. In Alpine regions several metres of snow build up each winter on the upper part of the glacier, or the *accumulation zone* (Fig. 4.2). That remaining after surface melting during the following summer, known as *névé* or *firn*, will be gradually transformed by compression, melting and refreezing into glacier ice. In this way the glacier surface in the accumulation zone will be built up by a

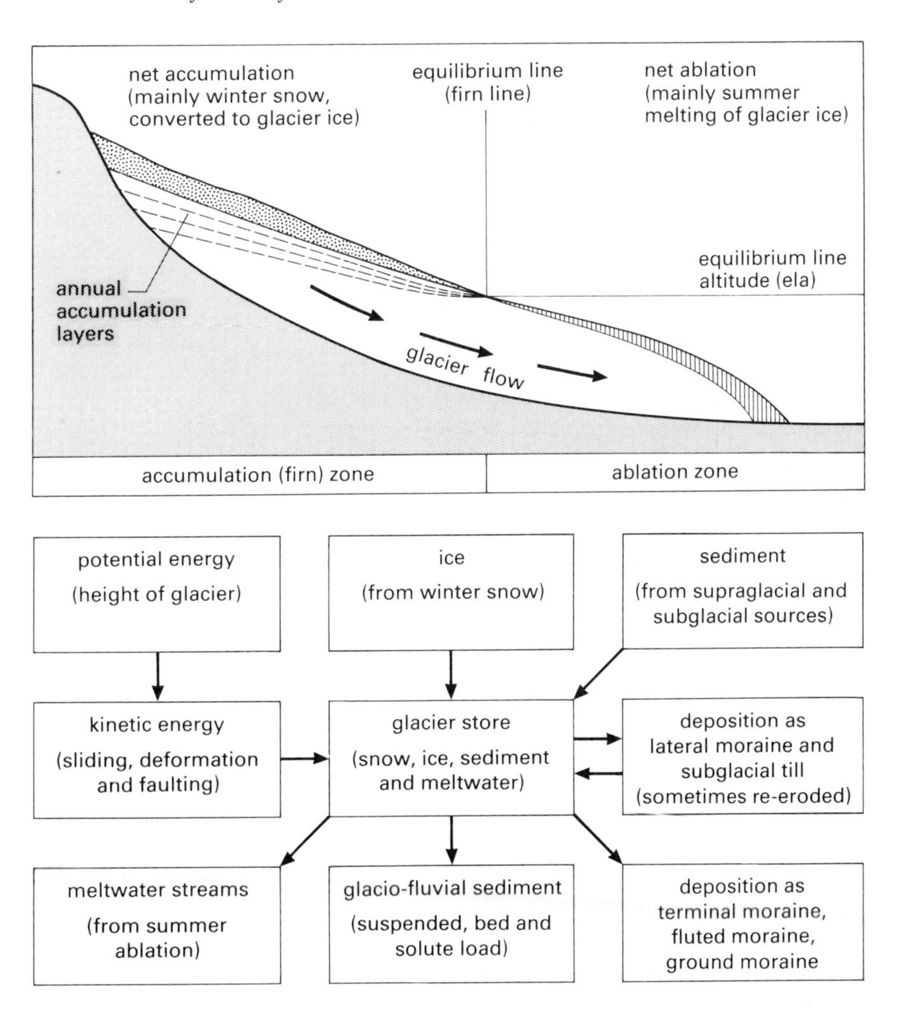

Figure 4.2 *Accumulation and ablation on a glacier*

Figure 4.3 *Main inputs and outputs of the glacier system*

series of annual layers. On the lower part of the glacier, snow also collects in winter but because of reduced altitude summer temperatures here are higher and all of this snow is soon melted. The glacier surface itself is then ablated, hence the term *ablation zone*, thus releasing large quantities of glacial meltwater; close to the glacier snout ablation may be so intense that the ice is lowered each summer by 10 m or more. The accumulation and ablation zones of the glacier are separated by the *equilibrium line*; this marks the change from increasing ice volume (above) to decreasing ice volume (below). In a large ice-sheet, such as that of Antarctica, accumulation occurs over a large central area, where the winter snowfall is much less than in the Alps but ablation is also greatly reduced by the lower summer temperatures; the ablation zone, of more limited extent, occupies a relatively narrow band around the periphery of the ice sheet. Much of the loss of ice is due to the calving of icebergs, rather than direct melting of the ice surface by the sun's rays.

Because a glacier is continually being added to in its upper parts, and reduced in its lower parts, there is a compensatory flow of ice from the accumulation to the ablation zone. This is the basis for viewing glaciers as *geomorphological systems*, or to be more specific as *open systems*, which are characterised by inputs, throughputs and outputs not only of *mass* but also of *energy* (Fig. 4.3). The most obvious inputs are snow and ice, and the major output is meltwater. It is at least theoretically possible that these inputs and outputs will exactly balance, in which case a condition of *equilibrium* or *steady state* will be established. This will be represented by a glacier whose snout will neither advance nor retreat; in other words, the forward motion of the ice at the snout will be precisely offset by melting back.

It is believed that geomorphological systems naturally tend towards a steady state condition, though in the case of glaciers changes of climate leading to greater winter snowfall (input) or more intense ablation (output) continually delay the attainment of this condition. One important mechanism that is relevant here is *negative feedback*, a process by which the system controls itself in the face of changing inputs and outputs. For example, if, as a result of reduced winter temperatures, snow accumulation is increased and is not offset by greater ablation, the glacier will enlarge and its snout will advance; in other words it will not be in a steady state. However, this advance will take the glacier snout farther downvalley into a warmer area. Here a greater input of heat energy, related to the higher temperatures, will lead to an increase in meltwater production, to the point at which the greater winter snow accumulation will be balanced; thus the glacier will have returned to a steady state condition, but will now occupy a more advanced position (Fig. 4.4).

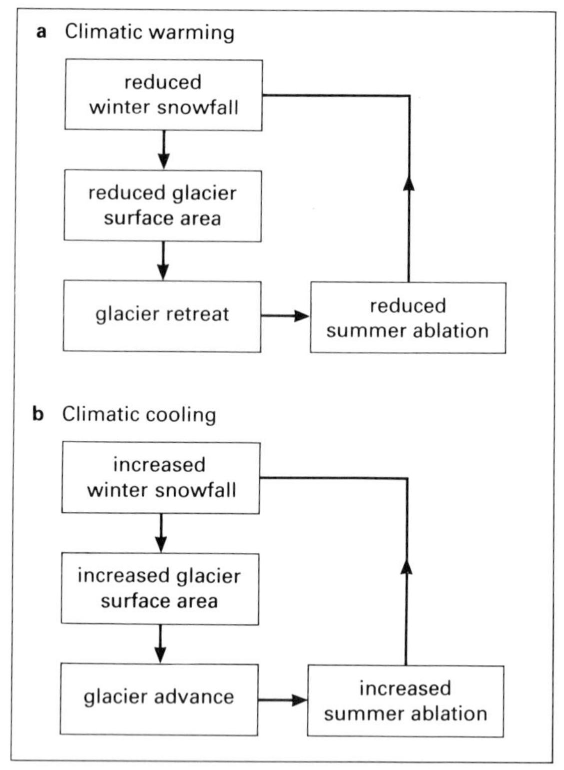

Figure 4.4 *The response of glaciers to climatic change. In* ***a*** *climatic warming and reduced winter snowfall results in glacier retreat, with the snout eventually becoming stable in an up-valley position. In* ***b*** *climatic cooling and increased winter snowfall leads to glacier advance*

It is important to realise that glacial systems involve not only ice and water, but also sediment, hence the allied concept of the glacier as a *sediment transport system*. Sediment inputs are derived from erosion beneath the ice, by processes such as plucking and abrasion (pp. 87–88), and from the weathering of slopes above the glacier surface; outputs consist of coarser material, which is mainly deposited on moraines, and finer sediment, which is washed away by meltwater streams.

Studying the inputs and outputs of glacial systems can clearly help us to understand the form of glaciers and their geomorphological activities. For example, over a period of years accumulation may exceed ablation, so that the glacier has a *positive mass balance*, and significant glacial advances will occur. In the late sixteenth century in Europe, a cooling of the climate, in the order of 1°C mean annual temperature, led to the onset of the Little Ice Age in the Alps. Many glaciers advanced by 1–2 km, and in some areas this led to the abandonment or even destruction of farms and villages. After 1850, a warming of the climate resulted in *negative mass balances* of glaciers and initiated a period of glacial retreat which lasted until about 1970. Since then, however, glacier snouts have again moved forward, in the case of Glacier de Tsidjiore Nouve by 300 m in 15 years (Fig. 4.5). Some of these advances are threatening expensive hydro-electric installations in the Pennine Alps of Switzerland.

Where inputs of snow and outputs of

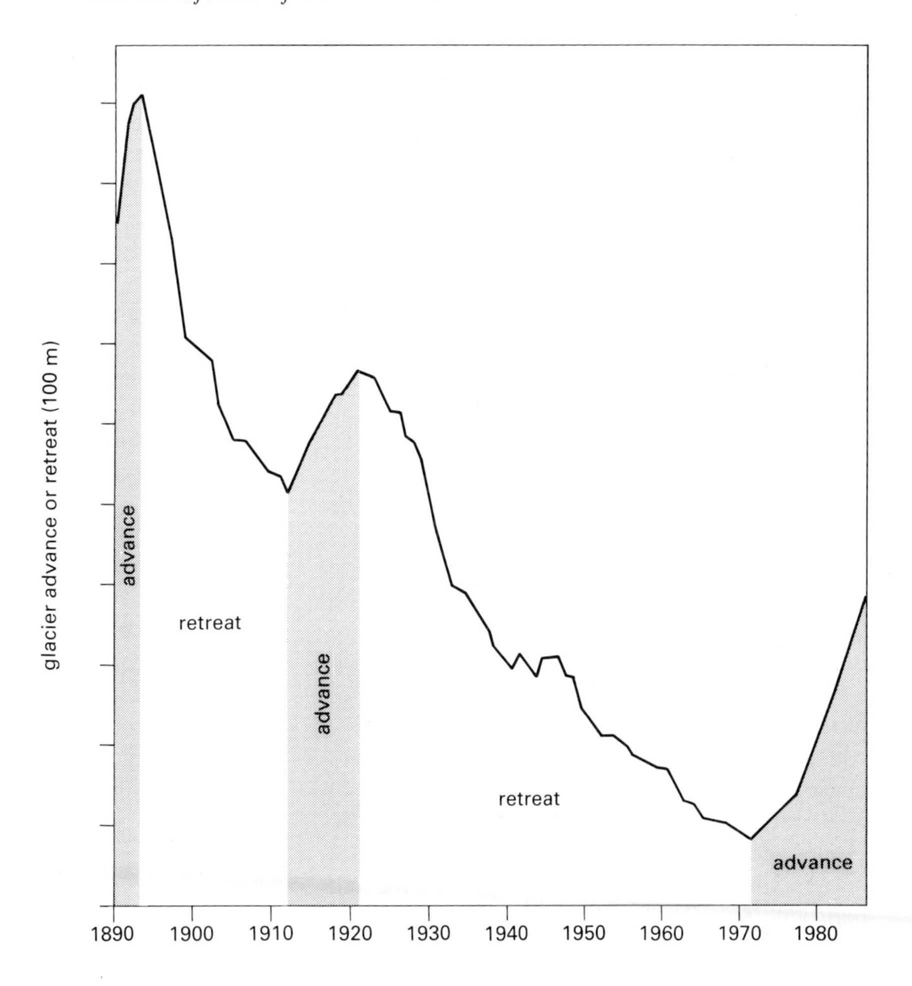

Figure 4.5 *The advance and retreat of Glacier de Tsidjiore Nouve 1890–1986*

meltwater are both high, the glacier will have a large *total budget* (accumulation plus ablation), and the glacier system will be characterised by a rapid throughput of ice. In other words, for a balance to be maintained between accumulation and ablation, velocities of flow need to be high, otherwise there will be excessive build-up of ice on the upper part of the glacier. If the latter does occur, it too will eventually cause rapid flow, and a sudden advance of the glacier snout as part of a *glacier surge*. Large total budgets are associated with regions such as the Alps, Himalayas and Rockies, and small total budgets with polar glaciers and ice-sheets. It has been argued that in the former glaciers will, because of their faster flow, erode much more effectively than those of polar regions.

Temperature characteristics and flow of glaciers and ice-sheets

It is tempting to suppose that all glaciers, consisting of snow that has been transformed into ice, are similar; in reality, this is far from being the case. Glaciers in mid-latitude mountain areas, such as the Swiss Alps, are at approximately 0°C throughout their depth, except in winter when their uppermost layers may be chilled to −5°C or less. They are thus on the verge of melting, or to be more exact are at *pressure melting point*, and during the summer generate large quantities of meltwater both on the ice surface, and within and at the base of the ice. Such glaciers are referred to as *temperate* or *warm glaciers*; and because there is always a layer of meltwater between the bottom of the glacier and bedrock, they experience quite rapid and effective *basal sliding*. Glaciers in sub-polar and polar regions, such as Spitzbergen, Baffin Island, Greenland and Antarctica, are characterised by much lower temperatures. Near the surface, the ice may be as cold as −20° to −30°C, even during summer; and though the temperature of the ice increases with depth, it may well be below 0°C at the glacier base. Such *cold glaciers* are therefore frozen to bedrock and cannot undergo basal sliding, with the result that their erosive powers may be even further diminished (p. 87). Moreover, there is no possibility of the formation of meltwater within and at the base of the ice. In some sub-polar environments, glaciers may be in a transitional stage, with negative temperatures in their upper layers and temperatures of 0°C in their lower; these are referred to as *warm-based cold glaciers*.

Most glaciers flow at a very slow rate; indeed, when standing on a glacier one is rarely conscious of any movement at all. Temperate glaciers move generally at a daily rate of 5–20 cm; the highest velocities are along the glacier centreline, and the least along the margins, where there is friction between ice and bedrock. In a downglacier direction, velocity increases from the head of the accumulation zone to a maximum at the equilibrium line; thereafter velocity is reduced across the ablation zone to a minimum at the glacier snout. There are, too, changes in ice velocity through the year. Temperate glaciers flow more rapidly in summer than in winter because meltwater penetrates by way of open crevasses and may reach the base of the moving ice. Occasionally glaciers experience, over a short period of time, what is known as *fast sliding*. Observations have shown that the Allalin Glacier, occupying a steep, glacially smoothed bed on the western side of the Saas valley in Switzerland, attains a peak velocity of 4 m/day for a few days in September/October of each year. It is now known that such fast sliding produces, in the presence of small rock steps and roches moutonnées, large subglacial caverns. These may grow to the extent that the overlying ice collapses suddenly. In 1965 such a collapse, and the associated shock, triggered off a catastrophic slide of the lower part of the Allalin glacier; one million tonnes of ice overwhelmed a dam-construction site, killing 88 workmen.

The actual mechanisms of glacier flow are complex, but in simple terms two types of movement can be identified. As stated above basal sliding is particularly effective in temperate and warm-based cold glaciers, where there is always a film of meltwater at the glacier base resulting from the escape of heat from the earth, or *geothermal flux*. In small valley and cirque glaciers, up to 90 per cent of the total ice flow will be in the form of basal sliding; in larger valley glaciers this figure is reduced to approximately 50 per cent. The second main type of glacier flow is *internal deformation*, otherwise known as *creep*. When ice is subjected to pressure, as at depth within a glacier, individual ice crystals are deformed and recrystallised. Since the glacier comprises countless millions of such crystals, it begins to behave as a plastic substance. Evidence of this can be seen in subglacial caverns and tunnels, where the ice has often moulded itself to the shape of the underlying rock surface in a very striking way. Internal deformation may be concentrated along narrow lines within the glacier, resulting in a banded structure of fine grained blue and coarser white ice, known as *foliation*. Although internal deformation is active in temperate glaciers, it is relatively more important in cold glaciers, where sliding is reduced or non-existent.

PROCESSES OF GLACIAL EROSION, TRANSPORT AND DEPOSITION

Glacial erosional processes

The occupation by present day glaciers of deep and often spectacular glacial troughs, the occurrence of such landforms in areas of past glaciation, and the evidence of intense geomorphological activity by glaciers described on p. 81, all point to the great erosional powers of glacier ice. However, such an *erosionist* view of glaciers and ice-sheets has by no means always been universally accepted. In the early part of this century, the so called *glacial protectionists* argued that glaciers actually reduced, by their very presence, the effectiveness of processes such as freeze-thaw weathering and fluvial erosion. It is obvious that whilst some arguments, such as that glacier ice at 0°C throughout insulates the subglacial rock surface from atmospheric temperature changes and thus hinders weathering, were valid, the protectionist case as a whole was overstated. Even so, it is now recognised that under certain circumstances, as when the ice is flowing very slowly or is actually frozen to bedrock, glaciers may have relatively little erosive power. Indeed, in some areas of eastern Greenland, landscapes have been found which, although subjected to Quaternary glaciation, display only fluvial characteristics, such as V-shaped valleys, interlocking spurs and soil-mantled slopes. For the most part, however, glaciers have had a very powerful erosive impact, and have transformed the landscapes they occupied.

Glaciers and ice-sheets are believed to erode mainly by the two processes of *abrasion* and *plucking*. However, it has become increasingly apparent that other processes play a part in the formation of what are regarded as typical glacial landforms.

Abrasion occurs when fragments of rock, either frozen into the base of the glacier or trapped between the moving ice and underlying bedrock, are used as tools to gouge, scratch and polish the rock; the process has been likened, in simple terms, to a sandpaper effect on a massive scale (Fig. 4.6). Abrasion is clearly most effective where basal sliding is relatively rapid, as in temperate glaciers, and where there is a ready supply of basal rock fragments; these can be derived from the fracturing of bedrock by plucking, the melting out of debris within the lower layers of the glacier, or from weathering of supraglacial rock faces. The particles used in abrasion are themselves subject to considerable wear, and are eventually reduced to fine sand and silt that can be washed out, together with the fine particles worn from the solid rock, by basal meltwater streams; hence the *glacier flour* which gives to these streams their milky appearance. Although glacial abrasion, carried out by glaciers moving at a few cm a day, may seem a slow process, there are reasons to believe that it is, in fact, highly effective. Careful measurement of the fine sediment emerging from glaciers by way of meltwater streams has revealed surprisingly large quantities. For example, in 1981 and 1982 respectively, the small Glacier de Tsidjiore

Figure 4.6 *A glacially abraded surface, exposed by the recent recession of Glacier de Ferpecle, Switzerland*

Nouve in Switzerland released 9491 and 8702 tonnes of suspended sediment; if this is distributed over the area covered by the glacier, an annual lowering of the glacier bed by 0.89–0.99 mm/annum^{-1} is implied. This would be sufficient to deepen the glacial valley by 900–1000 m over a period of one million years! The actual landforms resulting from abrasion are polished and scratched, or *striated*, surfaces; glacial grooves up to several metres in depth, formed where the basal ice flow is concentrated along certain lines; and streamlined rock outcrops.

Plucking involves the detachment from bedrock of large fragments of rock, up to a metre or more in diameter; these are then dragged at the base of the glacier or, more usually, actually incorporated within the basal ice layers. As a result, irregular rock faces, with the appearance of having been quarried, are developed on the downglacier sides of valley steps and roches moutonnées. Although it is an indisputable fact that plucking occurs, the process remains imperfectly understood. It is not due, as was once thought, to the glacier freezing on to bedrock and wrenching parts of it away; solid rock is very much stronger than ice, so that the latter would fracture, not the former! It is possible that very large boulders within basal ice are used to crush and break away smaller bedrock obstacles. Usually, however, plucking seems to be effective only where the rock has been already weakened in some way. For instance, plucking operates well in jointed rocks, which are mechanically less strong than unjointed rocks; hence the term *joint-block quarrying*. It is possible that these rocks are actually broken up, beneath the glacier, by the penetration into the joints of meltwater, which subsequently freezes and expands, giving rise to a process akin to freeze-thaw weathering. The problem here is that, beneath a temperate glacier which is perhaps 200 m thick and at 0°C throughout, temperature changes are usually very small, and effective rock breakdown difficult to envisage. One hypothesis is that rock fracturing beneath glaciers is due to pressure release or dilatation (p. 52). For instance, as a glacier slowly erodes, by abrasion, a valley in granite, it replaces solid rock with a density of 2.5–3.0 with ice having a density of 0.9. The reduced load on the valley floor allows the formation of sheet joints and the splitting away of rock fragments that can be transported away in the basal ice layers. Another view is that well jointed rock is unstable, and the collapse of steep rock faces, for example on valley steps beneath the ice, contributes much basal debris.

Other processes that are now accepted as important contributors to glacial erosion in the broad sense are weathering and collapse of rock faces above the glacier and the action of running water beneath the ice. Peaks standing above the glacier surface, known as nunataks, and valley walls are subject both to severe attack by freeze-thaw weathering and, following glacial retreat, the large scale collapse of over steepened rock faces. Study of Glacier de Tsidjiore Nouve, referrred to earlier, has shown that between 8000 and 11 000 tonnes of morainic debris may be derived from supraglacial rock faces in a single year. Subglacial streams, best developed beneath the glacier ablation zone, flow at high velocities and under considerable pressure. Using glacial debris as tools, they are capable of incising deep potholes and gorge-like valleys into solid rock. Such a process can be fairly termed glacial, since if the glacier were not present the erosive power of the water would be much diminished.

Glacial transportational processes (Fig. 4.7)

Large quantities of sediment, ranging in size from large joint bounded boulders to fine silt, are transported by glaciers on the ice surface (*supraglacial*), within the ice (*englacial*), and at the base of the glacier (*subglacial*). Supraglacial debris can fall directly on to the glacier margins, within the ablation zone, from valley sides. However, the vast increase in surface debris near many glacier snouts indicates that the release of englacial debris, as a result of ice ablation, is important. The latter consists at

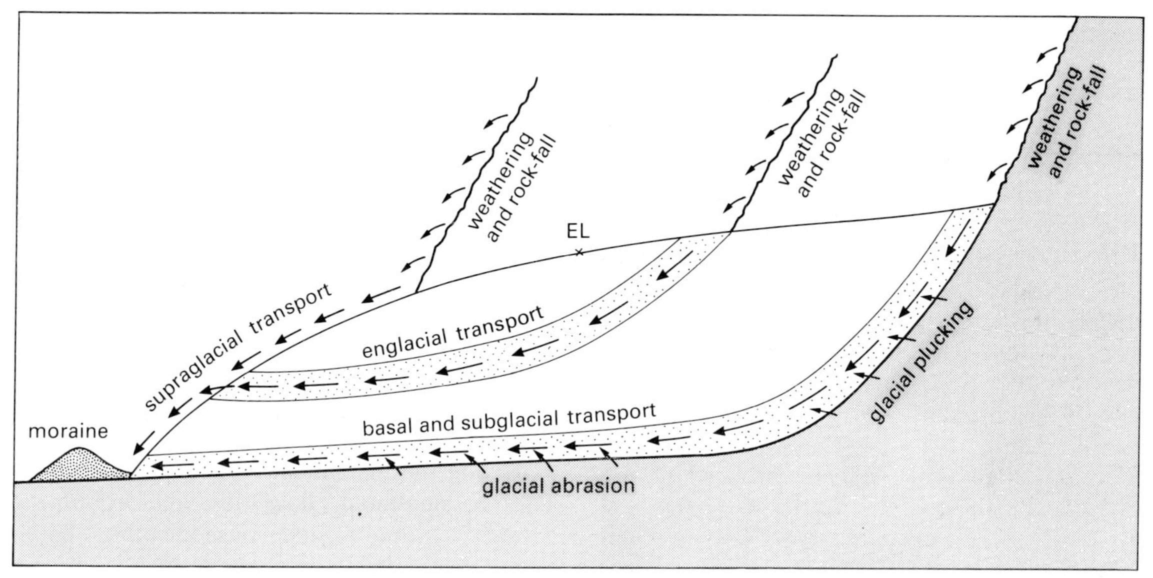

Figure 4.7 *Glacier transportational processes*

least partly of material which has fallen on to the glacier surface, from above, in the accumulation zone, mainly during the summer season when rock faces are free of snow. This surface debris will subsequently be buried by winter snowfall, which will in turn gradually be transformed into ice. Over many years layers of ice and debris are built up, giving the glacier a stratified structure. Subglacial debris is derived mainly from abrasion and plucking; the material is subsequently crushed, rolled and dragged along the glacier bed, thus becoming generally finer and more rounded than supraglacial debris. Some subglacial sediment may become incorporated within the lower layers of the glacier by *regelation*, or refreezing. Where pressure on basal ice is increased, for example, as it slides over a rock obstacle, melting will occur; however, downglacier of the obstacle, as pressure is reduced, the resultant meltwater will again freeze on to the glacier base.

Glacial depositional processes

Much of the sediment load of a glacier is removed and deposited by meltwater. The coarser fragments, however, tend to remain on or within the ice, until they are released and dumped at the glacier margins. Whilst remaining on the ice surface, supraglacial debris tends to be concentrated along the margins, as *supraglacial lateral moraine*, or approximately along the centre line of the glacier, as *medial moraine* (Fig. 4.8). Near the snout, however, as englacial debris melts out at the glacier surface, there may be a widespread layer of *ablation moraine*, up to a metre or more in thickness. One notable feature is the way in which layers of surface debris can protect the ice from the sun's rays, reducing ablation. As a result, supraglacial lateral and medial moraines grow into ice-cored ridges rising up to 30 m above the general glacier surface. The sediment covering the supraglacial moraines is partly supplied by the melting out of zones of concentrated englacial debris, known as *debris septa*.

Sediment is also deposited in large quantities at the base of the glacier, particularly where the ice becomes enriched by glacial sediment. Towards the glacier snout, as the forward velocity is reduced, bottom melting gradually releases rock particles from the ice; these are then lodged on to the underlying surface, hence the formation of the deposit known as *lodgement till*, which is particularly thick and extensive when formed by large ice-sheets.

Figure 4.8 *A supraglacial medial moraine, resulting from the junction of tributary glaciers from the left and right of the peak, La Vierge, in the top right of the photograph. Note the angular nature of the moraine, which results from its origin as a product of supraglacial weathering rather than subglacial erosion*

Meltwater, or *glacio-fluvial*, activity is important both in removing sediment from the glacier itself, and from the zone of deposition immediately beyond the glacier snout, known as the *proglacial zone*. During summer, as air temperatures rise above 0°C, ablation of the ice surface releases vast quantities of meltwater, particularly on temperate glaciers. For example, the stream draining the Gornergletscher, in Switzerland, has a maximum summer discharge of over 35 m^3/s^{-1}, whereas the discharge of the winter months is virtually constant at 0.2 m^3/s^{-1}.

During the summer melt, a dense network of *supraglacial* streams develops on the glacier surface; many of these are able to penetrate the glacier, by way of crevasses and moulins, to form *englacial streams* and, when eventually they reach the base of the ice, *subglacial streams* (Fig. 4.9). One important function of the latter is to wash out much of the fine sediment produced by glacial erosion, thus preventing the build-up of excessive amounts of sediment between the glacier and bedrock, and allowing abrasion to continue effectively. There is a pronounced daily rhythm in the flow of these meltwater streams, with a late afternoon peak reflecting the maximum daytime temperatures, and a minimum flow just before dawn. However, major and unpredictable floods sometimes occur; these are known as *glacial outbursts*. The principal cause is the accumulation of large quantities of meltwater, along the margin of the glacier, on its surface, or even within the ice. These lakes sometimes empty very rapidly, and have proved a serious hazard in Alpine areas; today artificial tunnels are often constructed, beneath the glacier itself or through bedrock, from known sites of temporary lakes, in order to prevent the build-up of meltwater to a dangerous level. Such glacial floods occur on a particularly massive scale in Iceland, where melting of the ice-caps is locally increased as a result of volcanic activity next to or even beneath the ice. The large lakes which form in a depression of Vatnajokull, next to the Grimsvotn volcano, provide a spectacular example. These develop over a period of 5–10 years, to the point at which the volume of meltwater may be as high as 7.5 km^3. Eventually this water literally raises the ice of Vatnajokull from its bed, and escapes rapidly through a 40 km subglacial tunnel to the Skeidarasandur beyond the glacier snout. The resultant flood is stupendous though short lived, lasting usually for one or two days; in the 1934 outburst the discharge of the meltwater stream was estimated to peak at 50 000 m^3/s^{-1}, by comparison with the mean discharge of the Thames at Teddington of 64.7 m^3/s^{-1} in 1980! Fortunately, the area affected by these great floods,

Figure 4.9 *Glacial meltwater streams emerging from beneath Haut Glacier d'Arolla, Switzerland*

referred to in Iceland as *jokulhlaups*, is an uninhabited outwash plain.

As stated above, meltwater streams, particularly those flowing beneath glaciers, have high velocities and thus a great capacity for transporting sediment. However, as the streams escape from the ice their velocities are suddenly reduced and much deposition, particularly of coarser sediments, occurs close to glacier margins. Finer sediments can be transported farther, with the result that *grading*, from coarse to fine, is often characteristic of the glacio-fluvial deposits of the proglacial zone. Moreover, since the deposits are built up by successive summer flows they tend to be stratified, and thus contrast with the unstratified deposits resulting from direct glacial deposition by processes such as marginal dumping and lodgement. The sediment washed out by meltwater streams can pose serious problems, particularly where the water is being utilised in hydro-electric schemes. Thus, field monitoring over the period 1968–80 has revealed that the glacier Nigardsbreen, in Norway, releases each year between 10 700 and 32 400 tonnes of sediment. Such a volume can quickly fill human made lakes, choke tunnels for water transmission, and damage generating equipment. The sediment therefore needs to be filtered out or disposed of in some way, even if the cost is high. For example, a natural sediment trap in the form of a rock-basin lake, below the Glacier du Mont Miné in the Swiss Alps, became almost entirely filled with sediment during the late 1970s and early 1980s. It was worthwhile for the Grande Dixence SA, a major hydro-electric undertaking which was utilising the meltwater from this glacier, to excavate 100 000 tonnes of sediment in the autumn of 1982, in order to restore the lake as an effective trap!

THE LANDFORMS OF GLACIATED REGIONS

Glacial erosional landforms of upland regions

Study of a mountain area which is at present *glacierised*, such as the Alps, Himalayas or Rockies, or which during the Quaternary was occupied by glaciers, such as Snowdonia, the Lake District or the Grampians, reveals the presence of a number of highly characteristic landforms.

Glacial cirques are large hollows, arcuate in plan and bounded by steep head and side walls. In Snowdonia, 84 cirques have been identified; these face mainly to the north-east, and are developed at the heads and along the margins of the many glaciated valleys of the area. In detail, the most important features of cirques are: the plucked appearance of the bounding walls; the relatively smooth floor, indicative of abrasion; the frequent occurrence of rock basins, which on the melting of the cirque glacier become occupied by small lakes; and rock lips which are smoothed on the inner side and plucked on the side away from the cirque (Fig. 4.10). In Britain the lips of cirques are often occupied by small terminal moraines, related to the final stages of cirque formation in the late-glacial period.

Study of present day cirque glaciers in areas such as Norway has shed light on cirque formation. At the upper limits of these glaciers there is usually a deep crevasse, or *bergschrund*, formed as the ice pulls away from the head wall; this bergschrund may penetrate to the underlying rock, at a depth of some 30 m. In the *bergschrund hypothesis* it is argued that freeze-thaw action at the base of the crevasse breaks up the rock of the head wall; the loosened fragments are then incorporated within the glacier and transported away. Thus the head wall is subject to a form of plucking, which leads to gradual enlargement of the cirque as a whole. Another process which may be particularly active during warmer periods, when the cirque glacier is reduced in size, is freeze-thaw weathering of the head wall above the ice.

Some of the rock debris from plucking and weathering becomes trapped within the basal layers of the glacier, and is used to abrade the cirque floor. Cirque glaciers in Norway have been shown to experience much basal sliding; indeed the glacier as a whole may slide in a rotational fashion, referred to as *rotational slip*, as shown in Fig. 4.10. This would help to account for the semi-circular long-profile of many cirques, and the presence of rock basins, exposed when the glacier melts.

Where an individual mountain is occupied by three or four cirque glaciers, each eroding its head wall, narrow ridges are eventually formed

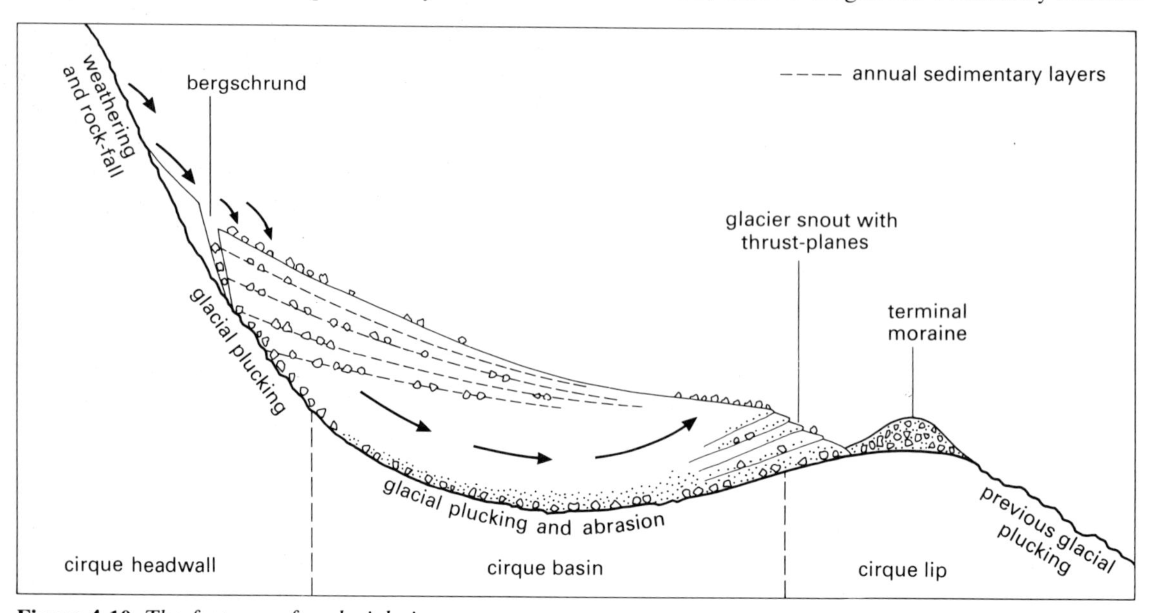

Figure 4.10 *The features of a glacial cirque*

Figure 4.11 *An arête at Engstligengrat, above Adelboden, Switzerland. The ridge separates the sites of former cirque glaciers to right and left. At points where the arête crest is smooth, the ice on either side appears to have become joined; separating these points are high, rugged peaks (such as that in the middle distance)*

between the individual cirques (Fig. 4.11). These sharp-crested *arêtes* may in time be lowered or destroyed, giving *cols* which link the cirque basins. At a late stage high, steep-sided peaks, or *horns*, may become isolated in the process; these are not well developed in Britain, but are very characteristic of Alpine regions, where the Matterhorn is the most famous and spectacular example.

Glacial valleys, which when particularly deeply cut are referred to as *glacial troughs*, usually display a U-shaped cross-profile, by contrast with the V-profiles of the pre-glacial river valleys which were followed by the Quaternary glaciers. The latter effected both lateral erosion, removing the spurs between former tributary valleys to give *truncated spurs*, and vertical erosion or *glacial overdeepening*. It is believed that, as a result of powerful glacial abrasion and plucking, the floors of Alpine valleys were lowered by 300–600 m, hence the form of striking glacial troughs such as the Lauterbrunnen valley (Fig. 4.12). In coastal Norway and Alaska, where massive valley glaciers were able to cut well below sea-level, over deepening by some 1000–1500 m may have occurred, giving rise to features such as Sognefjord, Hardangerfjord and Lynn Canal. One common result of glacial over deepening of the main valley was to leave tributary valleys, occupied by smaller and weaker glaciers, hanging, hence the term *hanging valleys*; the streams from these now commonly descend to the main valley floor by waterfalls. Another feature resulting from vertical erosion by a large valley glacier is the very steep valley head, or *trough end*; this is formed where a number of small cirque or tributary glaciers unite to give a trunk glacier of great thickness and erosive power.

Figure 4.12 *The deep glacial trough of the Lauterbrunnen valley, Switzerland*

The cross-profiles of large glacial valleys often display a valley in valley form, with the characteristic U-shaped trough incised into the lower part of a more open valley, perhaps the pre-glacial river valley. Remnants of the old valley profile are represented by *alp benches* above the shoulders of the glacial valley. In many cases, the benches themselves show evidence of glaciation, in the form of morainic deposits, though the ice here has been relatively inactive, at least compared to the main valley glacier. In post-glacial times, valley profiles have been modified by the accumulation of large quantities of glacio-fluvial deposits, resulting in the formation of a flat floor, and by freeze-thaw weathering of the valley walls, producing *deglaciation scree deposits*.

The long-profiles of glacial valleys are characteristically irregular (Fig. 4.13). The near vertical trough end is succeeded downvalley by relatively level sections, sometimes actually *rock basins* eroded into solid rock, and steep valley steps, or *rock steps*, which commonly show evidence of former glacial plucking. Such long-profiles appear to result from selective over deepening; thus basins frequently coincide with outcrops of weak, closely jointed rock that can be easily eroded, whilst the steps mark bands of more massive, highly resistant rock. There are also many minor irregularities, usually small projections of hard rock that have been abraded on the up-glacier stoss slope and plucked on the downglacier lee slope; such features are known as *roches moutonnées*.

Glacial depositional landforms of upland regions

Within glaciated upland valleys, morainic mounds and ridges are common features. Although these vary greatly in scale and form, several individual types are recognised. These all have one feature in common: the sediments they contain are heterogeneous, varying from large boulders to fine sand and silt, and are not layered, or in other words are unstratified.

Terminal moraines form when the glacier snout remains stationary for a period of years. Supraglacial debris, plus any englacial sediment released by ice melting, accumulates as a ridge which is broken at points where meltwater streams emerge from the glacier (Fig. 4.14). When a glacier undergoes several periods of retreat, separated by stillstands, a series of approximately parallel moraine ridges, or *recessional*

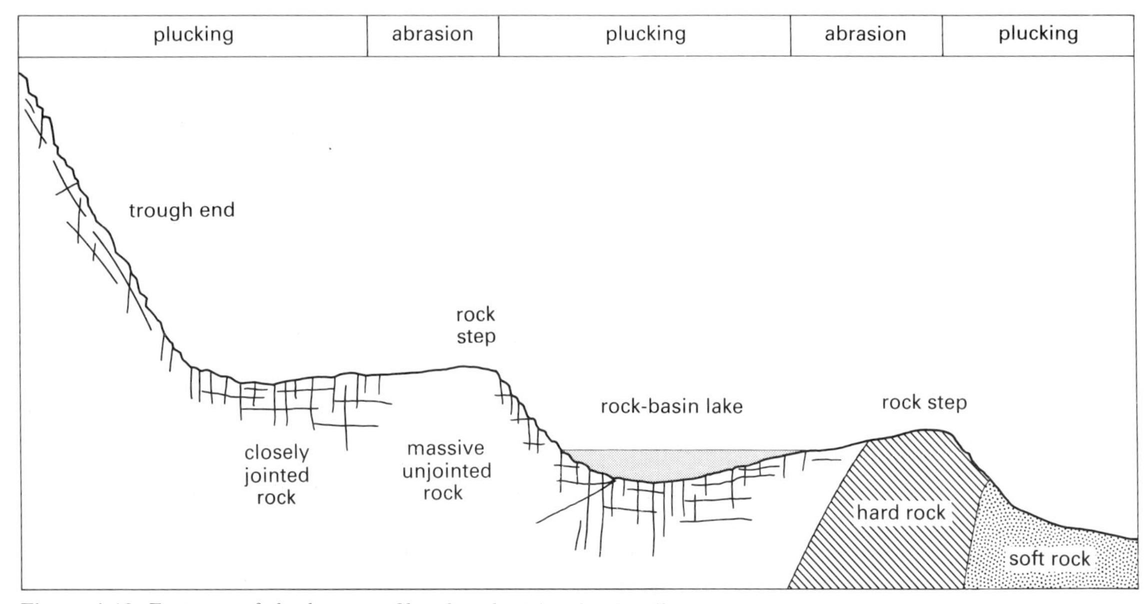

Figure 4.13 *Features of the long-profile of a glacial upland valley*

Figure 4.14 *The terminal-lateral moraines of the Fee-Gletscher, Saas-Fee, Switzerland. These moraines are the product of glacial advances during the past 5000 years, and have been left by a retreat of the glacier, amounting to approximately 1 km since 1850*

moraines, will be developed. In areas where the glacier snout is experiencing continuous retreat, as at Fjallsjokull, Iceland, between 1945 and 1965, small closely spaced *annual ridges* may form. During summer, subglacial water soaked debris is squeezed out from beneath the glacier margin; in winter, when ablation ceases, the ice front, although generally receding, will advance slightly, pushing this morainic material into a low ridge.

Lateral moraines comprise debris which has slid off the glacier surface into depressions along the ice margins. Note that supraglacial lateral and medial moraines, described on p. 89, are usually destroyed by a major glacial recession, the sediment formerly resting on the ice surface being spread widely over the proglacial zone. If the glacier surface is lowered, ridges of debris dumped at the glacier edges are then left high on the valley side. Like most morainic ridges, including terminal moraines, these are asymmetrical in profile, with a steep proximal slope formerly against the ice, and a gentler, more stable distal slope away from the ice. In the Alps, several minor glacial advances and retreats during the last 5000 years, known as the *Neoglacial period*, have resulted either in very large individual lateral moraines or a series of smaller ridges, or *nested moraines*, with the youngest next to the present day glacier and the oldest farthest away (Fig. 4.15).

Fluted (radial) moraines comprise low ridges, running approximately parallel to each other, which have been formed at right angles to the glacier snout, that is in the direction of ice flow. They are formed subglacially, where the ice has overridden bedrock obstructions. In the lee of these obstacles, caverns are formed; owing to the weight of the ice on either side, water soaked morainic debris is forced up into the caverns, preventing their roofs from closing down. With continued sliding of the glacier, the caverns thus become elongated to form debris filled tunnels, sometimes several hundreds of metres in length. These are eventually exposed as fluted moraines by glacier recession.

Landforms resulting from ice-sheet glaciation

Although, under conditions of severe glaciation, uplands can become entirely buried beneath a thick and extensive ice cover, as, for example during the Quaternary, when the Cairngorms were overridden by a Scottish ice-sheet moving north-eastwards, lowlands generally display the results of ice-sheet glaciation more effectively. The resultant landforms are in some ways similar to those produced by valley glaciers in uplands, namely rock basins, abraded surfaces, and terminal moraines. However, the whole scale of activity is vastly

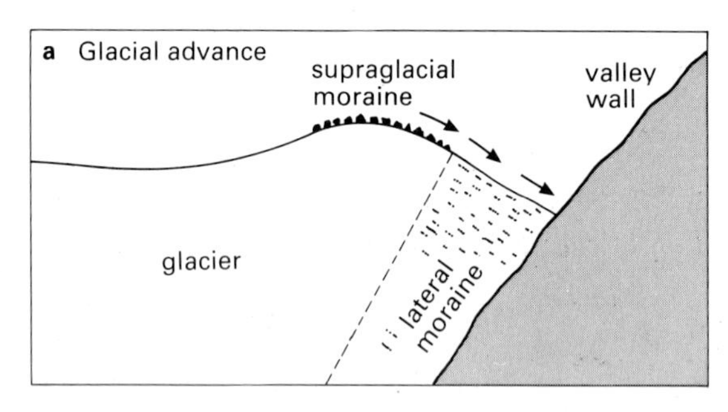

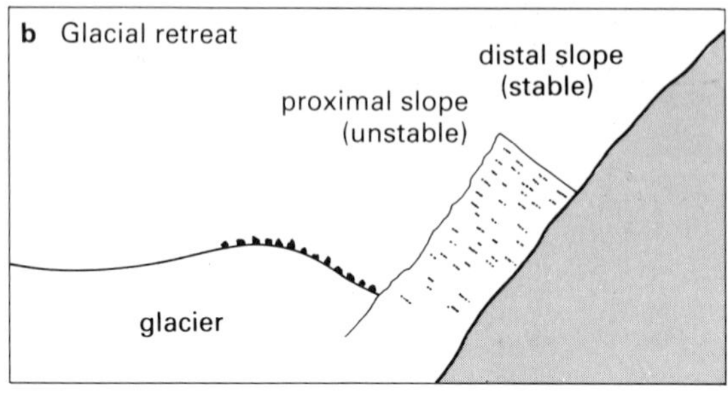

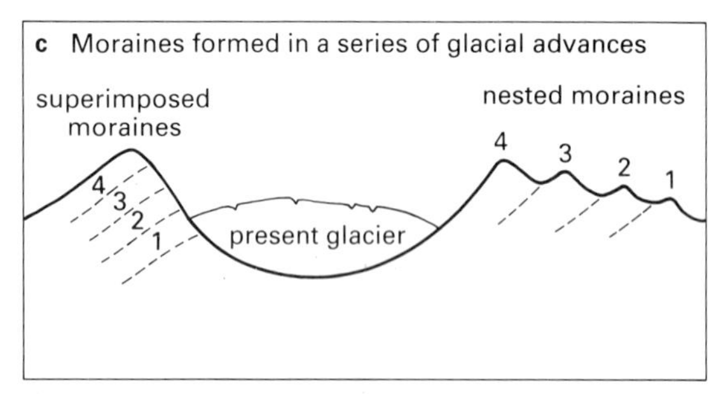

Figure 4.15 *The formation of Neoglacial lateral moraines in the Alps. Glacial advance (**a**) is associated with sliding of supraglacial sediment from the ice margins, to accumulate as a lateral moraine between the ice and the valley wall. Glacial retreat (**b**) leaves this moraine high on the valley wall; the moraine slope facing the glacier (the proximal slope) will be affected by mass movements and running water and will be eroded to a greater or lesser extent. In a series of glacial advances (**c**), morainic deposits may be laid on top of each other, to give superimposed moraines, or deposited as a series of ridges (nested moraines) which are progressively younger towards the glacier*

different, and certain individual processes, notably glacio-fluvial transport and deposition, are so characteristic that a separate treatment is justifiable.

Observations of existing ice-sheets, as in Antarctica and Greenland, indicate that in their central parts they are marked by very low ice velocities and basal temperatures below 0°C. However, towards their margins the ice-sheets become more active, as basal ice becomes warm and meltwater is able to form, thus accelerating basal sliding. Within this peripheral ice, threads of high ice velocity appear to develop along the lines of pre-existing valleys; or at the ice-sheet margins tongues of ice, or *outlet glaciers*, extend outwards, displaying many of the features of valley glaciers. It therefore seems probable that erosion becomes more effective towards the outer parts of an ice-sheet. A study of the area formerly covered by the Laurentide ice-sheet of North America has shown that the density of occurrence of lakes, occupying rock basins scoured out by the ice, is greatest in a semi-circular zone surrounding a large central area, where lakes are less numerous and erosion was evidently less intense. Outside this zone of maximum erosion is, of course, one in which glacial and glacio-fluvial deposition was dominant.

The erosional landscapes most often associated with ice-sheet erosion consist of low lying, relatively level plains, with many rounded or streamlined hills and innumerable rock basins, as in the Laurentian Shield of Canada, the Fenno-Scandian Shield of northern Europe or, on a more limited scale, the *knock and lochan* country of north-west Scotland (Fig. 4.16). These demonstrate the selective erosion of the ice, which has scoured out weak rocks and fault lines, and abraded and smoothed harder rock outcrops. The total amount of erosion carried out by lowland ice-sheets should not, however, be exaggerated. For example, it has been estimated that the average amount of glacial lowering has usually been in the order of tens of metres, by contrast with the 1000 m or more effected by the largest valley glaciers. In fact, the Shield areas referred to had been reduced by sub-aerial erosion to surfaces of low relief long before the onset of Quaternary glaciation.

Where upland areas have been affected by

Figure 4.16 *The Finnish landscape near Lahti. The numerous lakes and islands are the result of differential erosion of the ancient Shield rocks by the Pleistocene ice-sheet, and deposits of glacial and glacio-fluvial sediments*

ice-sheets, as in the Cairngorms, glacial erosion has been even more selective. On the high summits and plateaux, pre-glacial features such as tors and associated weathering deposits are surprisingly well preserved, whilst the valleys have been powerfully deepened by glacial erosion. It is evident that the ice-sheet was *protective* over the high ground, but strongly *erosive* where rapidly flowing ice streams within the ice-sheet were able to form.

Lowland ice-sheets, and associated melt-waters, are responsible for the formation of a range of depositional landforms. Direct deposition, such as the lodgement and dumping of glacial sediments, derived either from preglacial weathered layers stripped away by the advancing ice or from glacial erosion, results in extensive *till plains*, which occupy wide extents of North America and western Europe. In these areas, pre-existing hills and valleys were buried beneath great thicknesses of till, sometimes hundreds of metres in depth. These deposits are usually formed by a succession of glacial advances; for example, the till plain of East Anglia is the product of at least three separate glaciations. Till plains may be flat, featureless landscapes, or may be diversified by *drumlins*. These are low streamlined hills, usually no more than 50 m in height, and up to 1 km in length, and with a relatively blunt end on the upglacier side and a long tapering tail in the direction of ice flow. The long axes of drumlins, and of the stones contained within them, can thus be used in the reconstruction of former ice-sheet movements. The actual till comprising the plains consists of a mixture of fine clay and silt, plus many rock fragments which are rounded and striated, hence the former term *boulder clay*. Direct ice-sheet deposition may also form large terminal and recessional moraines (p. 94), though some so called morainic ridges are more the result of glacio-fluvial deposition (p. 98).

Streams running from the margins of lowland ice-sheets have, particularly during periods when the ice is decaying, high discharge and large transporting capacity. Large quantities of sand and gravel are washed from the ice and deposited as *outwash plains* or *valley trains* extending many kilometres from the ice-sheet margin. The outwash plains, consisting of layered, or *stratified*, deposits which contrast with unstratified till, gradually build upwards as huge fans, possessing gentle gradients away from the ice. However, in the late stage of development, as the ice surface is lowered by ablation, the meltwater streams dissect the outwash deposits, leaving a series of sand and gravel-capped plateaux. Valley trains consist of extensive infillings of glacio-fluvial sediment deposited by meltwater along pre-existing valleys.

Other glacio-fluvial features forming along the ice-sheet margins, or beneath the ice, are

Figure 4.17 *An esker at Holylee, west of Melrose in the Tweed valley, Scotland*

kames and *eskers*. Kames are mounds of sand and gravel which may be deposited in various ways. Some are ancient deltaic formations, laid down by meltwater streams flowing into ice marginal lakes; others form in thin ice, where surface melting produces depressions and exposes the subglacial surface, on which sediment accumulates; and some may represent large ice crevasses which become occupied by sand and gravel, giving mounds of sediment when the ice finally melts away. Eskers are long, narrow and often winding ridges of stratified drift (Fig. 4.17). They are widely regarded as the casts of subglacial streams, whose loads were laid down, within the ice tunnel, as flow was impeded close to the ice margin, for example by the presence of a lake whose surface was above the tunnel exit. As the ice-sheet retreated, such eskers were progressively extended; indeed, in Finland some large eskers can be traced over hundreds of kilometres. Another interpretation is that the ice tunnels became choked by sediment, as the meltwater streams were reduced in discharge during the final stages of deglaciation, when the ice mass had been greatly depleted by ablation. Whatever the reason for the accumulation of glacio-fluvial sediment, the latter is finally revealed as an esker ridge when the ice melts away.

In areas such as Finland, glacio-fluvial landforms are magnificently developed. In addition to valley trains, kames and eskers, there are very large moraine-like ridges, referred to as the Salpausselkas, extending broadly west-east across the southern part of the country. These record stages in the recession of the Finnish ice-sheet during the last 10 000 years, at a time when there existed a great marginal lake, known as the Baltic Ice Lake. The Salpausselkas actually consist mainly of glacio-fluvial sediments laid down along the northern edge of this lake, in the form of large deltas which have coalesced to form near continuous ridges; on their northern sides massive eskers, representing the streams which brought these glacio-fluvial sediments, can be observed at many points.

One final effect of ice-sheet glaciation is the frequent modification of the pre-existing drainage pattern. In areas of selective glacial scouring, there develops in the post-glacial period a disorganised drainage system, with numerous small lakes fed by many short streams, as in the glacially eroded Lewisian Gneiss areas of the Western Isles of Scotland. In some instances, large ice-sheets have advanced against the slope of the country, as in West Germany, where ice from the Baltic region moved southwards towards the higher ground of the South German plateaux; as a result, meltwater was forced to flow along the ice margin. The resultant streams were also

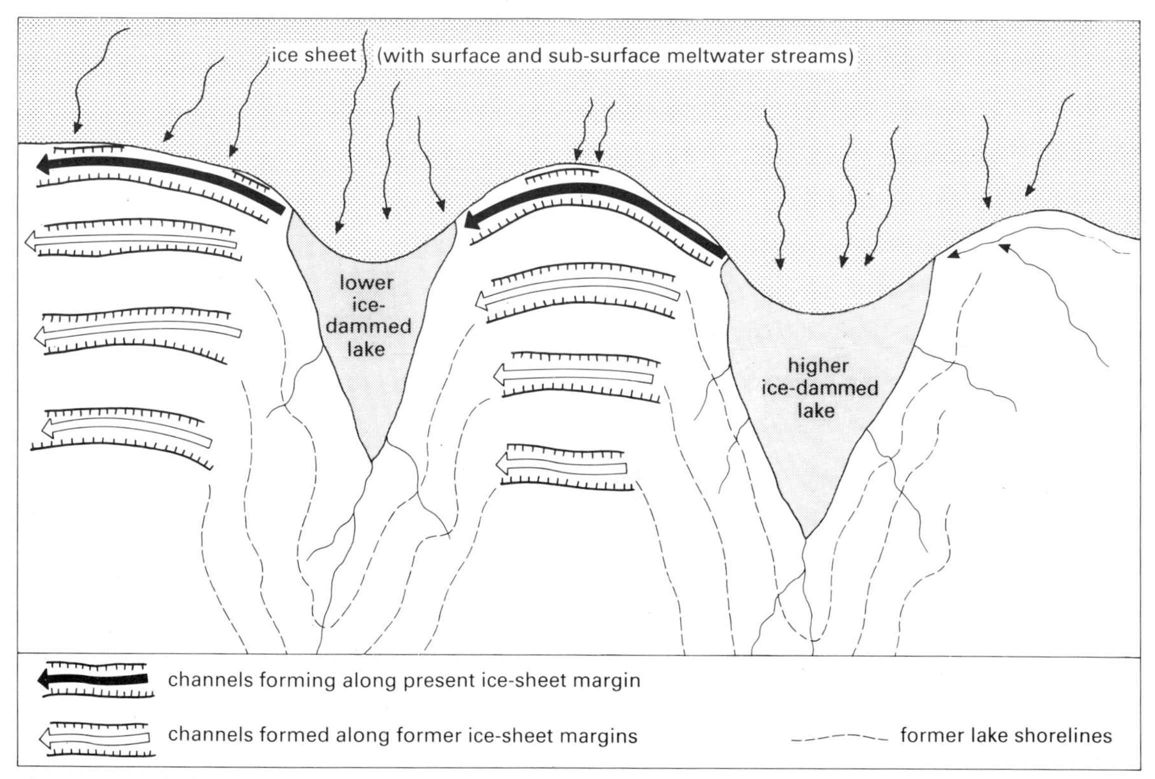

Figure 4.18 *The formation of proglacial lakes and overflow channels. The series of channels marks retreats in the ice-sheet margin and progressive lowering of the ice-dammed lakes*

swelled by water draining towards the ice from unglaciated regions, and were thus capable of eroding large valleys, as in the famous *Urstromtäler* of the north German plain. In detail, ice-marginal drainage is often complex. Where valleys run at right angles towards the ice-sheet, the edge of which acts as a barrier, *proglacial lakes* form. The water levels of these rise until there is spillage from higher to lower lakes; if the lakes persist for a sufficiently long period, the escaping water can cut deep, steep sided channels, known as *glacial overflow channels* or *spillways* (Fig. 4.18). Many examples of such glacial diversions of drainage have been identified in Britain. For example, it is widely believed that, during the Quaternary period, lakes were dammed up between the escarpment of the Chiltern Hills and an ice-sheet margin to the north. In this instance, the overflows were away from the ice, and were responsible for cutting the deep gap at Goring now followed by the Thames and, possibly, the smaller gaps at Wendover and Tring to the north-east.

More recently, study of so called glacial overflow channels has cast doubt on interpretations based on the former existence of proglacial lakes. Many of these channels in upland Britain have curious up and down long-profiles; in other words, there is a central hump, from which the channel floor slopes away in opposite directions. There is a similarity here to eskers, which often climb up one side of a ridge, and then descend the other. Moreover, the evidence of the lakes having once existed, such as old shorelines, deltaic deposits and lake floor clays, is often slender or controversial. There has thus been a growing belief that the channels are the result of subglacial erosion, by water flowing in tunnels at the base of the ice-sheet, and under such great hydrostatic pressure that it could be forced to run uphill, and erode in the process! Such subglacial channels, which are thus the erosional counterparts of eskers, vary greatly in scale, from deep but narrow trenches rather like railway cuttings, to the large *tunnel valleys*, up to 100 m or more in depth, of Denmark and north-west Germany.

PERIGLACIAL ENVIRONMENTS

The most important distinguishing feature of periglacial environments is the development of permanently frozen ground, or *permafrost*, containing masses of ice, known as *ground ice*, on a variety of scales. This phenomenon reflects the overall severity of the climate; indeed periglacial climates have been defined as having a mean annual air temperature of 3°C or less, implying a short cool summer period and a long harsh winter. Under severe conditions, as in central Siberia, the average annual temperature may actually be below −10°C. However, there is a good deal of variability in periglacial climates. In areas such as Siberia, winters are extremely cold, with the mean January temperature as low as −43°C, and snowfall is very limited in amount; yet summer temperatures are quite high, with the mean July temperature up to 19°C. By contrast with these continental conditions, more maritime periglacial climates, such as that of Jan Mayen Island, north of Iceland, have less severe winters, with a mean January temperature of some −30°C but much cooler summers, with a mean July temperature as low as 5°C. Winter precipitation, as snow, is greater than that of summer, whereas in continental climates winter snowfall is only a quarter of summer rainfall. In high mountain areas, for example non-glacierised tracts of the high Alps, winter temperatures are again severe owing to the factor of altitude, with a mean January temperature as low as −13°C, summers are cool, and the precipitation is very great, often in excess of 1500 mm/annum^{-1}, much falling as winter snow.

Permafrost

Permafrost is defined as a layer of frozen ground that does not completely thaw in summer; the surface of the permanently frozen

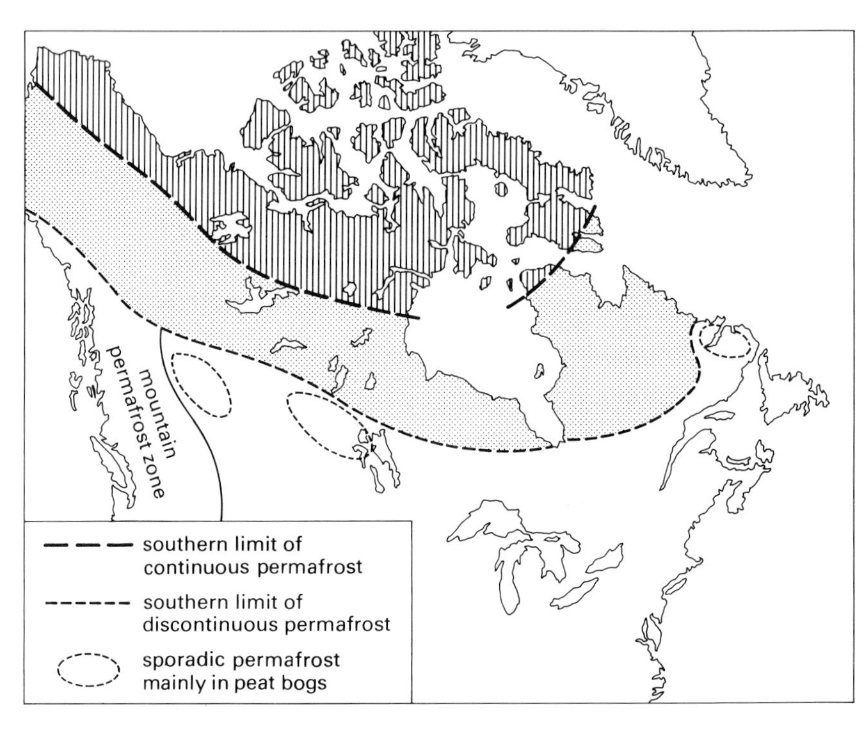

Figure 4.19 *The distribution of permafrost in Canada*

layer is known as the *permafrost table*. Above the table, annual summer thawing produces a layer of material, referred to as the *active layer*, which refreezes each winter. Within the permafrost freezing may be irregular, so that unfrozen zones, or *taliks*, occur locally. Taliks are also found in the active layer when, during winter, it is frozen from the ground surface downwards. Permafrost varies greatly in character and thickness; it reaches maximum development in continental interiors, but declines towards the southern margins of the periglacial zone and towards the coast (Fig. 4.19). *Continuous permafrost* is formed under the most severe climatic conditions, where mean annual air temperatures fall below −6°C; the ground is everywhere frozen, except beneath large lakes and major rivers, such as the Mackenzie in northern Canada. *Discontinuous permafrost* occurs where mean annual temperatures are between −6° and −1°C; the areas of frozen ground form either where the subsoil is relatively dry, or in well shaded locations, such as north facing slopes in the northern hemisphere. Eventually, as annual temperatures rise towards 3°C, the permafrost is developed only locally, in the most favourable conditions, as *sporadic permafrost*. In the tundra regions of Siberia the permafrost commonly reaches a thickness of 300–400 m and in northern Yakutia, where the winter temperatures fall below −50°C, a depth of 1600 m has been recorded. Farther south, in the coniferous forests, the thicknesses are reduced to 20–30 m, and the permafrost becomes discontinuous. It seems certain that in many areas the permafrost is partly the product of past climatic conditions related to the Quaternary glaciations; in that sense the permafrost is *relict*. This helps to explain the reduced thicknesses of the permafrost in Canada by comparison with Siberia; large parts of the latter were not glaciated, and there was no ice cover to hinder the penetration of the intense cold into the ground.

Permafrost and its related features are of considerable significance to human activities in cold environments, such as Arctic Canada and northern Siberia. For example, with the onset of winter and the freezing of water contained within the active layer, upward expansion of the ground surface, referred to as *frost heave* (p. 104), occurs widely. This can cause serious structural damage to roads, bridges and houses. Moreover, human actions can affect the permafrost itself, for instance where removal of the vegetation cover, or the stripping away of soil and gravel layers, exposes the permafrost table to rapid summer melting. This can create an impassable landscape, of innumerable mounds, hollows and small ponds; this is known as *human induced thermokarst* (see also p. 103).

The direct effects of permafrost on landform development are negligible, for the ground remains frozen and inert. Indirectly, however, permafrost is a major influence on geomorphological processes. One effect is to render rocks impermeable, so that the underground circulation of water is halted. During summer, when the winter snows and upper ground layers thaw, there is an abundance of surface water. In flat or gently undulating areas, the soil becomes waterlogged and surface pools, swamps and *thaw lakes* are abundant. Moreover, the processes within the active layer owe much to the permafrost, which prevents soil water drainage and thus promotes the formation of ground ice when winter comes.

The active layer reforms each spring, as daytime temperatures rise above 0°C, and throughout summer increases in thickness, sometimes to 3–6 m. Many factors influence the depth of melting, other than air temperatures. Coarse gravels thaw rapidly, owing to their high conductivity, but peaty soils insulate the permafrost and limit thawing. Vegetation cover is important; for example, coniferous trees shade the soil from the summer sun, and also prevent much winter snow from reaching the ground. Where vegetation is destroyed, thawing of the ground will be accelerated and the active layer will be unusually deep.

Ground ice and related features

The formation of ground ice is characteristic of most periglacial environments. Sometimes the

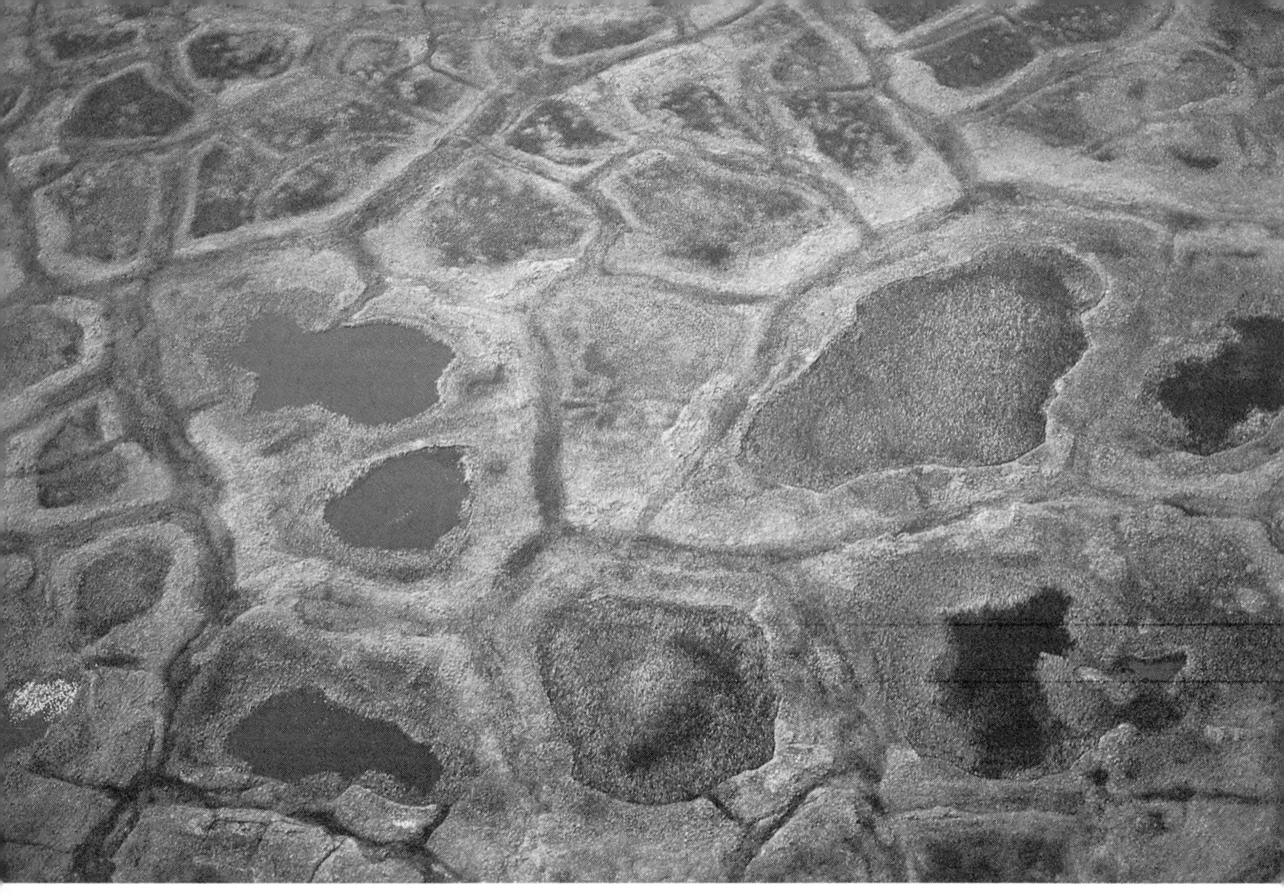

Figure 4.20 *Ice-wedge polygons, Barrow, Alaska. Note the low centres of the polygons, some of which are occupied by surface water*

frozen ground contains relatively little moisture, giving rise to *dry permafrost*, but for the most part involves soils and bedrock containing significant amounts of soil and ground water. In porous soils, the amount of ice produced by freezing may actually exceed the volume of the mineral soil, hence the formation of what is known as *wet permafrost*.

Ground ice occurs in many forms, and on a variety of scales, from small ice needles known as *pipkraker*, which develop just beneath the soil surface, to large sills or domes of almost pure ice, reaching thicknesses of several metres. Three main types of ground ice are recognised. *Wedge* or *vein ice* forms where water from melting snow penetrates the ground via open fissures, and freezes to give *ice wedges*. The process occurs where the soil has contracted as a result of very severe cold, with temperatures down to −20°C, which develops a rectangular pattern of frost cracks; this is known as *thermal contraction cracking* (Fig. 4.20). The individual ice wedges grow each year, as meltwater percolates down their margins and freezes; at their tops they may be up to 1.5 m across, but they usually taper downwards to a point 3–4 m below the surface. *Segregated ice* comprises ice layers and lenses which form where the active layer has a high moisture content. As freezing occurs in winter from the ground surface downwards, moisture is drawn upwards to the freezing plane, resulting in the formation of ice bodies. The process is more effective in fine grained than in freely draining gravelly soil. *Intrusive ice* is formed, often on a large scale, where water flows into the frozen ground, for example, by upward movement in an artesian basin.

One feature of ground ice formation is the development of *ice-cored terrains*, in which there are many mounds or low hills underlain by ground ice. The most spectacular examples are *pingos*, or ice-cored hills, of which 1400 have been recorded in the Mackenzie delta. They are up to 60 m in height, 300 m in width, and contain an ice core with an overlying sediment layer up to 10 m thick. Two types of pingo have been observed: *open system pingos*, of the East Greenland type, form in valley bottoms where water seeps into the upper layers of the ground, freezes and forms large ice masses which dome up overlying sediments; *closed system pingos*, of the Mackenzie type, develop on the sites of small lakes and lake beds (Fig. 4.21). As permafrost grows, ground water beneath the lake is trapped by freezing from above and freezing inwards from the lake basin margins. The ground water then forms a talik which is increasingly compressed, with the result that the overlying sediments are forced upwards and, when the talik itself eventually freezes, an ice-cored dome is the end product.

Many other types of ice-cored mound have been recognised. Along the southern edges of the permafrost zone *palsas*, which are mounds of peat up to 7 m high and 50 m in diameter, are associated with peat bogs. They have been attributed to the formation of patches of ground ice beneath an uneven snow cover. Where the snow is thin, and a poor insulator, the winter cold rapidly penetrates the ground, but where the snow is thicker the ground is less deeply frozen. With the advent of summer, thawing may be inadequate to remove ground ice segregations formed beneath the thin snow; instead, over a period of years, these can grow to cause doming of the overlying peat.

Where there is extensive thawing of ground ice, a highly irregular surface consisting of hummocks, pits and basins is formed. There is a crude resemblance to the karst scenery of limestone terrains, with the result that the term *thermokarst* has been adopted to describe this phenomenon. Among the individual processes involved are the thawing of ice wedges, to give elongated depressions, and the ice cores of palsas and pingos, to produce circular depressions, often containing ponds, with surrounding banks of disturbed sediments. Also, the lateral migration of streams may

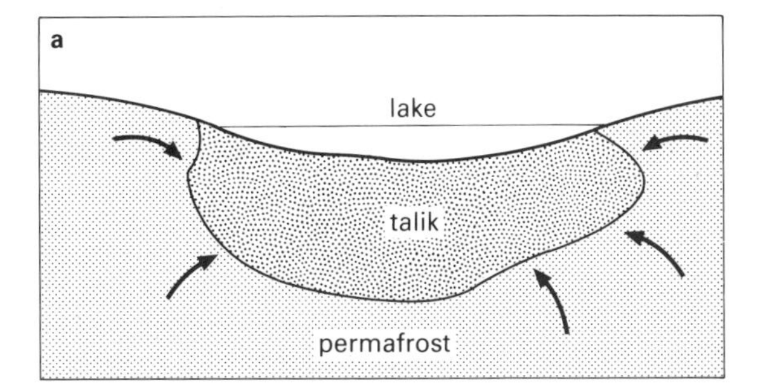

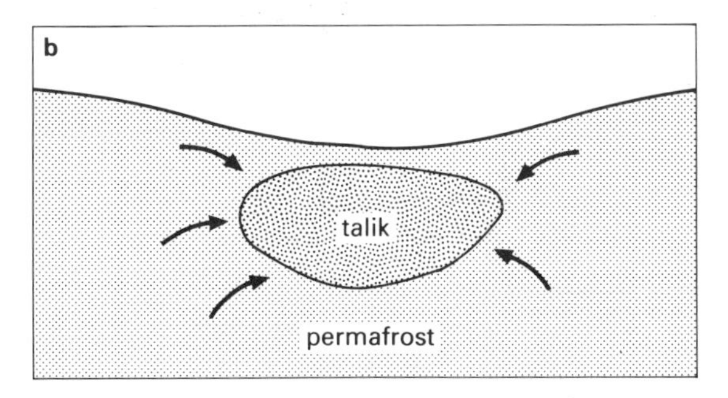

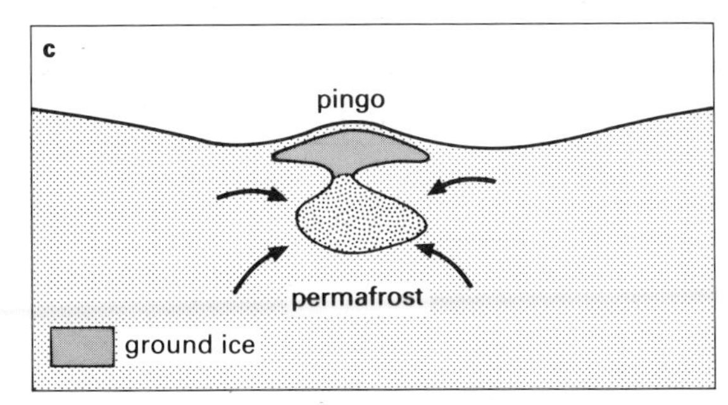

Figure 4.21 *The formation of closed system pingos*

expose ground ice formations, causing them to melt and collapse. Some of the most impressive thermokarst is found in central Siberia, where it has probably been caused by a warming of the climate; indeed, summer temperatures of up to 30°C are now recorded in the area. Large flat-floored depressions, known as *alases*, up to 40 m deep and 15 km in diameter, are widely developed (Fig. 4.22). It is believed that alases are initiated by the thawing of a network of ice wedges, to form numerous trough-like depressions separated by mounds up to 4 m high, referred to as *cemetery mounds* or *baydjarakhs*. Gradually the mounds collapse, leading to further melting of the permafrost; beneath the floor of the resultant alas

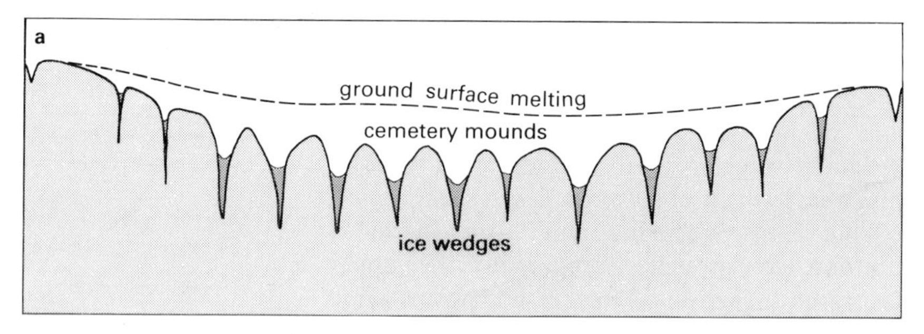

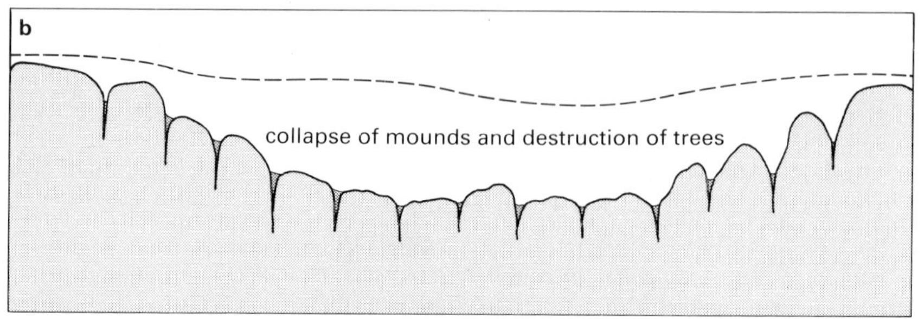

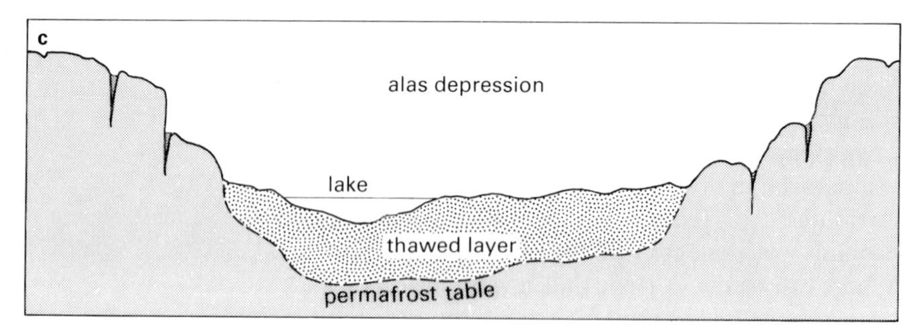

Figure 4.22 *Stages in the formation of an alas depression (see p. 103)*

depression, a large talik forms and, within the alas, thaw lakes are common.

Other periglacial processes

Frost action Daily fluctuations of temperature about 0°C are frequent in periglacial environments, particularly in spring and autumn. These, together with the annual freeze-thaw cycle, cause intense weathering of jointed and porous rocks, giving block fields, accumulations of scree, and frost-riven cliffs and tors. Within soil and regolith, the formation and decay of ground ice result in sorting processes and the development of *patterned ground*.

In very cold regions, thermal contraction cracking produces a polygonal network of fissures and cracks, which are enlarged by ice-wedges (p. 102). Where the precipitation is low, less than 100 mm/year, ice cannot form, and the fissures become occupied by wind-blown sand, or *sand wedges*. A more complex type of sorting results from the formation of ice segregations. As the active layer freezes in early winter, the formation of ground ice will result in *frost heave* of the ground surface, often by as much as 1–5 cm in a season.

In soils that are variable in coarseness, ice segregations will form most effectively in the finer materials; frost heave will then be irregular, forming a hummocky surface with many small *frost mounds*. In many instances, ground ice will form beneath the larger stones, which lose heat more rapidly by conduction, so that these are raised relative to surrounding finer particles. Over a period of time, there will be

Figure 4.23 *Stone stripes, resulting from solifluction and the lateral sorting of debris, Tinto Hill, Strathclyde, Scotland*

a high degree of *vertical sorting*, with the larger particles being raised to the surface, and the finer particles being washed down by meltwater. Where frost heave has resulted in a series of surface mounds, *lateral sorting* is caused by the sliding of stones down the flanks of the mounds, which are then left as areas of fines surrounded by borders of coarser fragments.

Processes such as these are responsible for various types of patterned ground. On near level surfaces polygonal or near circular networks of fines and coarse particles are formed. Among these are *stone polygons*, which comprise borders of frost shattered, frequently up-ended stones and high centres of moist mud, and *stone nets*, formed where the stone borders of the polygons intersect. On sloping ground, within the range 5–15°, polygons are replaced by *stone stripes*, which consist of lines of stones separated by broader strips of fine material, sometimes vegetated, running in the direction of maximum gradient (Fig. 4.23). Evidently sorting processes have been active on the slopes, but solifluction has prevented the formation of a regular network of polygons.

Solifluction This is the most characteristic transportational process in periglacial environments, though in many places, or at certain seasons, it is aided or replaced by slope wash, for example, over unvegetated ground during the thaw season. It is usually regarded as the slow flowage of waste material saturated by meltwater, even over slopes of quite gentle gradient; the process is also referred to as *gelifluction*. The process is most active in the uppermost 50 cm of the soil, where the structure has been opened up by small ice lenses and grains; with thawing, each particle becomes cushioned by its own film of water, friction is thereby reduced, and flowage can operate readily. Another important contributory mechanism is *frost creep*, which in some periglacial areas may actually exceed gelifluction in importance. This involves the net displacement of particles on a slope as a result of freeze-thaw action. As the ground freezes, frost heave raises the upper layers of the soil at right angles to the ground surface; with thawing the soil particles, under the pull of gravity, settle back more vertically. Over a long period of time, the resultant mass transport of soil material downslope is very considerable.

Measurements of the rate of solifluction as a whole have been made in several areas. In Spitzbergen, movements varied from 5 to 12 $cm/annum^{-1}$ on slopes of 7–15°; in Karkevagge, Sweden, rates of 4 $cm/annum^{-1}$ were recorded on slopes of 15°; and at Sachs Harbour, Canada, rates of 1.5–2 $cm/annum^{-1}$

were measured on a slope of only 3°. Rates of solifluction clearly vary from one site to another, depending on gradient, soil moisture content, vegetation and aspect. In the Yukon, Alaska, poorly vegetated north-east facing slopes were affected by relatively rapid movements, of 2.4–2.7 cm/annum^{-1}; on well vegetated south-east facing slopes the rate dropped to 1.6 cm/annum^{-1}; and on south-west facing slopes, dried out by the wind, the rate was only 0.7 cm/annum^{-1}.

Solifluction, with rainwash, transports frost-shattered debris down slopes to valley bottoms, where it either accumulates or is removed by streams. On many slopes, particularly in their lower parts, there are extensive sheets of solifluted material, which mask rock outcrops and give a generally smooth terrain. In detail, however, this sheet may contain *solifluction lobes*, consisting of mobile tongues of sediment which are highly charged with moisture and flow rapidly, and *solifluction terraces*, formed by accumulations of flowing debris. Solifluction also aids other processes, including *nivation*, or snowpatch erosion, which is responsible for the formation of rounded hollows and valley heads (Fig. 4.24). These appear to result from accumulations of snow which steadily eat their way into the slope, by a combination of processes. Melting snow provides water which can soak into the ground and freeze at night, thus breaking up the rock, and also aids solifluction and surface wash, which remove the resultant rock debris. Large snowpatches, over a long period, can develop relatively gentle *nivation hollows* into *nivation cirques*, which have steep frost-riven head walls and a form that is generally reminiscent of glacial cirques (p. 92).

Running water Most periglacial regions are drained by stream networks which are similar in form to those of other climates. However, there is one important difference: periglacial streams flow during a very short season only. This has led some authors to suggest that

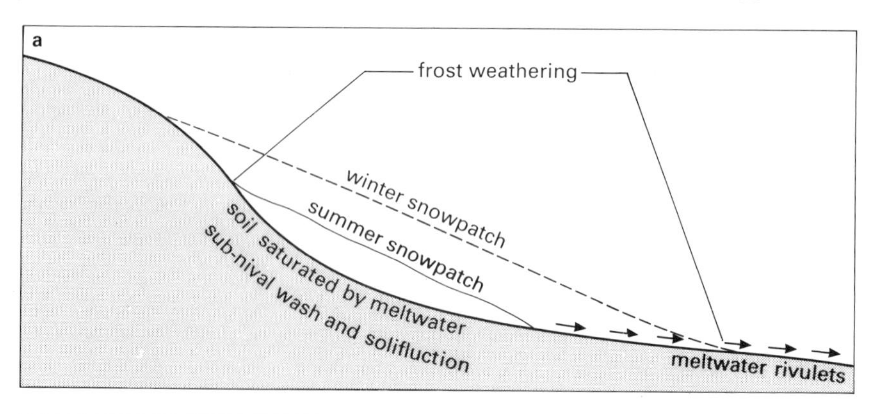

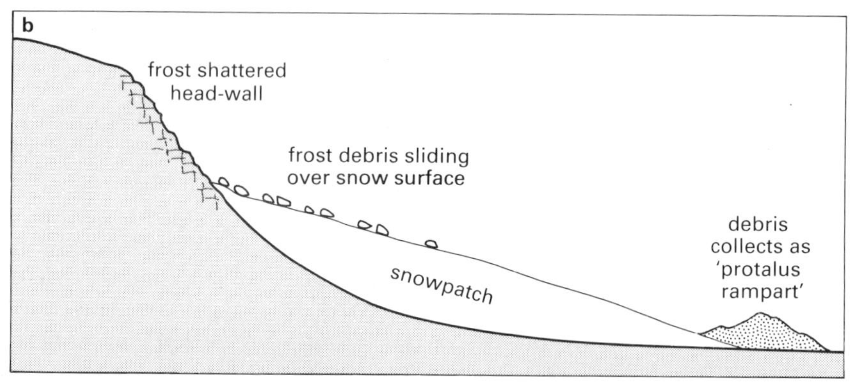

Figure 4.24 *The formation of nivation hollows (**a**) and nivation cirques (**b**)*

Figure 4.25 *Thermal erosion, involving melting of the permafrost and resulting collapse of the river banks, Footprint Creek, Barrow, Alaska*

stream action in periglacial environments is generally weak. The view is sometimes supported by the extensive build-up of sediments on valley floors, resulting from the rapid transport of weathered debris from valley slopes. Indeed, periglacial streams appear often to be overloaded, and thus incapable of moving all the sediment fed to them; the result is that valley floors are mainly broad, flat and occupied by braided streams. Braiding is known to be characteristic of streams with wide variations of discharge; in the Arctic there is both a strong seasonal contrast in run-off between winter and summer, and at certain times short term variations of discharge between day and night. Observations also show that it is common for periglacial streams to transport up to 90 per cent of total load as bedload. In valleys of this type, only *lateral* erosion is active, and usually takes the form of *thermal erosion* (Fig. 4.25). This takes place where a stream swings against the valley wall, removes slope debris and exposes the permafrost. This in turn melts at water level, to form an overhanging stream bank, known as a *thermo-erosional niche*. Eventually, the unsupported bank will collapse, and the process will begin again.

In some circumstances, however, periglacial streams are clearly capable of vertical down cutting, particularly where there is very rapid melting of winter snowfall. This can occur within a short period of only two to three weeks; up to 75 per cent of total annual run-off can be released within a few days, giving what has been termed a *nival flood*, or snow melt flood. In the chalk country of southern England many spectacular dry valleys appear to have been formed by such meltwater torrents during the Quaternary (Fig. 4.26). The chalk is normally a permeable rock, with little or no surface run-off. However, under periglacial conditions it was rendered impermeable by permafrost, which sealed all the joints and pores, so that meltwater streams, and in particular those flowing rapidly down steep scarp slopes, were able to incise steep sided and often flat floored valleys to a depth of 100 m or more. In some instances the meltwater erosion seems to have been astonishingly rapid. At Brook, in east Kent, a group of valleys, each up to 400 m long and up to 80 m deep, has been cut into the scarp face of the North Downs. There is evidence to show that these valleys were formed during a period of only 500 years, at the end of the final glacial period, when there was a brief episode of very snowy, cold climatic conditions in southern England.

Wind action This has not been responsible for the shaping of other than minor erosional landforms, such as undercut mushroom rocks and small depressions known as *wind troughs*, in

Figure 4.26 *Gullied chalk slopes near Oliver's Castle, Roundway, Wiltshire. The small valleys are probably the result of erosion by surface meltwater streams from snow on the chalk crests during the late-glacial period (10 800–10 300 BP)*

periglacial environments. Nevertheless, it has played a large role in the transport and deposition of fine sediments, resulting either from glacial and glacio-fluvial deposition or intense frost weathering. Wind action has been most effective in areas of low relief and sparse vegetation cover, experiencing very cold, dry and windy climatic conditions. Thus, during the Quaternary, the wind *deflated* vast quantities of silt from the extensive outwash plains, laid down by meltwater streams draining from the ice-sheets (p. 97). The coarser materials, including gravel and large stones, were left behind, to form *lag gravels* or *stone pavements*; within these, many individual stones were polished and shaped by the wind, forming *ventifacts*. The silt itself was transported, often over distances of hundreds of km, and deposited as layers of *loess*, known as *limon* in western Europe. These formations blanketed the pre-existing landscape, generally to a depth of 3–6 m, but reaching 150–300 m in parts of China. However, whilst wind action of this kind was active in the past, it seems to be a far less potent process under present day conditions; in other words, loess is strictly a *relict* deposit, not being added to today.

PERIGLACIAL LANDSCAPES

Periglacial environments are, as we have seen, associated with certain phenomena, such as permafrost, or processes, notably frost action and solifluction, that either do not occur at all or are much less active in other climatic regions. For this reason, it has been proposed that periglacial environments constitute a *morphogenetic region*, in which the landscapes and individual landforms are highly distinctive (p. 56). There is much evidence to support this view, not only in the presence of small scale features such as patterned ground, but in the frequent occurrence of larger scale landforms such as nivation hollows, dry valleys and asymmetrical valleys.

These features can be observed in *relict periglacial landscapes*, such as the chalk downlands of southern England, which experienced modification during the cold periods of the Quaternary. Along the escarpment face of the South Downs, or the Chilterns east of the Goring Gap, numerous rounded hollows are associated with spreads of frost shattered and soliflucted chalky debris, known as *coombe rock*, in the scarp foot zone. These features appear to represent former small depressions or valley heads which, during the cold periods of the Quaternary, became occupied by snow patches and were greatly modified and enlarged by nivational processes (p. 106). In addition, at some points very deeply cut and spectacular escarpment dry valleys, such as the Devil's Dyke, near Brighton, together with the valleys at Brook described on p. 107, appear to have been eroded at least in part by meltwater streams derived from winter snow accumulations.

In the less deeply incised valleys of the chalk dip slopes, it is common to find that one valley slope is steeper than that facing it (Fig. 4.27). For example, in the Marlborough Downs,

Figure 4.27 *The asymmetrical valley at Clatford Bottom, near Marlborough, Wiltshire. The steep valley side to the right (facing north-east) has been undercut by a former meltwater stream, forced to migrate towards the south-west by masses of solifluction debris, including numerous sarsen stones, moving down the active south-west facing slope (to the left)*

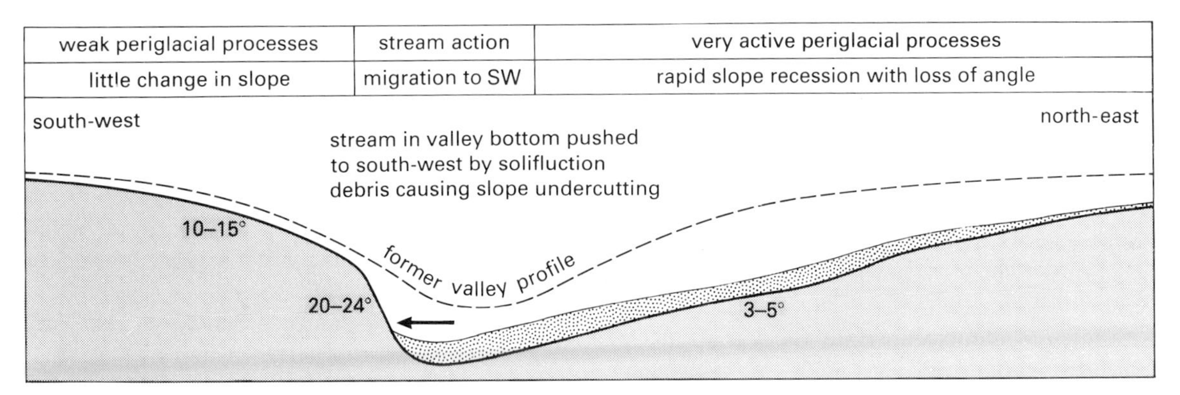

Figure 4.28

Wiltshire, north-east facing valley slopes are as steep as 20–24° and south-west facing slopes as gentle as 3–5°. Moreover, the gentle slopes are covered by a layer of coombe rock up to 4 m in thickness, whilst the steeper slope is mantled only by a thin post-glacial soil (Fig. 4.28). From this it can be seen that the gentle slope was, in terms of its geomorphological development, highly active under past periglacial conditions, which prevailed in this area until 10 000 years ago. One interpretation of these particular valleys is as follows: the north-east facing slopes, receiving little solar heat, remained largely frozen and inactive; in other words, processes such as frost action and solifluction operated on them at best very slowly. By contrast, the south-west facing slopes, receiving maximum insolation, experienced many cycles of freezing and thawing, promoting active frost weathering and solifluction; this apparently caused the slopes to retreat rapidly and decline in steepness. A last feature of chalk landscapes which has been ascribed to past periglacial activity is the smoothly rounded nature of the slopes, which are often convexo-concave in profile. This is believed to be the result of *mass wasting*, a combination of rapid weathering of the chalk, and effective downslope transport of the resultant debris layer by solifluction.

However, it would be wrong to assume that the present day chalk landscapes of southern England provide us with all the typical landforms resulting from periglaciation. For one thing, asymmetrical valleys elsewhere in

Europe are often quite different, in that it is the south-west facing slopes which are the steeper. This may have been due to the fact that snow was effectively blown off these slopes by strong south-westerly winds. As a result, meltwater would have been present in very small quantities, and thus frost action and solifluction would have been weakened by comparison with north-east facing slopes; on the latter, the build-up of snow would have provided the necessary meltwater to aid these processes. For another, other relict periglacial landscapes, such as that of Dartmoor in south-west England, possess features, notably the granite tors, which have no counterpart in the chalk. The controlling factor in the difference is clearly rock type. Whereas chalk is more or less uniformly weak, and very susceptible to rapid break-up by frost, granite is generally more resistant, particularly in areas where the rock joints are widely spaced. These more massive outcrops of granite have, therefore, not been destroyed but only modified by periglacial weathering, and remain upstanding as prominent rocky masses, surrounded by large blocks of granite which have been prised away by freeze-thaw weathering.

Studies of slopes illustrate the variations in landform evolution that occur in periglacial environments, as a result of variations in rock type and structure and the prevailing climatic conditions. At least four types of slope profile have been recognised, as follows: (i) steep, frost shattered cliffs, standing above accumulations of scree, as in Spitsbergen, where the periglacially modified slopes have been formed from glacially steepened valley walls; (ii) smooth, debris mantled slopes, resulting from very active solifluction, as in much of Arctic Canada at the present time; however, where hard rocks outcrop, these may give rise to tors; (iii) extensive basal concave slopes, rather similar to the pediments of semi-arid regions (p. 132) and resulting from surface wash processes and solifluction at the foot of steeper slopes experiencing rapid retreat; (iv) stepped slope profiles, produced either by the accumulation of solifluction deposits as terraces (p. 106), or the exaggeration of pre-existing benches, related to harder layers of rock, by nivation processes which have attacked intervening layers of less resistant rock.

ASSIGNMENTS

1 a. Explain how the mass balance and the basal ice temperature will help to determine (i) the rate at which a glacier flows, and (ii) the ability of a glacier to erode its bed.

b. What other factors are likely to influence ice velocity and the rate of glacial erosion?

2 Suggest ways in which the changes in glacial margins before, during and since the Little Ice Age (circa 1550–1850) may have influenced geomorphological processes and landforms in areas such as the Swiss Alps.

3 a. What types of evidence support the view that valley glaciers are, for the most part, very effective eroding agents?

b. Describe and explain the ways in which meltwater streams assist the geomorphological activity of glaciers.

4 Using a 1:50 000 Ordnance Survey map of a part of upland Britain affected by Quaternary glaciation:

a. identify the glacial cirques, and make a tracing to show their positions and outlines;

b. devise and apply a method of showing the extent to which these cirques face in a particular direction (or directions);

c. attempt an explanation of any pattern of orientation revealed by your study.

5 From the study of books and articles available to you, and from field visits, identify ways in which the landforms of your local area (within a radius of 10–20 km around your home) were affected by the climatic and geomorphological changes of the Quaternary.

6 a. Describe the main features of permafrost.

b. How does permafrost influence hydrological regimes in periglacial regions?

c. Describe and explain ways in which permafrost affects landform development in periglacial regions.

5

The Landforms of Hot Environments

The landforms of hot environments lie mainly between the Tropics of Cancer and Capricorn, the *intertropical zone* in the strict sense, but some occur in the extratropical zone, since hot deserts extend to beyond 30°N or S. Within this very large area, which comprises over 25 per cent of the earth's land surface, there are major differences in climate and, as a consequence, in the types and rates of operation of geomorphological processes. However, in very broad terms three main sub-zones may be identified.

1 The humid tropics (including equatorial, tropical humid and equatorial monsoon climates) are marked by high mean annual temperatures (27–33°C), small diurnal ranges of temperature, and very large amounts of rainfall (2500 mm/year or more). In many areas, this rain occurs throughout the year, with no pronounced seasonality. One characteristic feature is the great intensity of much of the rainfall.

2 The seasonally humid tropics (including the broad savanna belts of tropical Africa, and the tropical monsoon climate of the Indian subcontinent) show greater seasonal contrasts of humidity and temperature; in particular, the dry and wet seasons are usually strongly differentiated. Rain, falling mostly in the high summer season, often totals 500–1000 mm/year, and, as in the humid tropics, tends to be of high intensity. At times temperatures are significantly higher than in the humid tropics; for example, at the peak of the hot season in northern Nigeria, prior to the onset of the May rains, daytime temperatures can exceed 40°C. However, there are greater diurnal and seasonal ranges of temperature than in the humid tropics.

3 The arid and semi-arid regions, both within and beyond the intertropical zone, are characterised to a greater or lesser extent by aridity. In the true deserts, annual rainfall is less than 250 mm, but in the semi-desert fringes, for example, along the northern and southern edges of the Sahara, up to 500 mm can occur. This usually takes the form of a mini wet season, a shortened version of the adjoining savanna rainy season. In the interiors of hot deserts, rain is extremely rare; at Kharga, in southern Egypt, a period of 17 years without any rain has been recorded. When it does fall, desert rain is variable in type. Some desert travellers have frequently described cold persistent drizzle of low intensity. However, much desert rainfall, especially towards the desert margins, comes in brief storms, in the course of which 50 mm can fall within an hour. On the bare desert surface, this may cause rapid run-off, and give rise to dangerous *flash floods* in normally dry watercourses (Fig. 5.1). Deserts are also characterised by very high day time temperatures which, in summer, exceed 45°C in the air, and 60°C on rock surfaces, but low nocturnal temperatures, with ground frosts by no means uncommon.

The changing climate of the tropics

One of the greatest problems confronting mankind at the present time is that of massive famine in the tropical semi-arid regions of the earth. This is particularly true of the so called Sahelian and Sudanian zones which extend as a west-east belt across Africa along the southern edges of the Sahara desert. Here the desert margins appear to be advancing southwards at an alarming rate; for example by

Figure 5.1 *A flash flood in Wadi Al-Khanagah, Saudi Arabia, following a rainstorm in December 1985*

Figure 5.2 *Pleistocene lake sediments being subjected to rapid erosion near Magadi, in the rift valley of Kenya. The later stages of this erosion have been influenced by removal of vegetation cover, as a result of overgrazing by Masai cattle herds*

100–150 km between 1958 and 1975 in the northern Sudan. Increasingly, areas of scrub and grassland, and associated farms and grazing land, are being replaced by bare arid surfaces, shifting sands and extending dune systems.

This disastrous process of *desertification* has undoubtedly been both initiated and accelerated in recent years by human activities. As population pressure in the desert marginal lands has increased, the vegetation has been destroyed as the cultivated zone has been extended, serious overgrazing has occurred, and uncontrolled cutting of trees for firewood has become ever more common. This has exposed what are often fragile sandy soils to rapid erosion by running water and wind (Fig. 5.2). There have, too, been significant changes in the natural hydrological cycle, involving a serious reduction in the effectiveness of the rainfall. The amount of rainfall entering the soil and thus becoming available for plant growth has been diminished by increased surface run-off, causing lowering of ground water levels and the drying up of many wells and springs.

However, it is also apparent that, although desertification has been intensified by human activities, the underlying ongoing causes may well be climatic. The severe droughts in Africa of the early 1970s and mid 1980s were essentially the product of greatly reduced annual rainfall, perhaps related to either a long continuing trend towards climatic desiccation or shorter term cyclic changes from wet to dry and vice versa. For example, the idea of a 200-year cycle of drought has been proposed. Certainly, the evidence of the past shows clearly that the present day climate of the tropics cannot be safely regarded as characteristic, stable and unchanging. It is now believed that, with the extension of the great continental ice-sheets of the Quaternary into mid-latitute regions (Chapter 4), the climatic zones of the non-glacial areas were displaced towards the Equator. One view is that the Sahara was invaded from the north by the winter rains now characteristic of Mediterranean climates. At the same time, the southern margins of the desert would have encroached on to the savanna; for instance, in northern Nigeria there are massive sub-parallel dune systems still preserved in well vegetated, seasonally humid regions which are far removed from the Sahara (Fig. 5.3). It is possible, too, that some parts of the rain-forests of the humid tropics may have degenerated to savanna during the glacial periods. If we are indeed at the present time in an inter-glacial period which is approaching its end (p. 82), then it is to be expected that these past displacements of climates will recur – and indeed such displacements may have been initiated already.

The precise timing, nature and scale of past climatic modifications and their geomorphological and hydrological impacts, are still difficult to gauge. Indeed, there is a growing view that only certain desert areas, notably those of the western USA, were greatly affected by more rainy conditions, or *pluvial periods*, during the Quaternary. The larger deserts, such as the Sahara, are seen as having remained largely arid, except for a brief humid period at the very end of the last glacial period. In this respect, the evidence of ancient lake deposits and former lake shorelines is revealing. Perhaps the best example of a once greatly expanded water-body is Lake Chad in west Africa (Fig. 5.4). This is today a much shrunken remnant; its depth is now only some 8 m, whereas 10 000 years ago it was some 160 m deep and as large as the present Caspian Sea. Evidence for this so called *MegaChad* takes the form of old beach deposits; near Maiduguri, in north-east Nigeria, there is a relict barrier beach, 180 km from the existing lake edge and 50 m above the present water-level of Lake Chad.

In east Africa, many rift valley lakes are also much reduced remnants of their former selves. Raised shorelines on the southern slopes of Menengai volcano show that Lake Nakuru, Kenya, now on average only 3 m deep, was 180 m in depth only 10 000 years ago. It is very difficult to interpret the climatic implications of these former expanded lakes. Do they point to a *wetter* climate, or a *drier* climate in which

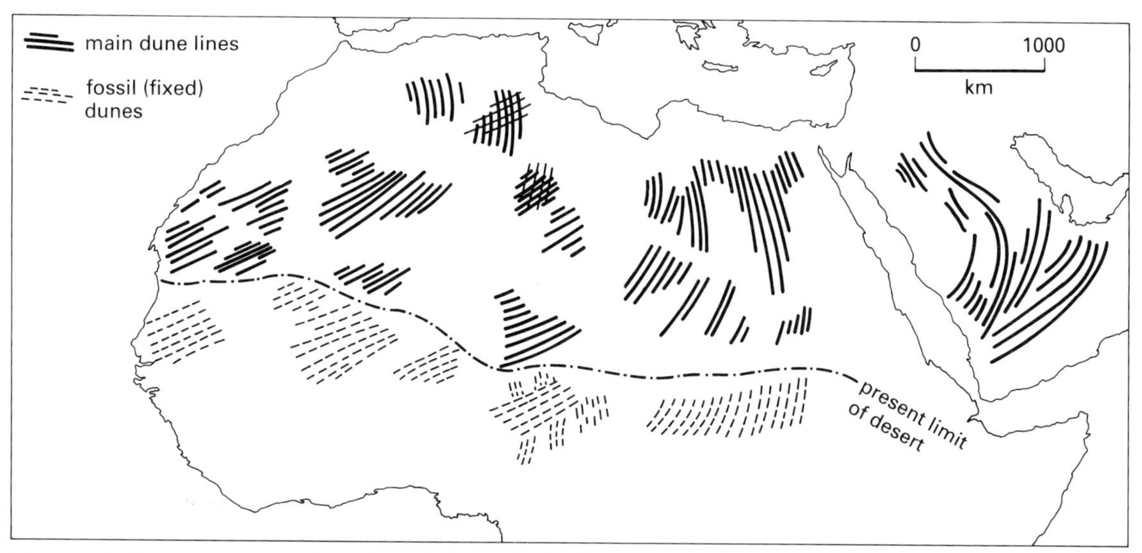

Figure 5.3 *Present dune trends and fossil dunes in the Sahara (see above and p. 129)*

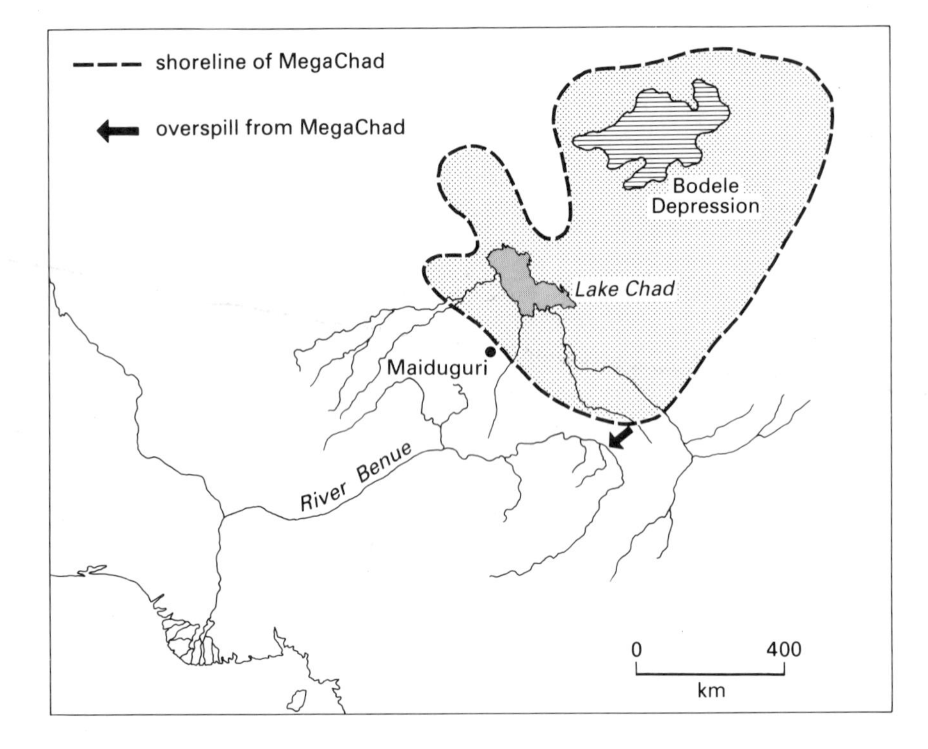

Figure 5.4 *The former extent of Lake Chad and its drainage. Note that at present Chad occupies a basin of internal drainage, but formerly overspilled westwards into the Benue system (see p. 113)*

surface run-off was more abundant? Do they reflect changed temperatures, with cooler conditions giving rise to reduced losses from evaporation? One suggestion is that the former Lake Nakuru would have depended on an average annual rainfall of 1330 mm (compared to the present 950 mm), and a mean annual temperature 3°C lower than at present.

LANDFORM DEVELOPMENT IN THE HUMID TROPICS

Weathering processes

Chemical weathering plays a dominant role in landform development in the humid tropics. In areas where the rocks are readily broken down into large quantities of sand and clay, deep *regoliths*, or weathered layers, accumulate, sometimes to depths of 30–60 m or even more. As a result, exposures of solid rock at the surface are quite rare, certainly by comparison with many temperate landscapes. In these circumstances, there are limited opportunities for mechanical weathering to operate effectively.

Several factors appear to have contributed to the formation of tropical regoliths.

(i) There is an abundance of soil moisture owing to the heavy rainfall; this moisture is required for the operation of processes such as hydrolysis.

(ii) The high prevailing temperatures speed up chemical reactions; indeed, it has been shown that the rates of such reactions are increased 2–3 times for every 10°C rise in temperature.

(iii) The dense rainforests supply decaying vegetable matter to the soil at an annual rate of 100–200 tonnes/hectare by comparison with the 20–25 tonnes/hectare of temperate coniferous forests. As it rots this organic material generates humic acids, another cause of chemical weathering.

(iv) The developing regoliths tend to be held *in situ* by the vegetation, even on slopes of 30–40°. The mixture of sand and clay itself constitutes a porous mass, acting rather as a giant sponge which retains soil moisture and promotes continual weathering of the underlying fresh rock.

Weathering in crystalline terrains

Crystalline rocks, such as granite, gneiss and schist, occur widely in the humid tropics; for example, granite and associated gneiss form the back bone of the interior uplands of the Malay peninsula, together with many outcrops in coastal areas. Such rocks are characterised by the presence of minerals such as biotite and feldspar, which are susceptible to decay by processes such as hydrolysis, and by the occurrence of joints, tiny fractures (microfractures) and crystal boundaries which allow acidulated rainwater to penetrate the rock. As the unstable minerals are selectively attacked, and minerals such as feldspar are broken down into clay, the initially hard and compact rock begins to change into a mass of platy fragments known as *gruss*. At a more advanced stage of weathering, when all the unstable minerals have been weathered, the regolith will crumble into a structureless mass of clay and sand, the latter derived from stable minerals such as quartz which are relatively unaffected by chemical weathering, known as *residual debris*.

The weathering of crystalline rocks from the surface downwards is rarely uniform, but proceeds most readily along the major joints (Fig. 5.5). In this way, large joint bounded blocks will become detached from bedrock, and then gradually be weathered inwards. In the process, the corners of the blocks will be most effectively decayed, owing to attack from three sides, and rounded *corestones* will thus be formed (Fig. 5.6). At an intermediate stage of the weathering process, these corestones will be contained within a mass of clay and sand. However, at a late stage, they will themselves be consumed by weathering. As the regolith develops, the washing away of fine clay particles by percolating rainwater will become more active. Not only will the quartz content of the residual debris increase proportionately, but there will also be subsidence and collapse in the regolith, giving a pitted and irregular ground surface.

The development of humid tropical regoliths may, in ideal circumstances, proceed to a depth as great as 100 m. However, it is now realised that there is, in effect, a downward limit to weathering, where underground pressures are so great that joints are non-existent or tightly closed, with the result that water cannot penetrate the rock. Examination of borehole records and exposed sections has shown that the change from regolith to unweathered rock occurs in different ways. Sometimes there is a transition downwards, through zones of residual debris (representing advanced weathering), residual debris with many corestones (representing less advanced weathering), and partial weathering of joints (representing the early stage of weathering). However, it is not

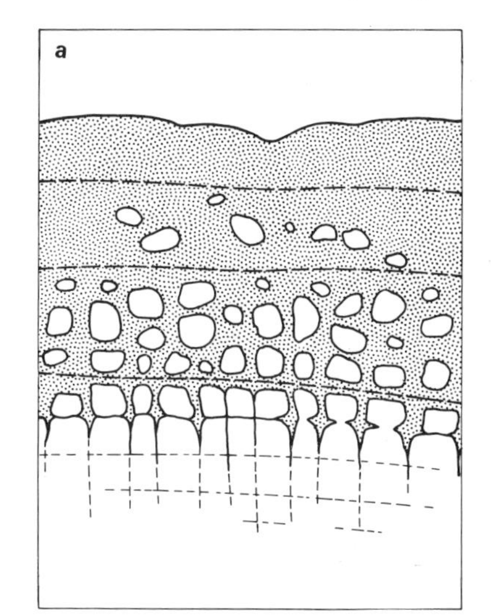

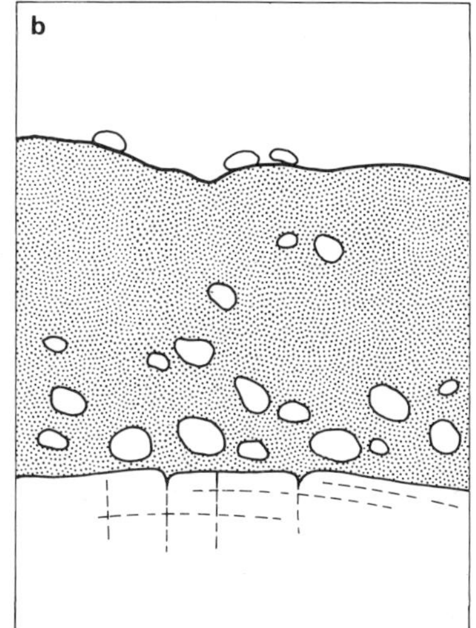

Figure 5.5 *The development and features of deep weathered layers. Note in **a** the zonation of weathering layers from the surface downwards: fully decomposed rock (residual debris); residual debris with corestones; corestones with residual debris; partially weathered rock. In **b** the weathered layer is entirely comprised of residual debris with relatively few corestones, and there is a well-developed basal surface of weathering*

Figure 5.6 *Granite corestones in deeply weathered rock at Genting Highland, near Kuala Lumpur, Malaysia*

uncommon to find an abrupt change from residual debris to sound rock, giving a clearly defined *basal surface of weathering*. The latter may coincide with a near horizontal sheet joint, in which case the basal surface approximates to a smooth surface.

Weathering in limestone terrains

In the humid tropics, deep weathered layers are by no means universal; rather they are confined to those rocks which yield abundant residual decomposition products such as quartz and clay. Limestone, when weathered, releases relatively little in the way of impurities, and is therefore characterised by regolith development on only a minor scale. Instead, in the presence of abundant rainfall and humic acids from decaying vegetation, there is intense *vertical solution*. This produces many deep hollows and *dolines* which grow into *cockpits* with steep rocky walls separated by conical hills; this is known as *cockpit karst*. In a more advanced stage of development, tropical limestone landscapes consist of vertical sided, tower-like hills, or *mogotes*, rising above extensive alluvial plains; such *tower karst* may be seen in parts of northern Malaysia and southern China (Fig. 5.7). The spectacular towers resemble in some ways the dome-like inselbergs typical of granitic terrains in the seasonally humid tropics (p. 121). However, they are the product of more direct weathering, not the process of deep weathering and subsequent stripping of the regolith operative in the latter regions.

In general, it is believed that surface karstic forms are more important in the tropics, and that underground karstification is less active than in the temperate zone. However, mogotes are often penetrated by caverns and underground passages, as at Batu Caves, Kuala Lumpur, Malaysia. Here, the main chamber has been greatly enlarged, leading to roof collapse and the formation of karst windows, comparable with features in temperate karst. Nevertheless, the main process in the later stages of tropical karst evolution is probably solutional undermining of upland limestone blocks, once cockpits have been deepened to the level of the water table and their floors permanently moistened. In this way, the hill slopes are continually undercut and steepened by basal solution, and the hill masses reduced to steep walled mogotes standing high above limestone plains which are crossed by surface streams and floored by alluvium.

Transport and erosion

The widespread occurrence of a deep regolith, even on steep slopes in many parts of the humid tropics, implies that transport processes here are relatively ineffective. Indeed, it has

Figure 5.7 *Tower karst adjacent to the Yulon River, Tangshuo, Guangxi, south China*

been argued that the decomposition of rock is more rapid than the transport of material over slopes, which in turn is more effective than fluvial erosion.

We may envisage three possible relationships between weathering, transport, erosion and regolith depth.
(i) Weathering rates exceed transport and erosion rates. This condition is necessary for thick regoliths to develop in the first instance.
(ii) Weathering rates equal transport and erosion rates. Such a steady state condition will maintain the regolith at a constant thickness.
(iii) Weathering rates are less than transport and erosion rates. Under this condition, regoliths will not be formed; or if previously developed under condition (i) are destroyed, leading to increasing exposure of the basal surface of weathering.

As a broad generalisation, it can be stated that (i) and (ii) appear most applicable to the humid tropics, and (iii) to the seasonally humid tropics (p. 118).

Rainwash is sometimes considered to be of little importance in areas of tropical rainforest, because the forest canopy intercepts rainfall and reduces rainsplash erosion, whilst porous regoliths favour rapid infiltration at the forest floor. Nevertheless, it has been observed that rainwater running down tree trunks can cause localised erosion. Moreover, one study in a Malaysian forest revealed that, over a period of only three months, 1–2 cm of soil were lost from steeper slopes under conditions of heavy rainfall.

Mass movements appear to be generally of greater significance than surface wash in the humid tropics. They take the form of land slides, slips and slumps on the steeper slopes, and soil creep on the gentler slopes. Movement may be concentrated in the sub-soil, beneath an upper layer where there is stabilisation by the root net. Factors favourable to landsliding include the presence of a regolith of little mechanical strength, and heavy rain which saturates the soil and so loads it with water that slope failure occurs. Soil creep is promoted by constant wetting and drying, leading to the swelling and contraction of clay minerals, and the removal of fines by eluviation causing settlement and disturbance of the soil. Although slopes occupied by forest appear to be stable in the field, there is much indirect evidence of the work of mass movements on the convex,

Figure 5.8 *The channel of the Sungei Selangor, Malaysia. Note the numerous large boulders, which represent corestones carried to the river by mass movements of weathered debris on the valley slopes*

rounded hilltops and interfluves, and the large accumulations of corestones in river beds (Fig. 5.8). The latter have clearly been transported downslope within masses of finer sand and clay, which has then been washed away by stream flow.

Fluvial activity in the humid tropics may be a transportational rather than erosional process, in the strict sense of the term. It has been argued that because tropical rivers carry mainly fine sediments, sand and clay, they have very limited powers of corrasion. Nevertheless, it needs to be emphasised that humid tropical landscapes are characterised by networks of river valleys, often deeply incised and with smoothly graded valley side slopes, similar to fluvially dissected landscapes in temperate regions. What is not always clear is whether these valleys result initially from vertical stream erosion or merely from the selective removal of previously decomposed rock.

It is sometimes easy to overestimate the transportational powers of tropical rivers. Chemical weathering here releases large quantities of soluble silica which, theoretically, should move from the slopes into the rivers, by leaching and throughflow. However, measurements have shown that the solution loads of tropical rivers are much less high than expected, and not significantly greater than those of temperate rivers where chemical weathering is generally much less active. Additionally, the sediment loads of tropical rivers are also surprisingly low, commonly less than 100 mg of sediment per litre of water, by comparison with a peak of 100 000 mg/l^{-1} in the San Pedro river, in the arid south-west of the USA.

Such evidence points towards the conclusion that rates of geomorphological activity at present may be low rather than moderate in the humid tropics, despite the apparently favourable circumstances of abundant rainfall and high temperatures (p. 114). The deep weathered layers may not be the product of rapid weathering, but of a very lengthy period of slow weathering. One suggestion is that many of the solutes released by weathering are taken up by the dense plant cover, and are later returned to the ground when the vegetation dies. In other words, in the humid tropical environment, energy is used in constantly recycling nutrients and maintaining the rainforest, rather than in erosion and transport by streams! It is only when the forest is destroyed either naturally, through processes such as landsliding, or by human activities, involving cultivation, lumbering and construction, that geomorphological activity is increased. High sediment concentrations in tropical rivers are almost always found in areas where land within the catchment is being cleared for housing, excavated for roads, and so on.

LANDFORM DEVELOPMENT IN THE SEASONALLY HUMID TROPICS

As in the humid tropics, the climatic conditions here are generally favourable to chemical weathering. However, regoliths are less thick, in the order of 25 m in the wetter savannas, but only 6 m in the drier savannas. Nevertheless, their characteristics, such as the formation of corestones and residual debris, and the presence of the basal surface of weathering, are similar to those found in humid regions. One important factor is that, in the presence of a less dense vegetation cover, involving more scattered trees and bushes and a clumpy grass cover, with much bare earth particularly at the end of the dry season, rainwash processes are far more effective. As a result, the surface layers of the regolith are prone to rapid removal, especially by the early wet season rains. It is not clear whether or not regoliths in the seasonally humid tropics are largely relict features, persisting from a time when the prevailing climate may have been more humid. At the present time they are undergoing destruction as a result of drier climatic conditions, associated with a less protective vegetation cover than existed formerly.

Landforms resulting from the dissection and removal of regoliths

The erosion of duricrust layers

In many seasonally humid areas the upper parts of the regolith have been cemented into a hard, concrete-like layer, or *duricrust*. Of particular note is the reddish-brown *lateritic ironstone*, which is developed widely on the erosional plains of Brazil, tropical Africa, southern India and western Australia. As the weathered layer is leached of bases and soluble silica, the relatively insoluble oxidised iron (Fe_2O_3) and alumina (Al_2O_3) accumulate. Continual wetting and drying leads to the crystallisation of the iron, and the formation of a hard crust several metres in thickness. Beneath the ironstone layer lies a considerable mass of soft rotted rock which can be easily eroded if the crust becomes breached by streams. In some areas, such as northern Nigeria, an older primary lateritic crust stands some 20–30 m above a younger secondary laterite. The lateritic ironstones in Africa appear to be very old, dating from the Tertiary era.

A characteristic landform type in the tropical savannas is the *dissected laterite sheet* (Fig. 5.9). This comprises an extensive plain, itself underlain by largely undissected laterite, which has been eroded by fluvial action. Above the plain are numerous laterite-capped mesas, some 10–20 m in height over much of west Africa but up to 100 m high in southern

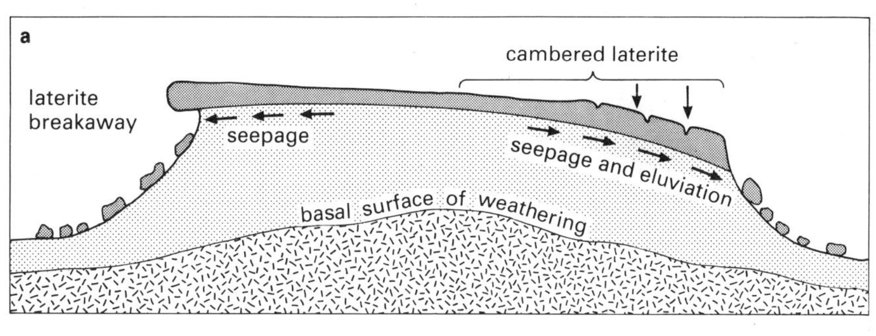

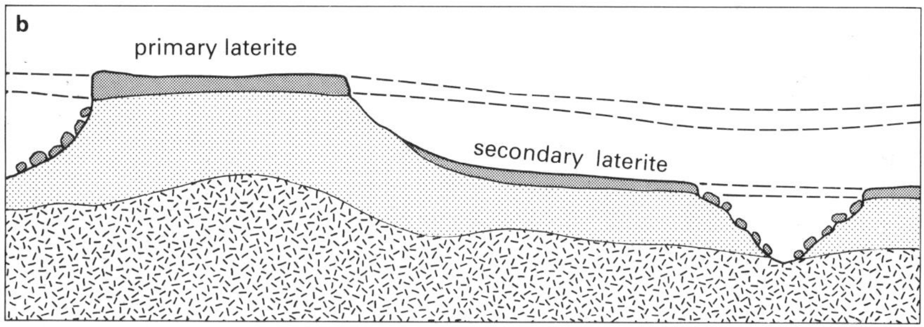

Figure 5.9 *Landforms associated with dissected lateritic crusts. In* ***a*** *a single laterite is involved; in* ***b*** *a secondary laterite, resulting from cementation of debris from the margins of the primary laterite, has been formed but is now undergoing dissection*

Uganda. These hills are protected at their summits by the hard, duricrust cap rock, but the underlying sands and clays exposed on the slopes are rapidly attacked by creep and rainwash. This promotes parallel slope retreat, thus undermining the laterite which collapses to litter the slopes with boulders. One active process in the wet season is spring sapping at the base of the ironstone. Rainwater percolating through the latter will be impeded by clay horizons beneath, and will migrate laterally to emerge at the mesa margins. Here, weathered material is washed out from beneath the laterite, which gradually settles to form a cambered structure.

The removal of regoliths

In many parts of the seasonally humid tropics, erosion of the regolith has been so severe that parts of the basal surface of weathering are now being exposed. For example, some rivers have cut down to reveal the basal surface in their channels. Where the surface is sloping, the rivers have then shifted laterally by a form of down-dip migration, since it is easier to undercut and remove regolith than to erode vertically into sound rock. More usually, however, there seems to have been a general lowering of the regolith surface, by combined stream and surface wash transportation, which has revealed the highest parts of the basal surface. In this way, the landscape has developed two contrasting elements: low, plain-like areas, underlain by regolith and alluvium; and higher, often dome-shaped hills underlain by solid rock. It is possible that such landscapes have been fashioned by several episodes of weathering and stripping (p. 123); land surfaces

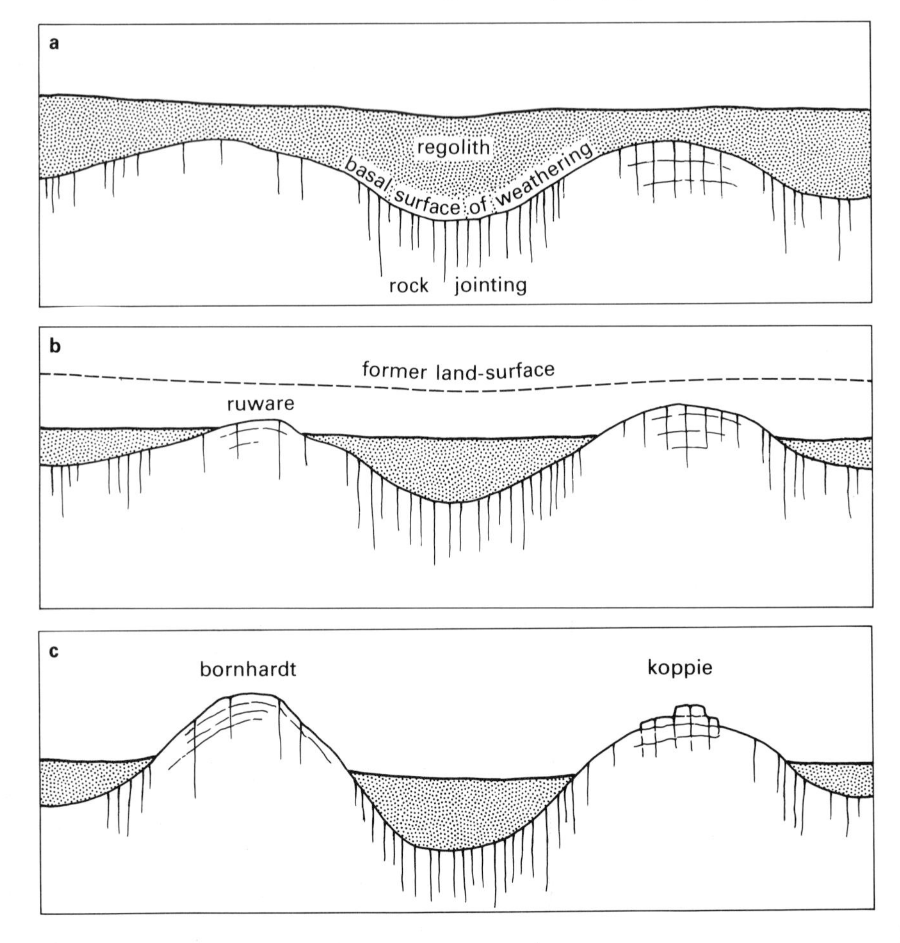

Figure 5.10 *The formation of etchplains (see p. 121)*

formed in this way have been termed *etchplains* (Fig. 5.10).

The landforms resulting from the removal of regoliths are as follows:

1 ***Tors*** are small masses of block jointed rock, projecting above the basal surface, and exposed when the soft sands and clays above and around them are stripped away (Fig. 5.11). The upper parts of tors often comprise detached and rounded corestones; sometimes accumulations of corestones alone form tors. Some authorities believe that tors in mid-latitude regions, such as Dartmoor in south-west England, are the product of past 'tropical' climatic conditions.

2 ***Rock pavements, ruwares and dwalas*** develop where the basal surface is undulating. Removal of the regolith exposes the high points of *domical rises*, to give near level rock outcrops or gently rounded, sometimes elongated hills (Fig. 5.12). The latter are initially very smooth, but weathering takes advantage of vertical and (particularly) curvilinear sheet joints to cause exfoliation and block disintegration over time.

3 ***Inselbergs*** (island mountains) are steep sided, isolated hills standing high above surrounding plains (Fig. 5.13). One common and distinctive type is the rock dome (*bornhardt*), with its near vertical or even overhanging sides and rounded summit profile, which is clearly determined by

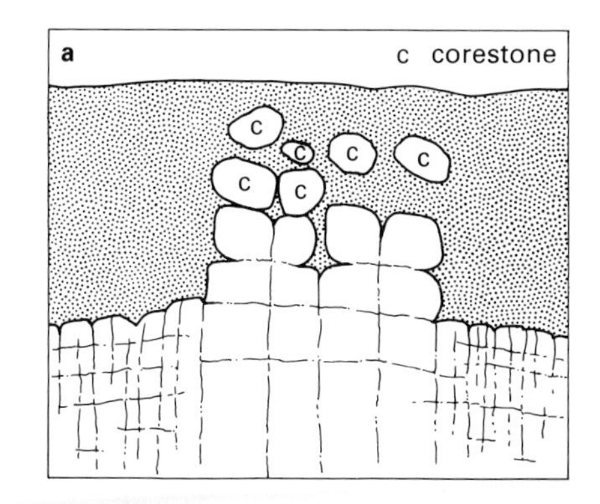

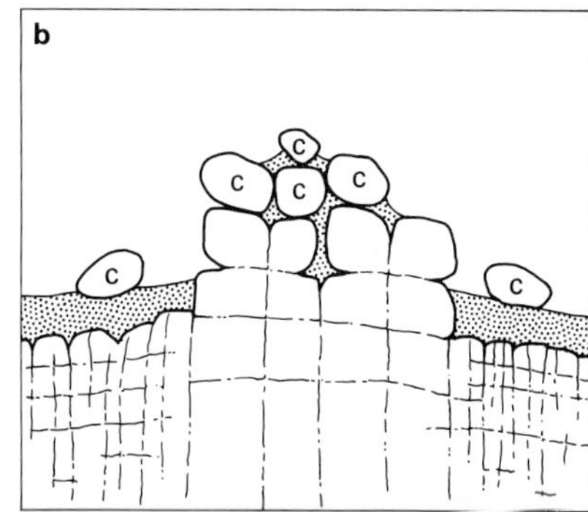

Figure 5.11 *The formation of tors* *(see p. 120)*

Figure 5.12 *A low rock-dome, or ruware, near Katsina, northern Nigeria. This dome appears to represent part of the basal surface of weathering, exposed by recent stripping away of overlying regolith*

Figure 5.13 *A large domed inselberg, or bornhardt, north of Harare, Zimbabwe*

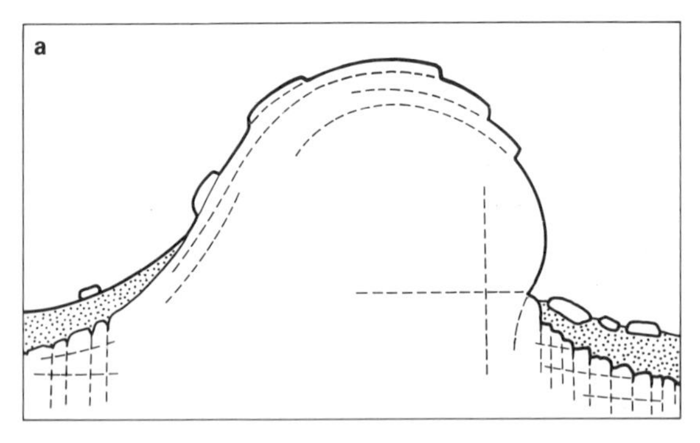

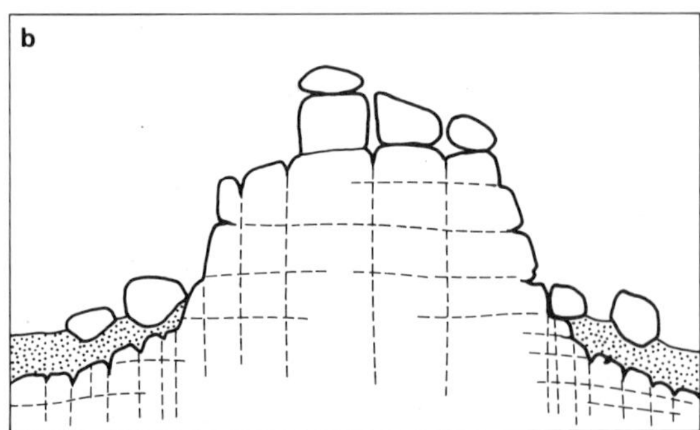

Figure 5.14 *Bornhardts (**a**) and blocky inselbergs (**b**) (see p. 122)*

massive sheet jointing in the rock, usually of a granite type (Fig. 5.14). By contrast, *blocky inselbergs* resemble large scale tors, developed where rectangular jointing is dominant. Where inselbergs, whether domed or blocky, are subjected to prolonged sub-aerial weathering and collapse, degraded forms referred to as *castle koppies* (*koppies*) are formed.

Although many inselbergs rise above plains underlain by rotted rock, some are found marginal to major erosional scarps, bounding extensive uplands and evidently undergoing parallel retreat. In granitic rocks, these scarps may be marked by *exfoliating half domes*. In some instances, dissection of the scarp by head-ward eroding streams has isolated hill masses, which have then become rounded into domed inselbergs as weathering exploits sheet joints. These *marginal inselbergs* thus result from backwearing, whereas those standing in isolation above deeply weathered plains may be interpreted as the product of the downwearing processes involved in etchplanation, and as representing emerged sub-surface domes; this is also referred to as the *exhumation hypothesis*.

Pediplanation and landform evolution

One hypothesis to explain erosional plains and inselbergs in tropical landscapes envisages that two processes of *scarp retreat*, or parallel slope retreat, and *pedimentation*, the formation of gently concave basal slopes by surface run-off, operate in conjunction. Over a very long period of time, they lead to the formation of a multi-concave surface (*pediplain*) above which stand residual hills, resulting from the reduction of uplands and interfluves by slope recession (Fig. 5.15).

In a general way, this hypothesis accounts satisfactorily for many of the major elements

Figure 5.15 *A pediplain with inselbergs, south of Sultan Hamud, Kenya*

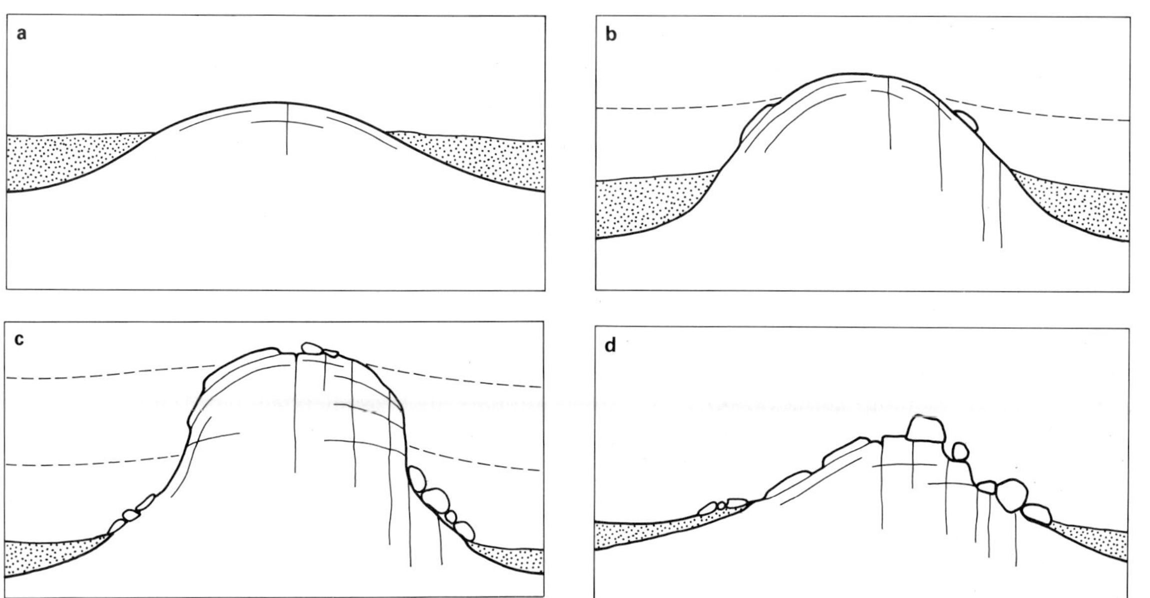

Figure 5.16 *The formation of inselbergs and koppies. In* **a** *the basal surface of weathering is exposed as a low dome (ruware) by the removal of regolith. In* **b** *and* **c** *the ruware is transformed into a major inselberg by successive episodes of deep weathering and stripping; in* **d** *the inselberg is reduced by exfoliation and block disintegration to a castle koppie (p. 122)*

in tropical landscapes, though it seems to take insufficient account of deep weathering and the stripping processes described above. On the other hand, the etchplain hypothesis poses its own problems. For example, regoliths rarely attain a depth of 100 m, so that sub-surface domes with a relief greater than 50–75 m cannot normally be envisaged. Yet some bornhardts rise to heights of 200–300 m or even more above the surrounding plain! One solution is to assume that such prominent inselbergs have arisen over a vast period of time, as a result of several episodes of weathering and stripping (Fig. 5.16). Throughout this development, the inselbergs would have progressively increased in height, simply because weathering of the rock forming them lagged behind that of the surrounding areas. This could be due to the fact that the bare rock of the domes rapidly sheds rainwater, and dries out to give an arid environment in which chemical weathering is restricted. At the same time, areas marginal to the domes would receive increments of water, and rock weathering here would be enhanced. The implication of this hypothesis is that prominent inselbergs are of great antiquity, perhaps dating back to Mesozoic times (approximately 100 million years ago); in other words, they are arguably the most ancient landforms of the earth's surface!

LANDFORM DEVELOPMENT IN THE ARID AND SEMI-ARID TROPICS

The landforms of hot deserts are in some ways highly distinctive. One well known feature is the presence of extensive areas of loose sand, fashioned by the wind into complex patterns of dunes; another is the angular nature of much of the scenery, with numerous flat topped plateaux and steep slopes rising abruptly from flat or gently sloping surfaces. One major problem of desert geomorphology is to decide how far these distinctive landforms are the product of processes acting today. As has been shown (p. 111), tropical deserts may have experienced past changes of climate, which have altered hydrological regimes and rates of geomorphological activity.

It has been widely accepted by geomorphologists that the legacy of the past is fundamental in deserts, but it is very difficult to determine precisely what that legacy is. There is evidence to show that hot desert landscapes have been evolving since before the Quaternary, with its world wide climatic fluctuations. For example, parts of the western desert of Australia are underlain by sheets of laterite (p. 119) and chemically rotted crystalline rocks related to a humid climate early in the Tertiary era. In late-Tertiary times, the area became more arid (the present rainfall is about 225 mm/annum^{-1}), and the laterite was partially stripped away. The present landscape comprises a plain with three main elements: laterite capped hills; exposed parts of the basal surface of weathering; and alluvial deposits comprising sediments from the old regolith which have been reworked more recently by desert flash floods.

The impact of the Quaternary climatic changes is more controversial. At some time, the desert margins were certainly affected by more humid conditions, as the evidence from Lake Chad and other tropical lakes shows. However, what happened in the desert interiors is less clear, and indeed some authorities now assume that these areas were largely unaffected by Quaternary rainy episodes. Yet it is difficult to equate this view with evidence such as the following. In the great Hoggar massif of the Saharan interior, there are not only numerous water carved valleys of considerable size, but also pockets of red soil typical of present day savanna regions. Botanical remains, too, indicate that parts of the Sahara were once occupied by open savanna woodland or steppe grassland. There are many signs of early human occupation of the deserts by people who fished lakes and rivers which no longer exist, hunted animals such as elephant and giraffe, and introduced cattle herding. In the Arabian desert west of Riyadh, limestones are penetrated by solution pipes to a depth of 30 m or more, although the present mean annual rainfall is about 100 mm. Moreover, in granite terrains here many low lying areas are underlain by chemically rotted rock, containing corestones, which is reminiscent of present day humid tropical environments (p. 115) (Fig. 5.17). Perhaps most striking of all, and of great importance in the economic development of Saudi Arabia, are the great quantities of fossil groundwater, lying at depths of several hundreds of metres beneath the surface of limestone and sandstone areas. Today, evaporation here greatly exceeds rainfall and recharging of the aquifer is impossible; thus this fossil water must testify to the occurrence of lengthy wetter periods in the past. It is surely impossible to believe that all the phenomena described can have resulted from

Figure 5.17 *A granite landscape near Arawah, Saudi Arabia. Broad wadis separate koppies, comprising weathered boulders. Deep weathering of the granite, under more humid conditions in the past, appears to have been followed by an episode of erosion of the weathered materials under arid conditions*

one brief pluvial period, lasting at most a few thousands of years, at the close of the final glacial period. Perhaps the earlier climatic changes, of which little direct evidence remains in the form of deposits or expanded lakes, were not great, and involved merely a doubling, or even trebling, of the present annual rainfall to about 300–400 mm/annum^{-1}. This would have been enough to increase surface run-off, and thus erosion, yet at the same time would not have encouraged a vegetation cover sufficiently dense or continuous to impede many geomorphological processes. For it is important to emphasise that, had the desert climates in the past become too wet, geomorphological evolution might have been slowed down rather than accelerated!

Weathering in hot deserts

It has been widely assumed that the considerable diurnal range of temperature in deserts, up to 30°C or more, leads to powerful thermal fracturing of rocks (p. 53). Certainly, many desert slopes and surfaces are littered by sharply angular rock fragments. However, many of these appear to be too large to have been detached by heating and cooling of rock surfaces, but seem more likely to have resulted either from the collapse of jointed rock faces, which have formed abundant talus deposits on the margins of limestone wadis, or from selective chemical attack along joint lines and bedding planes (Fig. 5.18).

Of great interest are the granite terrains of the central Saudi Arabian desert. Here numerous rocky hills rise steeply above flat wadi floors, beneath which there is first a layer of alluvium and then 4–5 m or more of rotted granite *in situ*. Rounded tor boulders are also abundant, and some granite outcrops are penetrated by numerous weathering caverns, which give to the granite an appearance of Gruyere cheese on a massive scale. Such landscapes are clearly the product of more active chemical weathering in the past. However, even today weathering has by no means ceased, as is shown by the numerous platy fragments littering rock surfaces, and the active exfoliation of thin surface rock layers, usually 1–3 cm in thickness. This disintegration is evidently not the result of thermal fracture alone, since the undersides of the rock fragments often show signs of chemical alteration. Processes such as

Figure 5.18 *The wall of a deep wadi, in limestone, Tuwaiq Mountains, Saudi Arabia, showing active collapse of well jointed rock under present day climatic conditions*

salt weathering and hydration (pp. 54 and 55), dependent on the availability of small quantities of moisture, seem to be mainly responsible.

Running water in hot deserts

It is the fashion for modern geomorphologists to attribute the dominant desert landforms (wadis, pediments, alluvial fans, erosional plains) to the action of running water, either at present or in the past. It is certainly no longer feasible to regard erosion, transport and deposition by running water as being secondary to wind action, as some early researchers believed. However, it may be that the pendulum has swung too far, and that, so far as present day processes are concerned, wind is somewhat underestimated by comparison with water!

Much has been written about desert flash floods which develop with alarming suddenness and sometimes drown unsuspecting persons camping in dry water courses. Such floods may be quite rare in desert interiors, but their scale can sometimes be startling. Wilfred Thesiger, in *Arabian Sands*, describes the effects of a major flood in the Wadi Aidam, in southern Saudi Arabia, at the turn of the century; even sixty years later, in the 1950s, palm trunks were to be seen jammed 6 m up in the rocky cliffs on either side of this 1000 m wide valley.

Where desert run-off does take place, it forms either stream floods or sheet floods.

Stream floods are confined to dissected uplands, which contain channels that are normally dry but become flooded after heavy storms. They are characteristic of deeply cut, flat floored and steep sided wadis, found in great numbers in the limestone cuestas west of Riyadh, Saudi Arabia (Fig. 5.19). However, apart from causing some local undercutting of the valley walls, the present day stream floods do not appear to contribute much to the formation of the wadis, which are probably the result of erosion by semi-permanent rivers during the Quaternary (p. 113). The present wadi floors are filled in, often to depths of tens of metres, by thick alluvial formations; the stream floods are merely reworking the surface layers of alluvium, and rarely make contact with the underlying rock floor. Moreover, the floods are rapidly depleted downvalley by percolation into the permeable alluvium; the latter supports a water table which is being replenished even under existing climatic conditions, and can be reached by shallow wells, often no more than 5 m in depth. For this reason, desert wadis are the focus of much settlement; indeed, the farmers and herders may construct small earth dams across the wadi floor, to impound stream floods and aid the process of percolation into the alluvium. The shallow ground water of the wadis should be contrasted with the fossil water, found in much larger quantities, and at much greater depths, in limestone and sandstone aquifers (p. 20).

Sheet floods consist of extensive flows which are not confined to narrow valleys or channels, but are spread widely over the ground surface. Clearly, such flows can occur only on gently sloping plane surfaces. These include rock pediments and alluvial accumulations at the base of scarps marginal to desert uplands. Here the sheet floods form directly from rain falling on to the pediment or fan, or result indirectly from the transformation of a stream flood emerging from a valley mouth. Sheet floods comprise a shallow layer of water, in which there may be many threads of high velocity flow; their powers of erosion and transport are necessarily limited.

The effects of sheet floods on landforms are somewhat controversial. One suggestion is that they are capable of eroding the near level surfaces which are characteristic of desert scenery. However, the counter argument is that the sheet floods develop only because such surfaces already exist! A realistic view is that, whilst sheet floods can carry out some erosion of exposed rock, their main function is to transport fine sediments from steep slopes, across the pediment to the zone of alluviation. Many pediments are partially covered by a thin layer of alluvium in transit; it may be that this is occasionally stripped away by an individual sheet flood, and that the rock pediment is then subjected to small scale erosion until the alluvial layer is restored.

Wind action in hot deserts

In the popular imagination, hot deserts are regions of unending sand dunes, where travellers can be lost in fierce sand storms. The

Figure 5.19 *A typical desert wadi in the shield area of Saudi Arabia. Note the steep, debris covered slopes, and the broad, alluvial valley floor. Present day run-off is infrequent and is mainly confined to the channel, marked by tamarix bushes, on the right hand side of the wadi*

reality is somewhat different. Individual sand seas, like the *ergs* of the Sahara desert and the *nafud* of the Arabian desert, are very extensive, yet still occupy only some 10 per cent of the total desert area. Far more important are the *reg*, or stony desert, consisting in part of weathered debris and in part of water deposited gravels and *hammada*, or rocky desert, with many rocky residuals and bare eroded outcrops.

Desert sand storms are assumed to have a powerful blasting effect, particularly where the wind is funnelled along depressions etched from joints or faults. However, most sand grains moved by the wind creep along the surface or *saltate*, which is a process involving jumping of grains in a turbulent air flow. They are mainly concentrated in a zone only 0.5 m above ground level, so that the vertical range of any abrasive effect is small. Whilst wind action is certainly capable of polishing hard rocks and undercutting weak rocks, it is hardly likely to play a significant role in the formation of major landforms such as mesas and inselbergs.

Wind erosion produces certain small weirdly-shaped landforms. Among these are *zeugen*, which are tabular masses of hard sedimentary rock standing up to 30 m in height and separated from each other by depressions, formed where the wind has been able to attack weak underlying shales (Fig. 5.20). Another common form is the *yardang*, an elongated ridge developed parallel to the prevailing wind direction. Yardangs show basal undercutting at their upwind ends only, and are thus distinguishable from pedestal rocks. Yardang-like landforms cover hundreds of km^2 around Tibesti, in the interior of the Sahara; they appear here to have formed over a long period, during which the wind direction remained virtually constant.

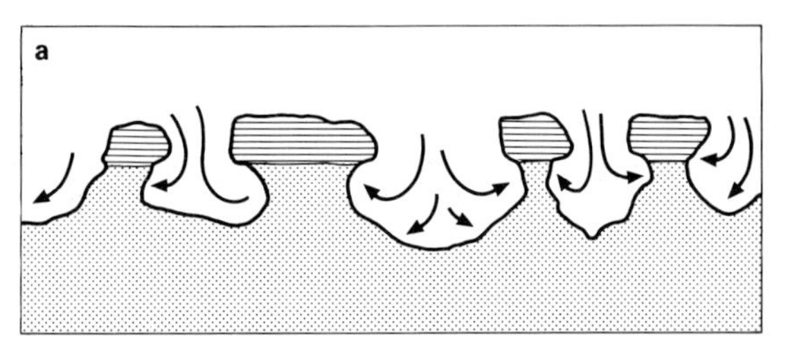

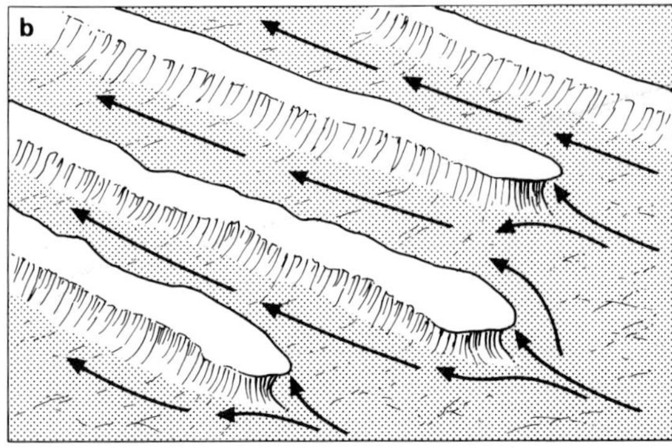

Figure 5.20 *The formation of zeugen (**a**) and yardangs (**b**)*

Larger features resulting from wind erosion include deflation hollows, the largest and most famous of which is the great Qattara depression of the western Egyptian desert. This attains a depth of 130 m below sea-level, and is reputed to have involved the removal of some 3000 km^3 of rock. It is almost certain, however, that such large hollows are of structural origin and are associated with downwarped or downfaulted areas. Concentration of moisture within them led to localised chemical weathering, causing granular disintegration and release of fine sediments which could be deflated, that is picked up and carried away by the desert winds. As the process continued, it became self perpetuating, for the deeper the depression, the greater the moisture present, and the more effective the weathering. The point would eventually be reached, however, when the depression floor actually became wet and marshy, so that deflation would effectively cease.

Wind deposition, to judge from the presence of great accumulations of wind-blown sand, appears to be highly effective in deserts. However, the evidence is a little misleading. The extensive sands of the Rub-al-Khali of the Arabian desert were actually deposited in a former arm of the Arabian Gulf during the Tertiary era. Within the Sahara, the great ergs usually occupy low-lying basins, and appear to consist of alluvial sands washed in from surrounding areas during pluvial conditions.

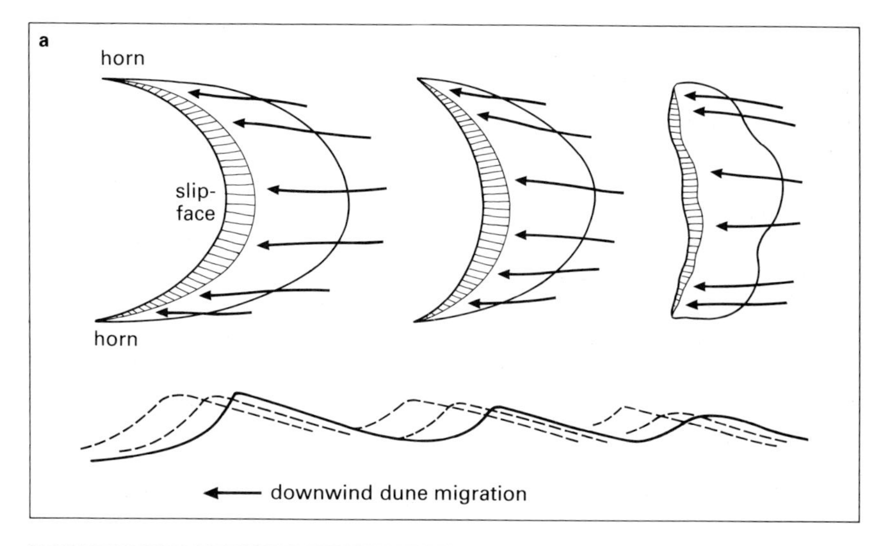

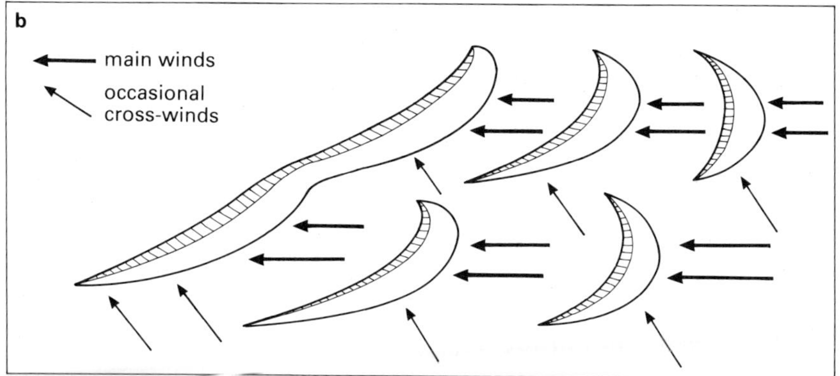

Figure 5.21 *Barchans (**a**) and longitudinal dunes (**b**)*

The associated sand dunes result merely from the reworking of *in situ* deposits.

Within large desert sand accumulations, the wind has fashioned sand dunes of varying scale and form. These may occur as large longitudinal ridges, up to a maximum height of 180 m and extending for nearly 200 km, or lower and broader dunes known as *whalebacks*. In the Sahara and Arabian deserts dune lines trend either north-south (in the north) or north-east to south-west (in the centre and south), reflecting the influence of the dominant winds (Fig. 5.3).

Smaller dunes are commonly of two types, the transverse crescentic dune (*barchan*) and the longitudinal dune (*seif*). Barchans are believed to form where the wind blows consistently from one direction (Fig. 5.21a). The dune begins as a small mound of sand, formed either by chance or on the lee side of an obstruction such as a rock or bush. Once in existence, the dune will trap more sand blown in by the wind. The fresh sand will be transported up the gentle windward slope, over the dune crest, and on to the steep lee face of the dune; this will cause downwind migration of the dune. The rate of migration will be slowest at the centre of the dune (where it is highest) and more rapid at its extremities; as a result it will develop horns.

Seifs form parallel to the direction of the wind (Fig. 5.21b). However, like barchans they are often asymmetrical in profile, and it seems that secondary cross winds assist their development (Fig. 5.22). Some may even result from the modification and amalgamation of barchans. Where cross winds blow, the windward horn of

Figure 5.22 *A seif dune at Sossusulei, Namibia*

the barchan will receive more sand, and will be extended, so much so that it may coalesce with another barchan. The steep faces of the seif also become orientated across the path of the secondary winds. When dune amalgamation occurs on a large scale, longitudinal dunes of considerable extent may result.

Landform types in the hot deserts

The landscapes of deserts vary greatly, depending on the degree of aridity, geological structure, climatic history and erosional history. Among the main landscape types are the following:

1 Areas of horizontal or gently dipping sedimentary rocks dissected by wadi systems Valley side slopes are steep or near vertical, and flat valley floors are covered by alluvium. Where erosion has reached an advanced stage, interfluves are reduced to inselbergs, often of mesa and butte form, and valley floors begin to coalesce as broad alluvial plains (Fig. 5.23). It is argued that lateral erosion by streams has been largely responsible for landform evolution in these conditions. Examples of such landscapes are the sandstone plateau regions of Libya and western Egypt, and the Monument Valley, Utah, USA.

2 The extensive, almost perfectly levelled erosional plains or pediplains (as in the African and Australian deserts) These result from the coalescence, over a long period, of innumerable rock pediments. The inselbergs rising above these plains are attributed to the destruction of uplands by parallel slope retreat (p. 122). The

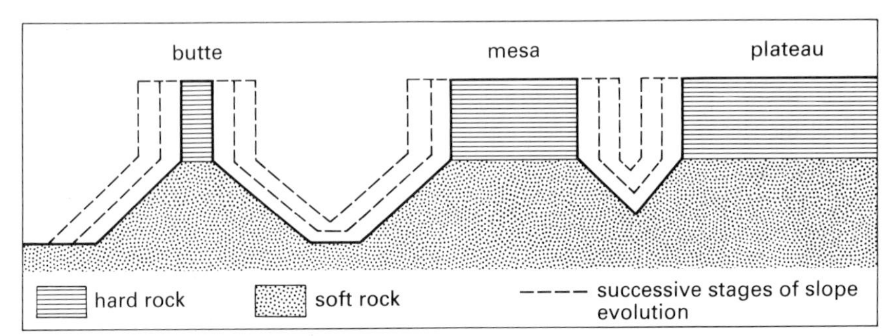

Figure 5.23 *The formation of mesas and buttes in the desert landscape*

Figure 5.24 *A reg covered plain, Plateau du Tademait, southern Algeria*

age of the plains is such that non-desert processes, such as deep weathering and stripping, may have contributed to their formation.

3 Broad areas of rocky or stony desert (hamada or reg) In these the rocky surfaces have been exposed as fine sediment has been evacuated by water and/or wind (Fig. 5.24). Such landscapes often form parts of the pediplains described.

4 Great accumulations of sand and sand dunes These form the ergs of the Sahara, such as the Grand Erg and Erg Chech, the nafud of the the Rub-al-Khali of Arabia, and the Great Sandy Desert of north-western Australia.

5 Mountain-rimmed basins (as in the western USA) These are associated with centripetal drainage, dissected upland blocks, steep boulder strewn mountain fronts, rock pediments and alluviated lowlands. The geological structure of these areas is strongly faulted; indeed mountain fronts are often eroded fault scarps. Landscape evolution appears to be at an early stage of development, at the opposite extreme from that of the ancient pediplains.

Landforms of the desert piedmont (Fig. 5.25)

The *piedmont zone*, or mountain foot zone, is situated between uplands and lowland plains of erosion and deposition (as in landscape (v) above). It has attracted the attention of geomorphologists for the reason that it is here that the dominant processes of the desert appear to be at their most active.

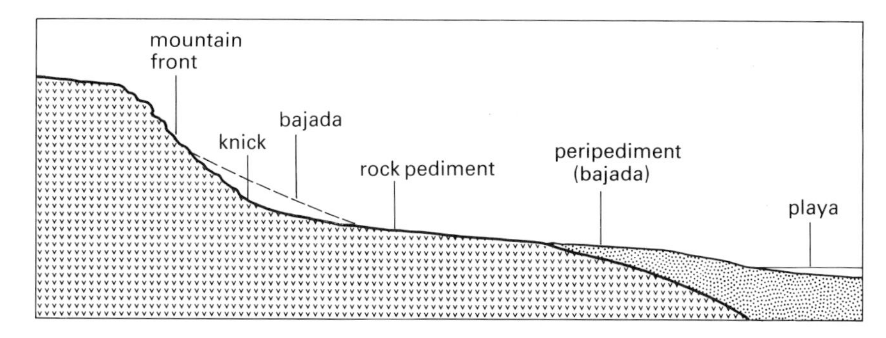

Figure 5.25 *Landforms of the desert piedmont*

1 The mountain front (or scarp) is a steep slope at 30°–90° rising abruptly from the gentler slopes beneath. Often it is occupied by boulders, released by disintegration of jointed rocks. The angle of slope is largely determined by the angle of these boulders; the mountain front is thus a boulder controlled slope, undergoing parallel retreat. The boulders on the slope are themselves affected by granular disintegration, and the resultant fine sediment is washed rapidly to the slope base.

2 The knick (piedmont angle) is an abrupt break in profile between the mountain front and rock pediment. It is regarded as a characteristic form of the arid environment. Usually, there is a change in the calibre of slope debris at the knick, from boulders above to alluvium below. The knick has been attributed to the lateral undercutting of the mountain front by running water on the pediment.

3 The rock pediment is a gentle concave slope ranging in angle from 7° on its upper part to 1° on its lower part (Fig. 5.26). It appears to be planed across the underlying rocks, irrespective of resistance to erosion. Frequently, it is veneered by fine sediment which is being transported from the mountain front. The concavity of profile suggests that running water plays a part in pediment formation. Among the theories of pedimentation are two of particular interest. The pediment is regarded by some as a *basal slope* left by active recession of the mountain front. Its angle is adjusted precisely to allow sheet floods to transport sediment from the foot of the mountain front to the peripediment below. Other authorities attribute pediment formation to lateral planation by running water, which undercuts the mountain front and causes it to recede. In this theory, the emphasis is on the active extension of the pediment, whilst according to the previous theory, it is regarded as a passive landform, subjected at most to minor trimming by sheet floods. Pediments are well developed in *pediment embayments* in the mountain front, formed where stream floods emerge from upland valleys. The streams swing laterally in the piedmont zone, undercutting the mountain front on either side, and thus gradually extending the pediment into the upland mass (Fig. 5.27).

Figure 5.26 *A pediment (foreground) developed at the base of a large residual hill (butte), Tuwaiq Mountains, Saudi Arabia. Note the occupation of the pediment by sand and gravel, and the evidence of water action in the shallow channel (bottom left of photograph)*

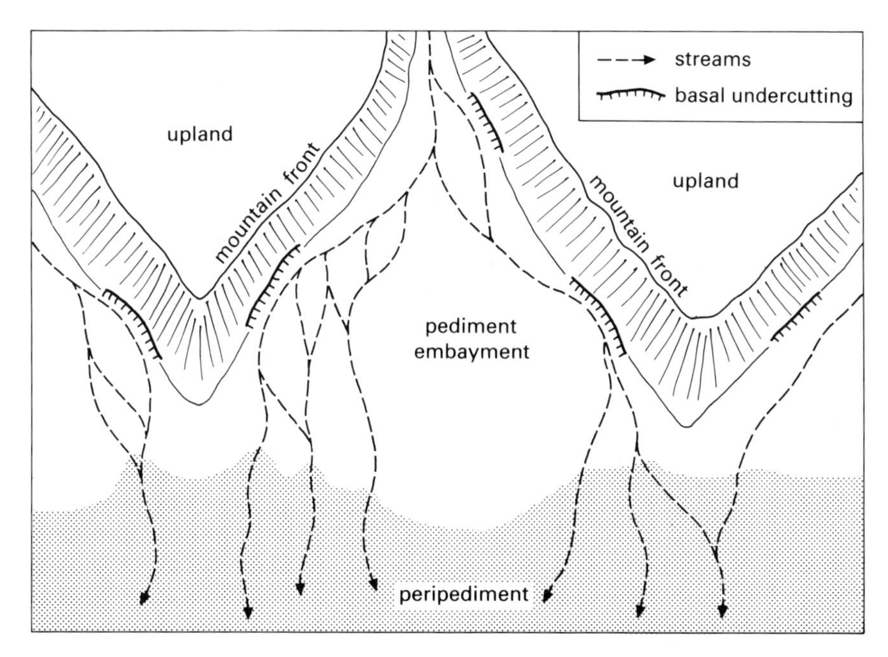

Figure 5.27 *Pediment embayments and recession of the mountain front (see p. 132)*

4 The bajada consists of a series of alluvial fans deposited by streams flowing from the upland to the piedmont zone (the term bajada is also sometimes used to describe the peripediment). The reduction of gradient causes the streams to deposit sands and gravels as alluvial cones and spreads, which may mask the upper pediment and knick.

5 The peripediment is a broad zone of alluvial sediments, laid down mainly by sheet floods beyond the lower margins of the pediment. The alluvial deposits reach considerable thicknesses, especially in areas of centripetal drainage like the downfaulted basins of the south-west USA. Temporary lakes form here after periods of rain, but are soon depleted by evaporation and replaced by a salt-encrusted plain or *playa*.

CONCLUSION

The geomorphology of hot environments is of particular interest for several reasons. These are areas of great environmental sensitivity, where relatively small scale climatic changes or ill considered human activities are liable to initiate rapid and far reaching landscape changes, which will retard economic development and exacerbate problems of drought, poverty and famine. On a more theoretical level, the study of tropical landscapes can shed light on the geomorphology of non-tropical regions, as in the case of temperate climates associated with landforms, such as tors, which were probably developed under past, much warmer climatic conditions.

Much can also be learned from tropical geomorphology about the factors which determine the rates at which landscapes evolve through time. Some authorities have argued that the prevailing climatic conditions of the tropics as a whole favour rapid geomorphological change. For instance, large temperature ranges in hot deserts should promote intense physical weathering; rapid run-off in semi-arid and savanna regions should cause powerful surface erosion; the high rainfall of the humid tropics gives rise to rivers of high discharge, and thus enhanced capacity for transporting sediment load and, in conjunction with the high prevailing temperatures, favours the rapid chemical decay of rocks. Various attempts have been made to measure *erosion rates* operative today in hot climates. This can be done, for example, by measuring the total amount of sediment being transported by a river over a certain time period, and then dividing this by the area of the river catchment, to give the *sediment yield*. This may be expressed either as volume of sediment per unit area of catchment, in $m^3/km^2/annum^{-1}$, or as the average lowering of the surface of the catchment, in $mm/annum^{-1}$. The results of actual studies have been rather conflicting, partly because of the disturbance of natural geomorphological processes in many areas by human activities such as deforestation and cultivation. However, some broad generalisations can be made:

(i) In the humid tropics erosion rates under natural conditions of undisturbed rainforest or well established secondary forest are probably moderate (but see p. 118). Although conditions favour rapid chemical weathering, erosional processes are reduced by the stabilising effect of the dense forest cover. It is only when there is environmental disturbance by humans or other agents that erosion rates are likely to become very high, particularly in areas of steep slopes. One estimate is that in the humid tropics the erosion rate is normally within the range 15–30 $m^3/km^2/annum^{-1}$.

(ii) In the seasonally humid and semi-arid tropics, erosion rates are mainly high. Observations show that sediment yield tends to increase as annual rainfall is reduced in total amount and becomes more seasonal in occurrence, so that the ground is protected for only part of the year by the vegetation cover. Maximum erosion appears to take place when the precipitation is in the order of 300–400 $mm/annum^{-1}$. The erosion rate for seasonally humid and semi-arid tropics may lie within the range 15–100 $m^3/km^2/annum^{-1}$.

(iii) In hot deserts, erosion rates may be comparatively low, or actually very low in the most arid desert interiors where run-off is quite rare. It may be that some desert landscapes are in a state of geomorphological inactivity; in other words, their valleys and slopes must be seen as relict features, developed in the past at a time when the climatic conditions favoured more active processes, and undergoing little change by current erosional processes (p. 58). Indeed, the erosion rate in tropical deserts may be as low as 0.5–1 $m^3/km^2/annum^{-1}$ at the present time.

ASSIGNMENTS

1 a. What evidence is there of climatic change within hot environments (i) over the past 50 million years, (ii) within the past million years?
  b. Show how these long and short term climatic changes may have influenced landform development in hot environments.

2 a. How, and for what reasons, do weathering processes in hot environments differ from those in a cooler region such as the United Kingdom?
  b. Why is it necessary to study regoliths and the basal surface of weathering in order to understand the form and origin of some types of landform in hot environments?

3 The nature of the vegetation cover is a very important geomorphological influence in the hot regions of the world.
  a. What evidence can you find to support this statement?
  b. Describe and explain some of the effects of human disturbance of the vegetation cover in hot environments.

4 Show how and why the importance of surface run-off, in the form of channel flow and overland flow, varies within hot environments.

6

Coastal Processes and Landforms

The sea is in most circumstances a very active geomorphological agent. On a stormy day, the expenditure of energy by waves breaking on a beach or against the foot of a cliff is considerable. Within the space of a few hours, wave action is capable of achieving significant changes, as during the great storm surge of February 1953, which affected the North Sea coasts of England, Belgium and the Netherlands. In a single night, shingle banks suffered large-scale breaching, and some cliffs were eroded back 10 m or more. Over months or years, much less powerful wave attack can significantly alter beach morphology, or cause appreciable cliff recession (Fig. 6.1). Clearly the coastline constitutes, in geomorphological terms, a dynamic environment, and one which provides an excellent opportunity for the study of active processes, such as the breaking of waves, the resultant transport and deposition of beach sediments, and the erosional modification of sea cliffs.

The time scale in coastal geomorphology

Despite the above, it would be wrong to suppose that all coastal landforms are to be explained in terms of currently acting processes alone. On many coasts, past events and conditions have left their mark. In the short term (up to 100 years), powerful individual storms may create identifiable beach ridges which persist, as a testimony to the storm's occurrence; or particularly large land slips, such as that at Dowland's Chasm near Seaton, Devon, in which 8 million tonnes of rock moved seawards by up to 400 m in one night in December 1839, may profoundly alter a cliffed coast. It is within this time span that most modification of coastal features by human

Figure 6.1 *Rapid erosion of cliffs in Barton Sand and Clay, near Highcliffe, Dorset. Note the absence of a beach, allowing the waves to attack directly the base of the unstable cliffs*

activity has occurred. In the medium term (up to 10 000 years), large relative changes of sea-level, having a profound influence on coastal form and evolution, can take place. For example, in the early post-glacial period, a large rise of sea-level resulted from the recession of the Quaternary ice-sheets and the return of vast quantities of meltwater to the oceans. The sea actually attained its present level only 6000 years ago, creating the existing coastal geomorphological systems, and initiating current episodes of coastal recession and deposition. Thus, in Holderness, east Yorkshire, the cliffs, developed in weak glacial deposits, have been driven back some 4 km since Roman times, and 29 villages have been lost. In the long term (up to 1 000 000 years), coastlines can be affected by many changes of sea-level, both positive and negative, as well as by changes of climate. This is especially true of the Quaternary period, the events of which have had a major impact on the world's coastlines. Indeed, many coastal landforms, particularly where developed in very hard rocks, have as yet been little changed by the existing geomorphological systems, and continue to display relict features of Quaternary period (p. 156).

The coastal geomorphological system

As with rivers (p. 38) and glaciers (p. 82), coasts can be regarded as geomorphological systems. There are inputs of energy (by way of winds, waves and tides) and sediments (principally from rivers and coastal erosion), and outputs of energy (expended by breaking waves) and sediment (in the form of beach and sea-floor deposition). If such a system attains a state of equilibrium, then coastal features such as beaches will undergo little change over time. In many instances this does appear to be the case, despite small scale movements of sediment up or down the beach on a day to day basis. However, as we have seen, in the mid and long term, important changes in the system are almost inevitable. Moreover, the coastal geomorphological system varies spatially, for reasons of changing geology and climate; and since the latter may change temporally, as in the Quaternary, spatial and temporal changes are often interlinked. Climate has perhaps been underestimated as a factor in coastal development, though climatic elements such as wind strength and direction influence wave generation and energy (p. 136). There is, for example, a contrast between coastlines in the humid tropics and those of cold regions (Fig. 6.2). In the former, the dominant deep weathering leads in many regions to a rarity of rocky cliffs and headlands, and provides the rivers with silt and clay to wash into the sea, rather than the coarse gravels needed to form shingle beaches. It is hardly surprising to find that much of the coast of western Malaysia comprises mud flats colonised by mangroves. In cold regions, cliffed coastlines in solid rock are more widespread, and their intense weathering by frost action yields abundant coarse debris for waves to fashion into large shingle structures. These features are also well developed in temperate regions which experienced periglacial conditions in the past.

WAVE PROCESSES

Waves are mobile undulations on the sea surface, resulting from the drag effect of the wind. They vary in size, as defined by *wave height* (the vertical distance between the wave crest and an adjacent trough) and *wave length* (the horizontal distance between successive wave crests) (Fig. 6.3). With each wave, there is a series of circular, or orbital, movements, produced by the drag of the wind on surface water particles. These are best developed near the sea surface, but decrease downwards, becoming barely perceptible at a depth equal to half the wave length. Waves move across the sea at a speed usually less than that of the generating wind. *Wave velocity* is expressed directly in m/sec^{-1}, and indirectly in terms of the *wave period*, or time interval in seconds between the passage of successive waves.

If the wind blows for several hours at a constant speed, or if the wind speed increases rapidly, waves will grow in size, with the

Figure 6.2 *Coastal features north of Kuantan. Malaysia. Note the granite corestones and outcrops in the foreground; these have been exposed by marine attack on the regolith of sandy clay. The bay bar comprises sandy material of granitic origin*

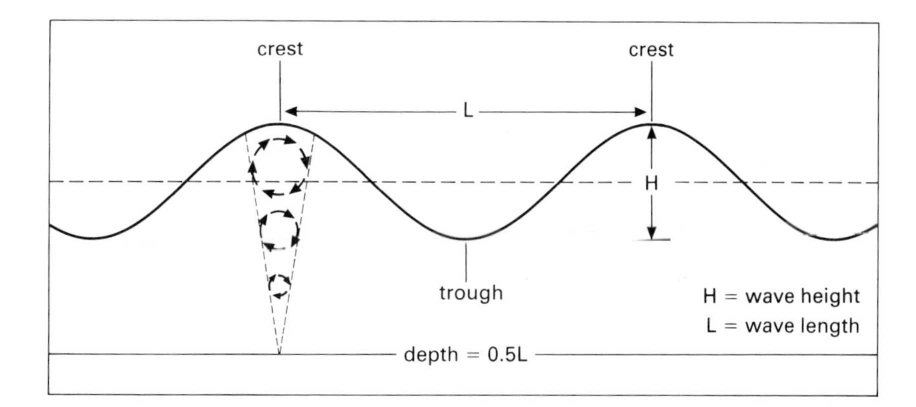

Figure 6.3 *Wave form and dimensions (see p. 136)*

leeward wave slopes being steepened by wind eddies. Where very high winds persist, waves may attain a height of 10–20 m, a length of 200–300 m or more, and a velocity of 15 m/sec^{-1}. One constraining factor in wave growth is the distance over which the winds can affect the sea surface. In a sea of limited dimensions, such as the English Channel or North Sea, the maximum size of wave expected for a particular wind velocity may not be generated. By contrast, in large oceans such as the North Atlantic there is ample space for maximum size waves to be formed. Thus, wave dimensions are a function not only of wind strength and duration, but also of *fetch*, or the distance between leeward and windward shores.

As waves approach the shore, they undergo several changes. With decreasing water depth, friction between the orbiting water particles and the sea bed slows down wave velocity, causing a reduction in wave length and period (Fig. 6.4). Since waves are effectively a means of transmitting energy, there is thus a greater concentration of energy in a relatively narrow zone. As the waves slow down, there is also an increase in wave steepness. The orbital movements become more elliptical, and eventually

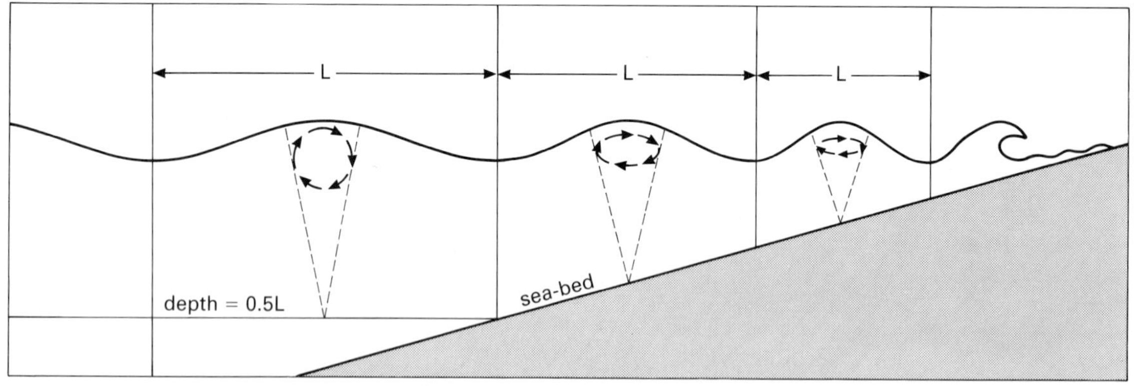

Figure 6.4 *The approach of waves to the shore (see p. 137)*

the forward movement of the water particles at the wave crest exceeds wave velocity. The wave form cannot then be sustained, the wave front collapses, and there is a rush of turbulent foamy water, known as the *swash*, up the beach. Thus, the wave energy is released as kinetic energy.

In the near shore zone, waves are also affected by *refraction*. When generated, waves have approximately parallel crests, and travel in the same direction as the wind. If the latter is oblique to the coast, the waves also will approach at an angle (Fig. 6.5a). However, as they enter shallow water and velocity is reduced, the waves become re-orientated and, when they break, may be nearly parallel to the beach. At the far point of a spit, the waves may actually swing round, as shown in Fig. 6.5b. Refraction may also affect waves approaching parallel to the shoreline. Owing to irregularities in the sea bed, giving localised shallowings, these waves may be refracted, so that *wave orthogonals* (lines at right angles to the wave crests, showing the direction of movement) will give a pattern as shown in Fig. 6.5c. As a result, there will be concentration of wave energy at same points, and dispersion at others. Also, some waves will break obliquely, even though initially the waves are parallel to the shore.

The effects of breaking waves

As explained above, when waves break *swash* is formed. However, the impetus of the water flowing up the beach is reduced by the gradient, and by the loss of water percolating into the beach. After a few metres, the flow becomes reversed, and the remaining water runs down the beach, gathering speed because of the gradient; this is *backwash*. Beach sediment, even of coarse calibre, is transported up the beach by swash, to be returned by backwash. The two movements tend to balance each other, so that there may be no net sediment transport.

However, field observations have revealed that particular wave forms are *constructive*, leading to the net transport of sediment up the beach, whilst others are *destructive*, resulting in the combing down of sediment. For example, long low waves with a period of 8–12 seconds produce a very powerful swash, and a much weaker backwash, whereas shorter waves with a period of 3–6 seconds display a steep 'plunging' break and a relatively feeble swash. Wind direction may also influence constructive and destructive action. Thus, a strong onshore wind may cause a surface flow towards the beach, and a compensatory return flow at depth or localised 'rip currents', both of which aid sediment transport away from the beach. Conversely, offshore winds can have a constructive effect.

Over a period of weeks, as wind, wave and tidal conditions alter, slight changes in beach profiles occur, though the beach system as a whole approximates to a steady state. During the year, there may be a seasonal rhythm to

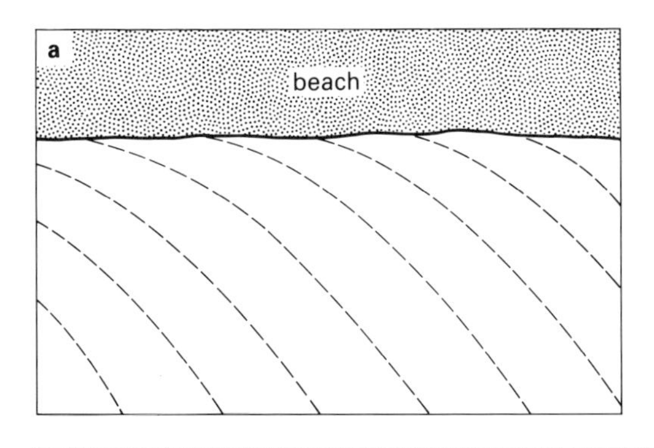

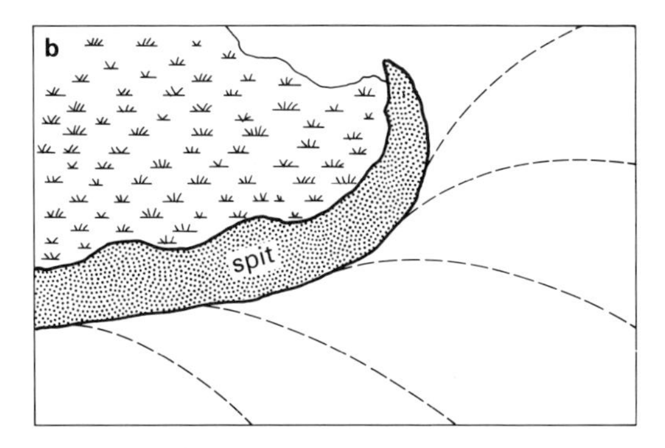

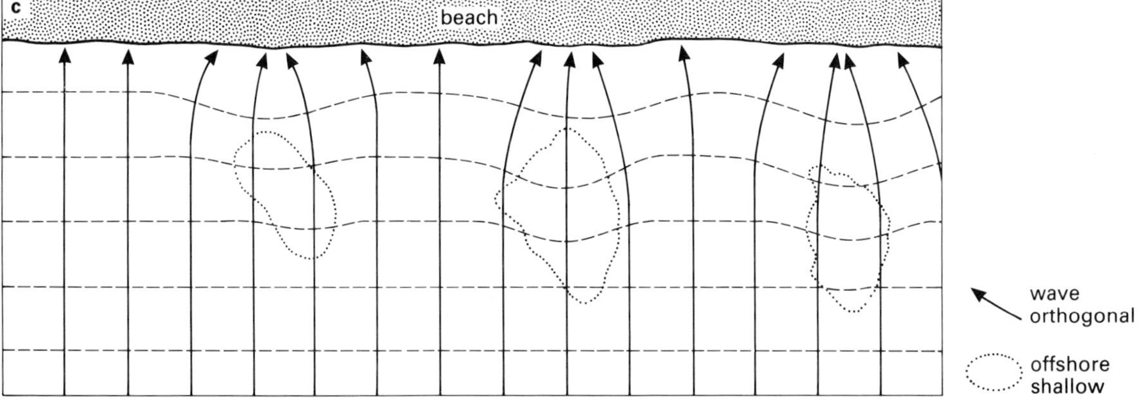

Figure 6.5 *Wave refraction (see p. 138)*

profile changes. Thus, in Britain, the stormy conditions of winter are generally destructive to beaches, whereas during the calmer conditions of summer beaches are built up. Over greater periods of time, as long term changes in weather patterns occur, beaches may experience progressive destruction or construction. At this time scale, other factors may come into play. For instance, as a result of constant pounding by the waves, beach particles are reduced by *attrition*, and the resultant finer particles may be transported offshore. Unless new beach material arrives, the existing beach will be depleted, whether the waves are destructive or constructive.

The nature and sources of beach sediment

Beaches are heterogeneous accumulations of boulders, cobbles, pebbles, sands, silts and clays, plus organic remains such as sea shells. These sediments can be studied by the method of particle size analysis, whereby the proportions by weight of a sample of beach material falling within given size ranges are plotted as a graph. Graphs for beach sediments are frequently asymmetrical, with a trend towards coarseness; that is, there is a greater quantity of cobbles (diameter exceeding 64 mm) and pebbles (diameter 4–63 mm), and less fine sand, silt and clay. This reflects the selective washing offshore of the finer material by wave action, leaving behind a residue of coarser material. The upper part of the beach in particular may comprise cobbles and pebbles, with a steep seaward slope, whilst the lower beach, exposed at low tide, is mainly of sand and at a gentler angle.

Since beach particles are constantly impacted against each other, and rolled up and down by swash-backwash, they quickly become worn by attrition, rounded, and reduced in size. Many cobbles and pebbles become almost perfectly rounded or, where derived from thinly bedded rocks, slightly flattened or disc-like. Sand grains, too, become smoothed and polished. Even so, many beaches, for example those in Dorset and Hampshire, are composed largely of sub-angular flints. These are being released by present day erosion of Quaternary plateau-gravels; there has been insufficient time, since incorporation into the beaches, for these to be rounded by marine action.

Beach materials are, in fact, derived from several sources, and are moved to the beach by a variety of processes, often along a circuitous route, and sometimes over a long period of time. Most beach sediments are derived originally from the breakdown of solid rock by subaerial weathering and erosional processes. However, relatively little material is the product of direct wave attack on solid rock exposed in sea cliffs (p. 148), except in areas where weak sands and gravels are exposed. Greater supplies of sediment are brought into the sea by rivers, and then redistributed along the shore by wave action. Another significant source may be the offshore zone, particularly where the sea floor is shallow and mantled by loose sands and gravels. It is not always clear how much onshore transfer of this sediment is occurring under present conditions; perhaps only sand is moved in large quantities, and from a maximum depth of 10–20 m. However, in the past, as the sea level rose during the post-glacial period, onshore sediment transfer was very considerable. As the shoreline of Britain shifted towards its present position, superficial deposits of glacial and periglacial origin which had accumulated on the dry sea bed were swept shoreward by the breaking waves. Some authorities believe that the majority of our beaches were formed in this way, but that they are now being depleted as the existing store of beach material is worn away by attrition.

Finally, the expanding role of humans in beach nourishment must be briefly mentioned. At many points, beaches are disappearing rapidly, either for the reason given above, or because local supplies of beach sediment are being cut off by sea walls and other cliff protection works. When holiday resorts are affected, as was Bournemouth in Dorset in the 1970s, action becomes imperative. One solution is to dredge large quantities of sand from the offshore zone and dump them on the beach. Such a measure is, however, only palliative, since the real causes of the problem are not being tackled.

Sediment transport on beaches

Sediment is moved by breaking waves directly up and down the beach (normal to the beach), or laterally along the beach (*longshore drift*). The first process, described above, leads directly to changes in beach profile, and the formation and removal of minor features such as beach ridges and terraces (*berms*). The second process redistributes beach sediments, leading to accumulations at particular points, as at the heads of bays, and the formation of landforms such as coastal spits.

Longshore drift occurs when waves approach the beach at an oblique angle. The swash runs up the beach diagonally, carrying sediment with it, whilst the backwash, under the influence of gravity, flows directly down the beach (Fig. 6.6). Over a period of time, this can result in a considerable net movement of beach material, in a direction that reflects the prevailing winds. In Britain, these are from the south-west, with the result that sediment transport is mainly west to east along the south coast, and south to north along the west coast. In the North Sea, however, the largest waves result from north-easterly winds, so that there is a dominant beach drift from north to south along the east coast. These directions of movement are confirmed by the coastal spit growth (p. 144), and by the build-up of beach material on the windward sides of groynes (Fig. 6.7).

Most beaches are far removed from the sources of their sediment, and thus owe their existence to longshore drift. As new sediments arrive, so existing sediments are carried away in a downdrift direction. Providing the two are balanced, the beach will remain in a healthy condition. However, if longshore drift is inter-

Figure 6.6 *Longshore drift (see p. 140)*

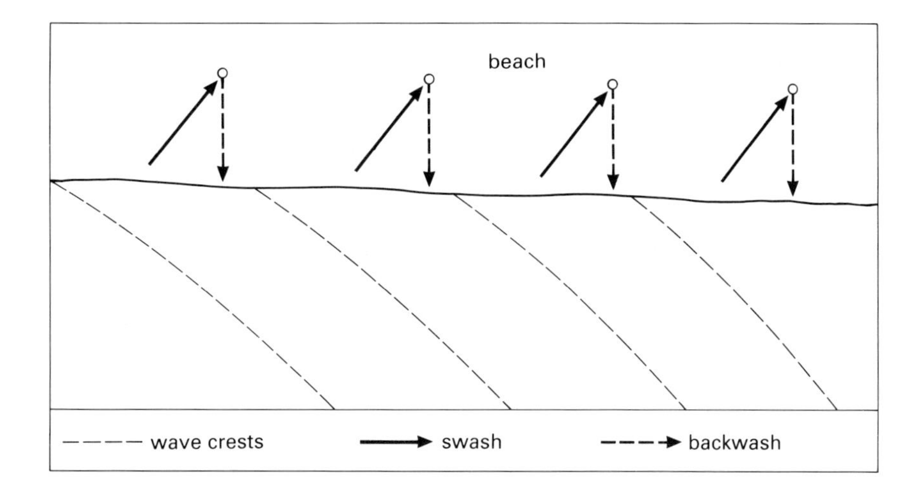

Figure 6.7 *The large groyne at Hengistbury Head, Dorset. This has held up sediment being transported eastwards by longshore drift, resulting in a broad accumulation of beach material*

rupted, either naturally or by human interference, serious consequences may result. Thus, as coastal erosion proceeds, bays are deepened and headlands become more prominent. The beach then becomes fragmented into a series of isolated bay head accumulations, and longshore drift past the headlands will at best be much reduced. If a coastal spit occurs downdrift from the area of erosion, it will be starved of beach sediments and will decline. An alternative possibility is that coastal erosion concentrates on exposed headlands so that as these are worn away the sediment supply for longshore drift is reduced. The rapid erosion of the outer spit of the double spit complex at Dawlish Warren, across the mouth of the Exe estuary in Devon, has been attributed to the destruction by the sea of once more extensive promontories at Langstone Rock and Clerk Point to the west.

Where a stretch of cliffed coastline is protected by a series of artifical groynes, constructed to hold back drifting beach sediment and thus maintain a protective accumulation at the cliff foot, the lack of beach material beyond the final groyne will give rise to *terminal scour*. In the absence of a beach capable of absorbing wave energy, the cliff will be undercut and will recede rapidly; as a result, the unprotected cliff will become 'set back' in relation to the protected cliff. Some of the most striking effects are seen where large harbour walls are built, and beach drift virtually ceases. For example, the extensive harbour mouth jetties at Newhaven, East Sussex, have led to long standing erosion problems at Seaford, immediately to the east.

Deposition of beach sediment

Beaches are the most common form of sediment deposition; indeed, they represent a major store of coastal sediment. However, as explained above, this storage is often temporary. Longer term storage occurs at points where beach drift is impeded, by natural features such as estuaries and headlands, where major accumulations occur as coastal spits and allied formations (Fig. 6.8). Under certain conditions, beach sediment may also be washed offshore, forming shingle and sand banks on the sea bed. This may result from a rapid tidal current, of up to 7 km/hour^{-1}, removing sediment from the end of a spit terminating in deep water. For example, the west running ebb current off Hurst Castle Spit, at the western entrance to the Solent, appears to have resulted in the formation of a series of banks, the Shingles, trending south-westwards across Christchurch Bay. Generally, however, tidal currents play little part in the modification of beaches, since velocities close inshore are usually less than 2 km/hour^{-1}, and the capacity to transport other than fine sediment is limited.

An interesting question is whether sea floor sediments which have come from the beaches can be returned to them by wave action. The use of radioactive tracers has revealed the possibility of limited movement of pebbles on the sea floor off Orford Ness, Suffolk, but there is no positive proof of an onshore drift. Sometimes beach sediment is washed into deep water, to form a *sediment sink*, containing material which has been permanently lost from the beach system.

Figure 6.8 *The complex of old beach ridges at Dungeness, a large shingle foreland which has been built up by constructive wave action since Roman times*

COASTAL DEPOSITIONAL LANDFORMS

1 ***Beaches*** are the most widespread coastal depositional features, though they are not found at the base of many steep cliffs. Many of the characteristics of beaches, including their composition and changes in response to wave action, are described above. Beaches are often contained within bays, hence terms such as *bay head beach* or, where the bay and the beach are very small, *pocket beach* (Fig. 6.9a). If the waves normally approach the bay at right angles, the beach will be symmetrical. But where the approach is at an oblique angle, the beach deposits will be concentrated, largely by longshore drift, towards one end of the bay (Fig. 6.9b). Moreover, in plan the beach will become orientated to face the direction of wave approach. Additionally, there is often sorting of beach material, with the coarsest particles accumulating at the downdrift end of the bay head beach. Here, too, the beach will tend to be steeper and higher.

One of the best known examples of beach sorting is at Chesil Beach, at the eastern end of Lyme Bay, southern England. This is a major shingle ridge, or barrier beach (p. 146), stretching for 25 km from West Bay to the Isle of Portland. At first sight, Chesil Beach appears to be a spit which has grown south-eastwards, to join Portland to the mainland, and is thus an example of a *tombolo*. However, it is more likely that the beach originated on the once dry floor of Lyme Bay, and migrated onshore during the post-glacial, or Holocene, rise of sea-level (p. 154). At present, Chesil Beach occupies an asymmetrical position within Lyme Bay, and runs nearly parallel to the dominant south-westerly waves, approaching up the English Channel. The constituents of the beach increase gradually in size south-eastwards, from dominantly 'pea size' shingle at West Bay to pebbles of 50 mm or more in diameter at the Portland end. At the same time, the beach increases in height to a maximum of over 13 m above mean sea-level. The reasons for the grading in size of the beach sediment are not entirely clear. One simple suggestion is that the coarser particles are transported along the beach towards Portland by large waves from the south-west, whereas the less powerful waves from the south are capable of moving back only the smaller material. However, a better explanation is that, owing to a progressive increase in water depth offshore as

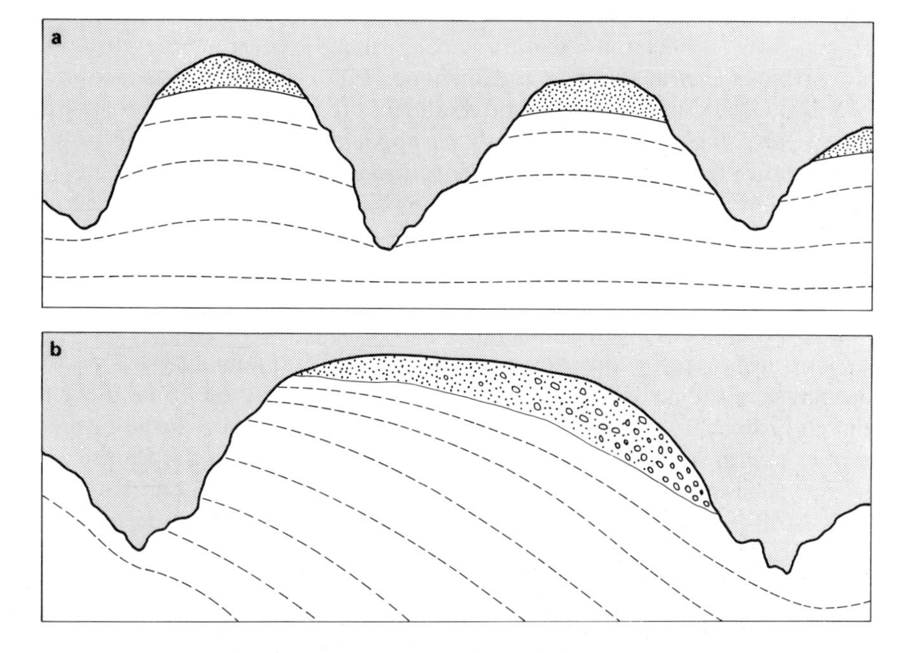

Figure 6.9 *Bay beaches*

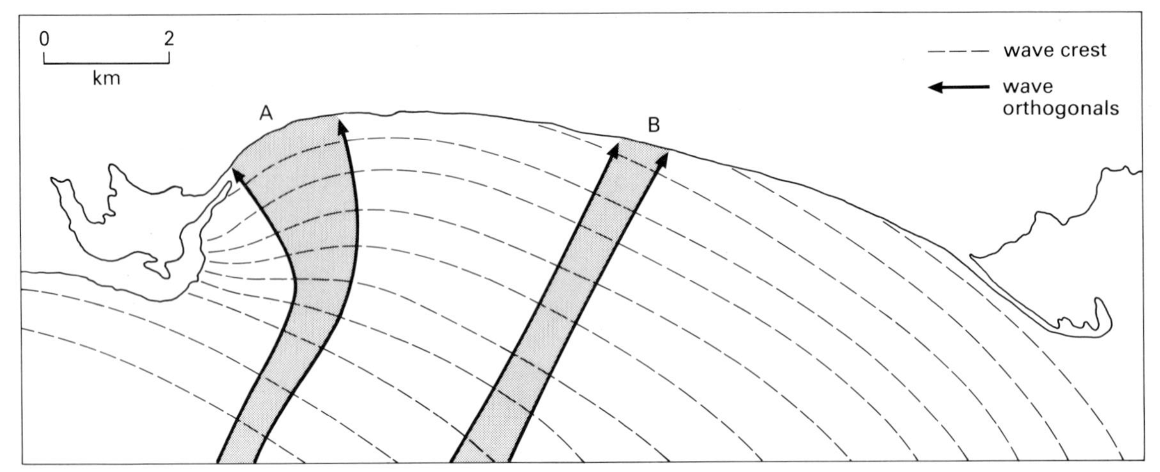

Figure 6.10 *Christchurch Bay, Dorset. Note the concentration of energy at* ***B*** *by comparison with* ***A****; the beach material at* ***B*** *is coarser than that at* ***A***

Portland is approached, larger waves of greater energy are able to build a higher beach comprising coarser constituents.

Within a large bay, with a continuous beach, both the shape of the bay, and of the beach, assume a distinctive plan form, akin to a mathematical curve. Thus, at the downwind end of the bay, the curve is very gentle; but, towards the upwind end, the curve becomes progressively more pronounced, especially if there is a prominent, sheltering headland at that end (Fig. 6.10). Such a feature, of which Christchurch Bay in southern England and Half Moon Bay in California are good examples, is known as a *log spiral bay*. The shape appears to be associated with increased wave refraction as the curve of the bay becomes sharper; similarly beach sediment size tends to decrease in the same direction.

*2 **Coastal spits*** are formed from beach sediment, transported by longshore drift, which has accumulated either where the coastline changes direction sharply, or where drift is held up by a river mouth or estuary. The shingle and sand is then fashioned into a projecting beach ridge, which will be extended, particularly if the sea bed is shallow, until a point is reached at which sediment is removed as rapidly as it arrives. In the case of an estuary, as the spit grows and the entrance is narrowed, tidal currents will increase in velocity, and thus wash sediment from the far point of the spit.

An example of a simple spit which appears to have attained a state of equilibrium with little change of form in the recent past and no significant growth occurring at present, is Calshot Spit, at the entrance to Southampton Water (Fig. 6.11a). In the case of a river mouth, the spit may be extended sufficiently to deflect the river, in a downdrift direction, by a considerable distance. Thus Orford Ness, in Suffolk, has grown southwards at a rate of 15 m/annum^{-1}, and has diverted the mouth of the River Alde by some 17 km.

Double spits are formed at the entrances to some estuaries, as at the mouths of Pagham Harbour, in West Sussex, and Poole Harbour, in Dorset. These might result from longshore drift towards the estuary mouth from either side. Alternatively, where longshore drift is dominantly in one direction, sediment may be washed from the end of one spit, across the estuary, to be fashioned by wave action into a spit on the far side. This is most likely to occur where there is a shallow foundation, such as a salt marsh or a drowned river terrace, on which the material can readily collect.

Spits sometimes prove to be fragile landforms, and suffer periods of severe erosion

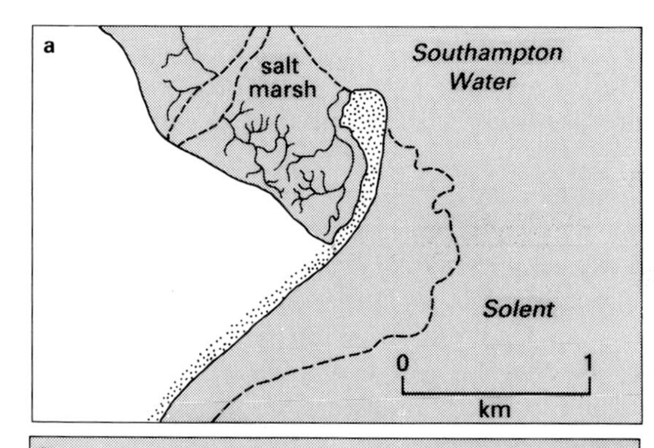

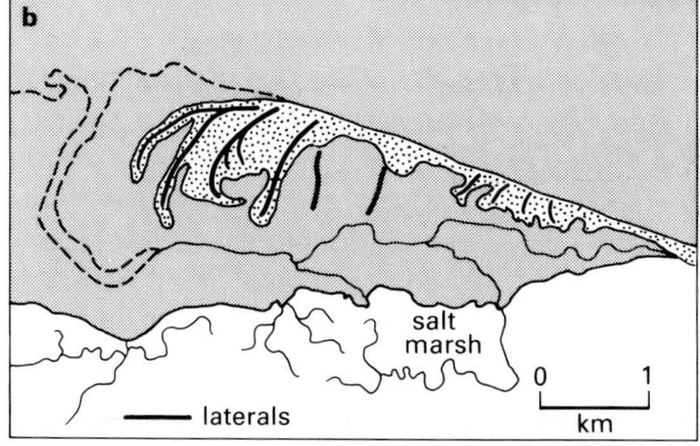

Figure 6.11 *Calshot Spit (a) and Blakeney Point (b) (see p. 144 and p. 145)*

(p. 141). From the evidence of old maps, Spurn Head, at the mouth of the Humber, has experienced several cycles of growth and decay. The spit across the mouth of Christchurch Harbour, in Dorset, has similarly grown several times to a length of 2–3 km, only to be breached by the sea, opposite to the harbour mouth. On each occasion, the 'dead' part of the spit was subsequently washed onshore, east of the harbour entrance. The last breach occurred in February 1935. Subsequently, the spit has not redeveloped, probably because the completion in 1938 of a large groyne at Hengistbury Head, to the west, effectively cut off the supply of beach sediment.

Other spits, by contrast, experience a long history of growth. In the process they develop a complex form, comprising a main beach ridge currently acted on by waves, and a series of inactive ridges on the landward side; these meet the main ridge more or less at right angles, and are referred to as *laterals*. An excellent example of such a *compound spit* is Blakeney Point, Norfolk (Fig. 6.11). It is noticeable that, at the far points of simple spits, the beach curves round in a landward direction. This may be due initially to the action of refracted waves (p. 138), but at a later stage the *recurve* may be further modified by secondary waves approaching the end of the spit from a direction opposite to that of the dominant waves. The individual laterals of a compound spit can be interpreted as representing successive stages in spit extension, in the manner shown in Fig. 6.12. This simple model of spit formation also shows that the main ridge tends to migrate inland, through wave overtopping, as growth proceeds; that sediment at the developing end of the spit comes partly from erosion of the older part of the main ridge; and that the main ridge undergoes some re-orientation, to run more nearly parallel to the dominant waves.

3 Coastal bars are accumulations of beach

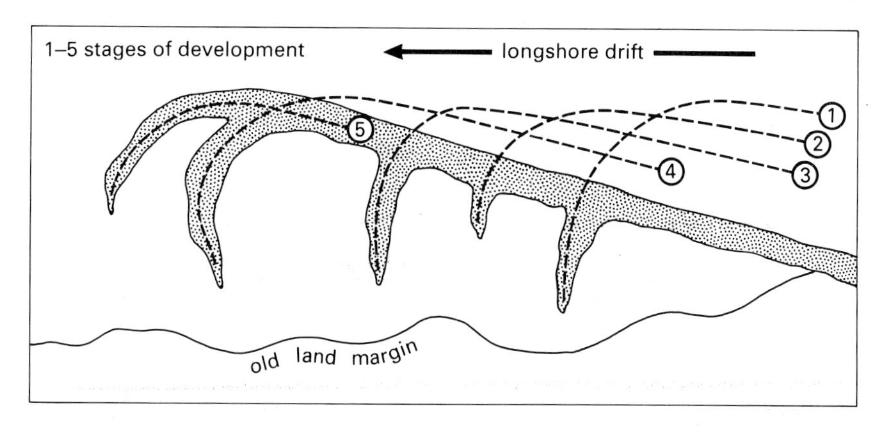

Figure 6.12 *The development of a compound spit*

material, orientated parallel to the coastline and often lying some distance offshore, hence the term *offshore bar*. At an early stage bars are submerged at high tide, but in time grow upwards as a result of further wave sedimentation. Many become further stabilised by the formation of sand dunes. Offshore bars are believed to be characteristic of shallow coasts with an extremely gentle gradient. The waves break well offshore, eroding the sea bed and throwing forward the resultant sediment to initiate the bar. Once in existence, the bar may either migrate landwards, as sediment is washed over its crest, or be extended laterally by longshore drift. In the latter process, bars may develop laterals, in the manner of a compound spit; indeed, the distinction between bars and spits is not always entirely clear. An outstanding example is the Bar, near Nairn, Scotland (Fig. 6.13). Where offshore bars do migrate onshore, they frequently extend between promontories, and enclose lagoons. This may be seen to the north of Start Point, Devon, where Slapton Ley and the small broad at Beesands are trapped by a shingle bar (Fig. 6.14).

Many coastlines are dominated by large bars. In some areas, an extensive and continuous bar is developed across the mouths of a series of bays and inlets, as at Martha's Vineyard, north-eastern USA; this is a *barrier beach*. In other cases, there is a line of offshore islands, separated by tidal inlets, as in the East Frisian Islands, off the North Sea coast of West Germany; these are *barrier islands*.

Barrier formations reflect several influences. Where coastal areas comprise weak glacial sands and gravels, rapid erosion releases large amounts of beach sediment, which are transported alongshore, to accumulate as a barrier beach enclosing coastal embayments. This is probably the origin of the extensive *nehrungen*, or *barrier spits*, of the southern Baltic coast. Alternatively, the entry into the sea of vast

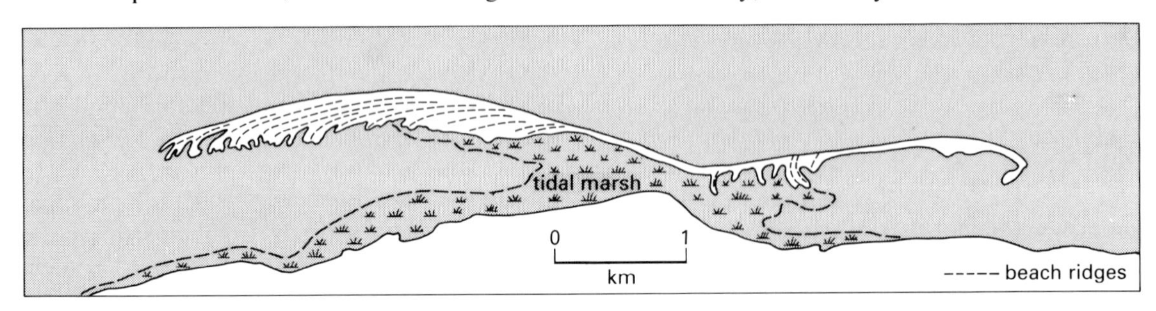

Figure 6.13 *The Bar, Nairn*

Figure 6.14 *Slapton Ley, Devon*

quantities of glacio-fluvial sediment may provide the material for barrier formation, as on the south coast of Iceland.

Other barrier bars can be related to the rise of sea-level during the post-glacial period, when sediment on the sea bed was collected into a beach and driven landwards (p. 140). In some instances, coastal dune ridges, which had developed on a bar, were submerged during the final stages of the marine transgression. The low-lying land inside the dunes was transformed into a tidal lagoon, alternately flooded and drained by way of gaps between the dune islands. At present, some barrier bars are continuing to shift landwards, as storm waves overtop them and transfer sediment on to the inner face; this mechanism is observable at Chesil Beach (p. 143). Alternatively, deposition is now occurring on the seaward side of some barriers, forming a series of sub-parallel ridges.

Finally, it should be noted that tidal conditions are influential, in that where the tidal range is small, as in the Baltic, barrier beaches are more likely to form, whereas with a large tidal range, barrier islands are more frequent.

Other coastal depositional features

Sand dunes are common features at the landward edge of extensive sand beaches, and on the constituent ridges of spits and bars. They are formed by onshore winds, which transport sand exposed and dried at low tide. The accumulation of this sand, to form dunes, is aided by certain grasses, notably sea couch and marram grass, which thrive in a dry sandy environment. The complex root systems bind the incoherent sand, and the rapidly growing stalks continually trap new sand. Where the supply of beach sand is abundant, as on the coast of Lancashire to the north of Liverpool, successive lines of dunes may form. The youngest of these dune lines, which grow rapidly to a height of 5–15 m, will be characterised by fresher and greener vegetation. The older dune lines, farther inland, will have a less healthy grass cover and a generally 'greyer' appearance. Dunes are, however, very fragile landforms. When the grass cover is removed or damaged, for example by human trampling, large hollows or *blow outs* quickly form, and may lead in time to the destruction of the dune. Moreover, when the seaward faces of dunes can be reached by powerful waves, owing to long term changes in the beach profile or the occurrence of exceptional storm conditions, erosion is often very rapid indeed.

Salt marshes are the result of accumulation of mud in sheltered locations, such as estuaries or the landward margins of spits and bars. They comprise fine sediment, carried in suspension in sea water, which is transported into these areas by tidal currents. At high tide, when for a time the water becomes relatively motionless, this material slowly settles out as a very thin layer. Over a period of time, however, the resultant accumulation can be considerable. Eventually, the mud will build up to a level at which it is inundated only rarely, by the very highest spring tides.

As with sand dunes, vegetation plays a vital role in the formation of salt marshes. At an early stage, the mud becomes colonised by salt loving plants or *halophytes*, such as marsh samphire, which help to trap mud. Later, other plants such as sea aster, sea lavender and marsh grasses form a more continuous cover, and the rate of sedimentation may rise to 1 cm/annum^{-1}. Eventually, the marsh will reach a height at which it can be relatively easily reclaimed, for pasture or other purposes, by the construction of a protective embankment to keep out the high tides. One interesting feature of a mature marsh is the presence of a complex system of channels, or *creeks*, whereby the tidal waters enter the marsh on the flood and drain from it on the ebb.

COASTAL EROSIONAL LANDFORMS

Coastal erosion, leading to cliff recession, is often a matter of serious public concern, particularly in areas where the cliff tops are built over. A series of coastal landslips at Barton-on-Sea, Hampshire, culminating in November 1974, led to the abandonment and subsequent demolition of houses placed in a precarious position, and posed a future threat to others. Such was the local concern that engineering works on the beach and cliff, costing nearly £300 000, were initiated, in an attempt to stabilise them and at least retard future erosion.

Of course, coastal erosion does not always have such alarming results. Much will depend on the geological composition of the cliffs, and on the degree of their exposure to high energy waves. In parts of southern and eastern Britain, where mainly soft rocks outcrop at the coast, the average erosion rate may be as high as a metre or more each year. However, in most instances only agricultural, recreational or waste land is affected. By contrast, where harder rocks outcrop, as in much of western Britain, cliff retreat may amount to only a few mm each year. Indeed, parts of the coast have experienced little change since the sea returned approximately to its present level some 6000 years ago.

Processes of wave erosion

When storm waves break against the base of a cliff, usually at high tide level, there is a sudden and large scale release of energy. Indeed, it has been calculated that the pressure exerted by such waves frequently exceeds 30 tonnes/m^2 over a very short time interval. This enables the wave to carry out *hydraulic erosion*, which breaks down incoherent rocks such as weakly cemented sandstones or washes away loose debris which has fallen to the cliff foot. Where the rocks are harder, but contain cracks in the form of joints and bedding planes, a process of *wave quarrying* can occur. In this, air contained within the cracks is suddenly compressed by wave impact, and then decompressed as the water recedes. There is an 'explosive effect' which can, in time, open up the cracks, weaken the rock structure, and even detach large blocks

Figure 6.15 *A deep wave notch, resulting from wave erosion of a raised coral reef, south of Mombasa, Kenya*

of rock. Breaking waves can also use available sediments, particularly cobbles and pebbles, to corrade the cliff base, undercutting it to form a prominent wave notch (Fig. 6.15). Often such *wave corrasion* is localised along lines of structural weakness, to produce caves or steep sided, narrow inlets known as *geos*. On limestone coasts, solution by breaking waves is also effective, often extending well above high tide level, where sea spray forms karren-type features and contributes to general cliff recession.

The most characteristic landforms resulting from these combined wave processes are cliffs and wave cut platforms. These are created by the removal, at sea level, of a wedge shaped mass from the land margin (Fig. 6.16). The cliff will continue to retreat, primarily as a result of wave undermining, though subaerial processes often contribute (p. 149). The platform is thereby extended, but also lowered as a result of corrasion by the waves crossing it. This erosion may be very selective, etching out lines of weakness, so that in detail the platform becomes very uneven, with narrow trenches separating ridges. One suggestion is that, as the platform becomes ever wider, more and more wave energy will be expended upon it, so that cliff erosion will be slowed down in the long run.

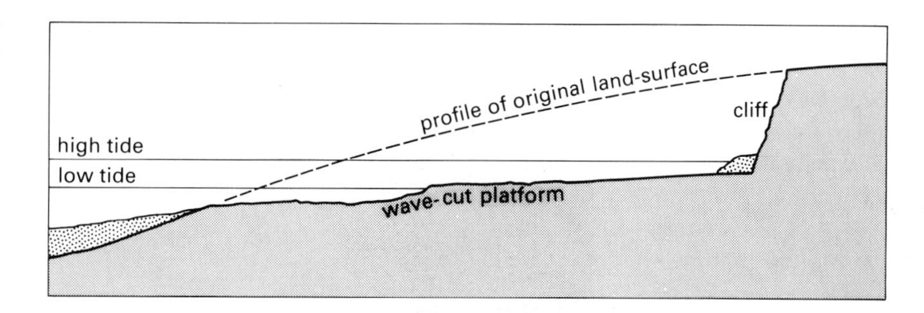

Figure 6.16 *The formation of a cliff and wave-cut platform (see p. 148)*

The forms of sea cliffs

Cliffs vary enormously in profile. The popular image of a cliff as a precipitous face, dropping vertically into a turbulent sea, is somewhat misleading. Such cliffs do, of course, exist, particularly in certain types of rock and where marine erosion is currently powerful; hence the terms *live* or *active cliffs* (Fig. 6.17a). However, a surprising number of cliffs comprise an upper, partly vegetated, and relatively stable slope (at 30°–35° in angle), and a lower vertical face which may occupy up to half the profile or even more; these are *bevelled cliffs* (Fig. 6.17b). In some instances, the upper part of the cliff is broadly rounded, and the lower part consists of a relatively gentle slope (at 20°–30°), leading down almost to high tide level; this is a *hogs back* cliff (Fig. 6.17c).

The major determinant of cliff steepness is the balance between the rate of erosion at the base, by waves, and the rate of recession of the face, by the action of weathering, mass movements (including rock slides, mud flows, solifluction and soil creep), and gullying by rainwater and spring flow. Where basal attack is very rapid, and the rock has sufficient shear strength to support steep faces, vertical cliffs are frequently formed, as in many of the limestone, sandstone and chalk cliffs around Britain's coastline (Fig. 6.18). However, where wave action is restricted, as in sheltered bays, or where there is a large cliff foot beach to absorb wave energy, cliffs are reduced in angle over time. Cliffs no longer subjected to marine

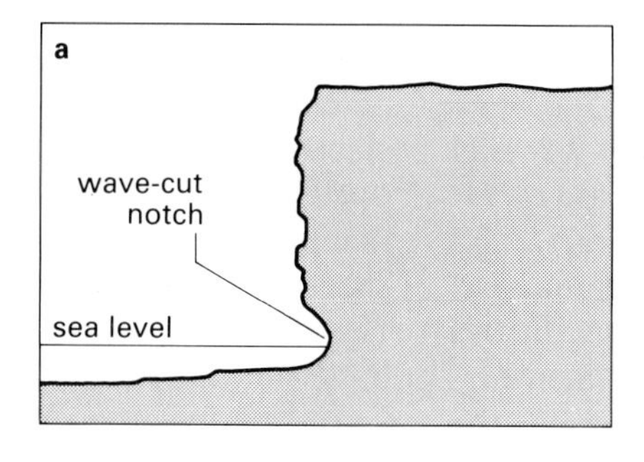

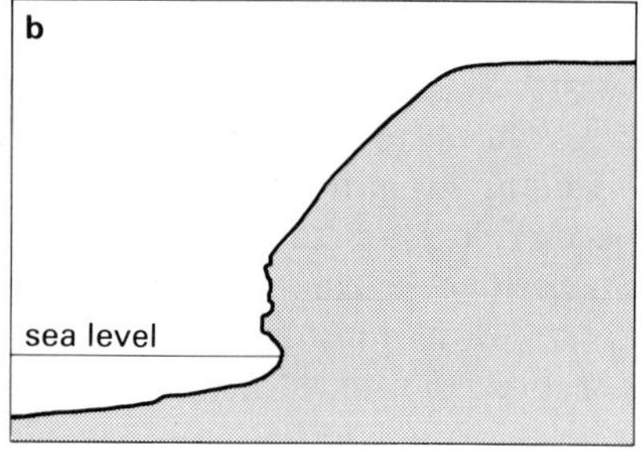

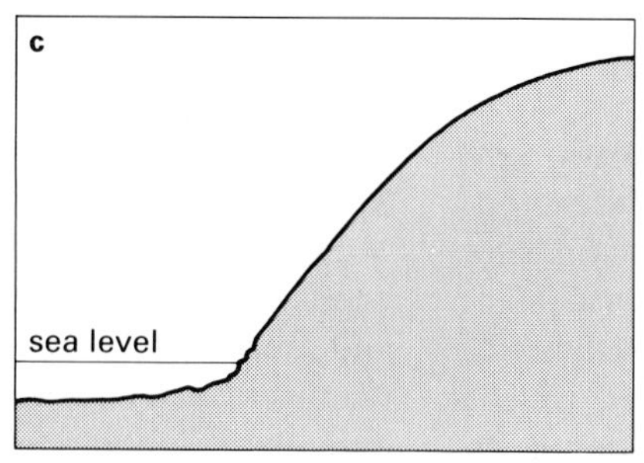

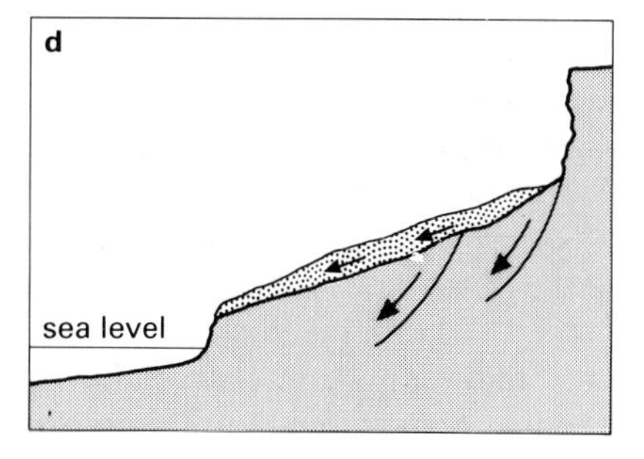

Figure 6.17 *Types of cliff: vertical (active) cliff (**a**); bevelled cliff (**b**); hogs-back cliff (**c**); undercliff (**d**)*

Figure 6.18 *Cliffs at St Govan's Head, Dyfed, being attacked by storm waves. The dip of the Carboniferous Limestone is gently seawards, and the cliffs are characteristically vertical or slightly overhanging. The numerous large boulders in the foreground are largely the result of toppling failure*

erosion, referred to as *inactive* or *dead cliffs*, are characterised either by an upper free face, with an extensive debris slope below, or, at a later stage of development, by a smooth, soil-mantled and well vegetated slope (Fig. 6.19). Even where wave attack is continuing, the lack of strength of the rock materials forming the cliff may lead to frequent rock falls, so that the upper face actually retreats more rapidly than the base, which is protected by the fallen material.

In detail, cliff profiles are strongly influenced by geological structure. For example, *benched cliff profiles* occur where horizontal strata of varying resistance to erosion outcrop at the coast. Where the structure consists of a weak layer of sand above, and a layer of clay beneath, the springs emerging at the base of the permeable sand 'sap' the upper cliff face, and by wetting the clays render them unstable and liable to rotational slips and mud flows. In this situation, the upper cliff may retreat inland by a distance of 100 m; the lower part of the profile will consist of an *undercliff*, the outer face of which is being eroded by the waves (Fig. 6.17d).

The angle and direction of rock dip are widely held to be key factors in cliff development. Where the strata are horizontal and uniform in type, cliffs are often vertical (Fig. 6.20a). Where the rocks dip gently seawards, and there are joints at right angles to the bedding planes, toppling failure is common. In this, tower-like masses slowly become detached, as the joints are opened by weathering from above, and fall over seawards, to give large bouldery accumulations at the cliff base; the cliff itself may even be slightly overhanging (Fig. 6.20b). Where the seaward dip is steeper (20° or more), rock slides are likely and part or all of the cliff profile may become characterised by smooth rock slabs, in effect exposed bedding planes (Fig. 6.20 and Fig. 6.21). Where the strata dip inland, there is greater inherent stability, as individual masses of rock, defined by bedding planes and joints, remain *in situ* even when loosened. The resultant cliff is steep, at 70–90° where the dip inland is relatively gentle (Fig. 6.19d). However, where the dip is steeper (at 30°–45°), and there are well developed joints at right angles to the bedding planes, the latter can act as slide planes, and the cliff will be less steep (Fig. 6.20e). However, it must be said that none of these are hard and fast rules. It is, for example, not unknown for vertical or overhanging cliffs to occur even where the seaward dip is steep (Fig. 6.20f).

Geological structure also influences the plan form of cliffs, at micro, meso and macro-scales. Marine erosion is particularly sensitive to lines of structural weakness, however slight; these become rapidly etched out by hydraulic action and subsequent corrasion. Because of this, many cliffs are highly irregular in plan, with individual joints or bedding planes eroded into

Figure 6.19 *A dead cliff near Milford-on-Sea, Hampshire. The cliff foot is protected by an extensive accumulation of shingle, and the cliff is weathering back to a relatively gentle angle*

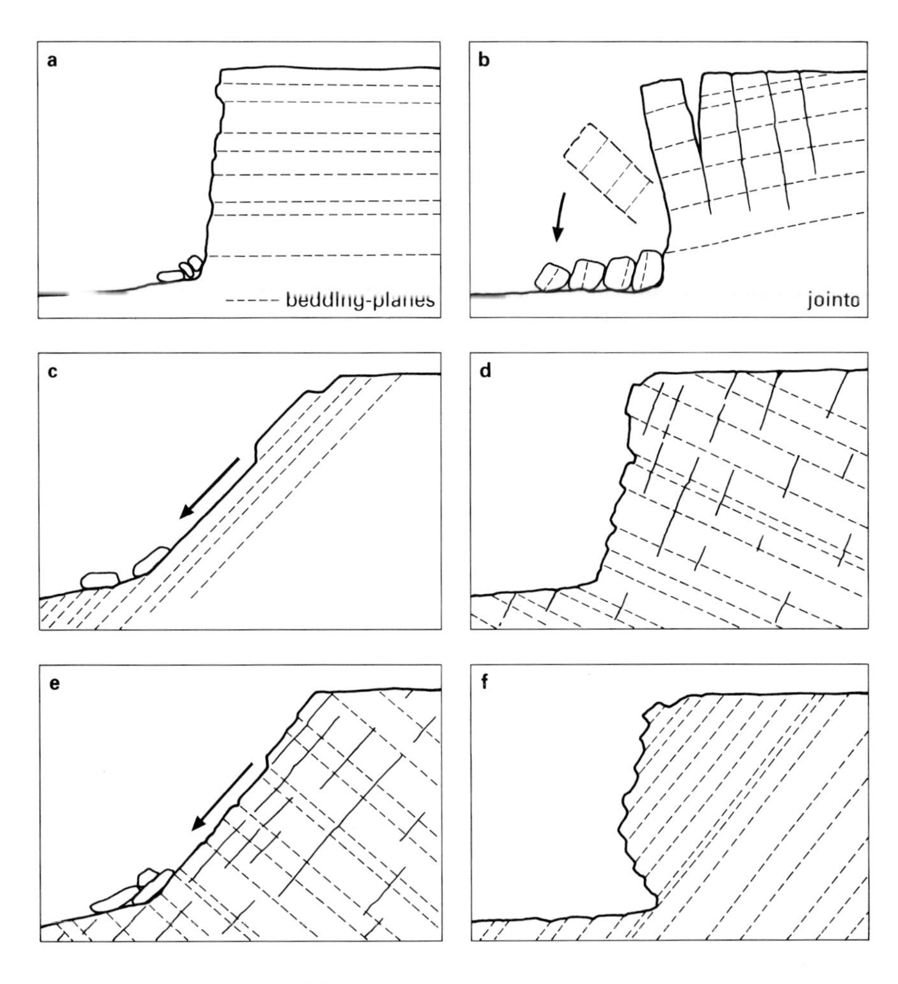

Figure 6.20 *The influence of geological dip on cliff profiles*

minor inlets, separated by 'mini' promontories. At the meso-scale, faults closely guide wave attack, as may be seen on the south Pembrokeshire coast west of St Govan's Head, where several magnificent geos, including Huntsman's Leap, mark vertical fractures in the Carboniferous Limestone. Long continued erosion of structural weak zones leads also to the detachment of steep rocky *pinnacles*, or *stacks*, and the formation of natural *arches* (Figs. 6.22 and 6.23). At a larger scale, in areas of complex geological structure comprising rock formations of differing resistance, marine erosion can form a series of bold promontories and wide bays. This is shown by the north Pembrokeshire Coast between St David's Head and Strumble Head, where there are several headlands formed by intrusions of hard igneous rock, with intervening bays eroded from relatively unresistant shales. Again, Carmarthen Bay in south Wales has been formed by marine attack in a broad zone of weak Coal Measures, sandstones and shales, formerly protected on the south side by a barrier of hard Carboniferous Limestone, now represented by the cliffs at Tenby (to the west) and Worm's Head, Gower (to the east).

The examples are either bays deepened by selective erosion which has increased the irregularity of the coast or cases where steady erosion has worn back the bays at the same rate as the exposed headlands. However, some have argued that beyond a certain stage, when the bays become occupied by extensive beach deposits and sheltered by the headlands, *regularisation* of the coastline can occur. Theoretically, the destruction of the headlands should lead eventually to an almost straight coastline, even in an area of diverse rock type. Cliffed coasts of this type do occur, as between Brighton and Eastbourne, in East Sussex. This coastline was once irregular in plan, owing to the drowning by the sea of the lower reaches of valleys running southwards from the South Downs. However, this is an area of homogeneous rock type, namely chalk, so that regularisation has been relatively easy. Whether such a process could ever be completed on, say, the coast of Pembrokeshire seems doubtful, to say the least.

CHANGES OF SEA-LEVEL AND RELATED COASTAL LANDFORMS

There is much evidence to show that sea-level, relative to the land, is undergoing, and has undergone in the past, significant changes. For example, careful analysis of tidal records has shown that the coasts of eastern England, Belgium and the Netherlands are sinking at a rate of 2.2–2.4 mm/annum^{-1}. Moreover, sites occupied in and near London during Roman times have been discovered at 5 m below the

Figure 6.21 *Cliffs in seaward dipping strata, Skomer Island*

Figure 6.22 *The chalk cliffs and stacks at Handfast Point, near Swanage, Dorset*

Figure 6.23 *The Green Bridge of Wales, an outstanding example of a natural arch, eroded from landward-dipping limestone strata near Flimston, Dyfed*

present mean sea-level. These relative rises of the sea result either from a depression of the earth's crust, or an increase of water in the ocean basins. The latter, known as a *eustatic movement*, must affect all the oceans equally, since they are interconnected. Approximately half of the observed sea-level rise in the southern North Sea is eustatic, and is the result of continued melting of the world's ice-sheets and glaciers; this is *glacial eustatism*. If current predictions about increasing levels of CO_2 in the atmosphere, and a resultant rise in temperatures by 5°–7°C in the next century, prove to be correct, many existing lowlands will be flooded. If all the remaining ice were melted, sea-level would rise by as much as 60 m.

However, there are also areas where the land is rising relative to the sea. Thus, study of an esker 60 km east of Helsinki, in Finland, has revealed that it is steadily emerging from beneath the sea, at a rate of 1.8 mm/annum^{-1}, to form a chain of small islands. The main process at work here is *isostatic uplift*. During the last Quaternary glaciation, southern Finland was occupied by a great ice-sheet, some 2 km in thickness. The weight of the ice was so vast that it caused a major depression of the earth's crust. With the deglaciation of the past few thousand years, there has been a relief of pressure and a return crustal movement, or isostatic recoil, that is still proceeding. This recoil, which cannot operate effectively until the ice has experienced considerable melting, tends to occur after the main eustatic sea-level rise. In southern Finland, the isostatic uplift is now 2.6 mm/annum^{-1}; this is only partially offset by the now reduced eustatic rise of 0.8 mm/annum^{-1}. Within Britain, Scotland is the main area of isostatic recovery, and again this exceeds the eustatic sea-level rise, so that in contrast to eastern England, the land is slowly emerging from beneath the sea.

Over long periods of time, eustatic and isostatic mechanisms, together with other forms of crustal movement referred to as *tectonic*, can give rise to major changes of sea-level. During the last glacial period of the Quaternary, when much oceanic water became 'locked up' in the continental ice-sheets of North America and Eurasia, the sea-level fell by 100 m or more. One result was that much of the present North Sea and English Channel became dry land. In the post-glacial, or Holocene period, climatic warming led, as shown, to a rapid eustatic rise of sea-level, the *Flandrian trangression*, which lasted in Britain until about 6000 years BP. Since then, the rise of sea-level has continued, but at a much slower rate. During the Quaternary as a whole, there were twenty or more rises and falls of sea-level of this magnitude. The picture is further complicated by the fact that in some parts of the world, such as New Zealand and the western USA, which are tectonically active, rapid land uplifts not in any way related to glaciation have occurred. Even Britain may have experienced a general uplift amounting to 200 m during the Quaternary. Thus, the many 'cyclic' changes due to glaciation have been superimposed on a 'falling trend' that has occupied the last 3 million years.

Coastal landforms due to rises of sea-level

When sea-level rises substantially, one obvious result is the inundation of the lower parts of river valleys, to form estuaries. In Britain, the Flandrian transgression produced many such features, ranging from the large scale Thames and Humber estuaries and the Firth of Forth, to medium sized but complex drowned valley systems, such as the branching *rias* at Kingsbridge and Falmouth in south-west England, to relatively minor inlets. Additionally, the submergence of areas of complex relief led to the creation of many islands, as in western Scotland, where additionally the numerous sea lochs are drowned valleys that had been deeply eroded by the Quaternary glaciers. A particularly well known example in southern England is the Isle of Wight. This has been isolated from the mainland by two processes: the inundation of a former river valley, that of the so called Solent River, which once flowed eastwards from the present Poole Harbour, through the Solent, to Selsey and beyond; and the marine erosion, in post-glacial times, of a barrier of chalk hills once extending from Handfast Point, near Swanage, in the west, and the Needles of the western Isle of Wight (Fig. 6.24).

At many places, especially on the hard rock cliffs of south Wales and south-west England, the rising sea-level of the Holocene has led to a revival of erosion. Cliffs which had been rendered inactive by the fall of sea-level during the last glacial period began to experience renewed wave attack. The sequence of changes was as follows (Fig. 6.25). In the cold glacial climate, the cliffs were profoundly modified by freeze-thaw weathering and solifluction. Free faces retreated, were reduced in extent by the upward growth of debris slopes at an angle of 20°–35°, or were even fragmented into isolated tor-like masses. In the process, the former cliffs became mantled by a layer of frost-debris, which increased in thickness towards the cliff base, where as a result of active solifluction aprons of what is termed *head* were spread over the exposed wave-cut platform. With the cessation of glacial conditions, and the resultant rise of sea-level, wave erosion began again at approximately the 'pre-glacial' level. The head deposits were stripped from the platform and in many areas from the cliff base, and marine attack on solid rock was renewed. This is one mechanism by which bevelled cliffs (p. 149) are formed. The stages in this process of cliff rejuvenation are well displayed at Manorbier Bay, Pembrokeshire. Within the sheltered bay itself, the sea has as yet succeeded only in forming cliffs in the head: to the west of the bay, bevelled cliffs have just begun to form; and to the east of the bay, well developed bevelled cliffs occur at some points. It is apparent that, in areas such as this, the general outline of the present coastline, with its bays and headlands, is closely similar to that existing during the last interglacial period. Thus, we have an example of a *relict coastline*, as yet little changed by modern erosion.

The effects of rises in sea-level on depositional landforms, such as beaches and bars, are discussed in a previous section (p. 147).

Coastal landforms due to falls of sea-level

The most common, if at times unobtrusive, landform resulting from falls of sea-level is the *raised beach* (Fig. 6.26). These are particularly well developed in much of western Scotland, where the '25-foot' (8 m), '50-foot' (16 m) and '100-foot' (30 m) beaches reflect changes of sea-level during the Quaternary glaciations. Owing to isostatic deformation (p. 154), these raised beaches are not horizontal. Thus, the so called 25-foot beach declines from a maximum height of 12 m in the vicinity of Mull, where the post-glacial isostatic uplift has been at a maximum, southwards into north-west England, where it coincides with present sea-level. There are, too, many raised beaches of Quaternary age in areas such as south Wales, where the *Patella* beach lies 2–3 m above high-water mark, south-west England, and at isolated points along the south coast, as at Portland Bill where there are two well preserved raised beaches at between 18 m and 6 m Ordnance Datum (OD).

Raised beaches take the form of raised wave-cut platforms, or *raised beach platforms*, of variable width and backed by a degraded cliff,

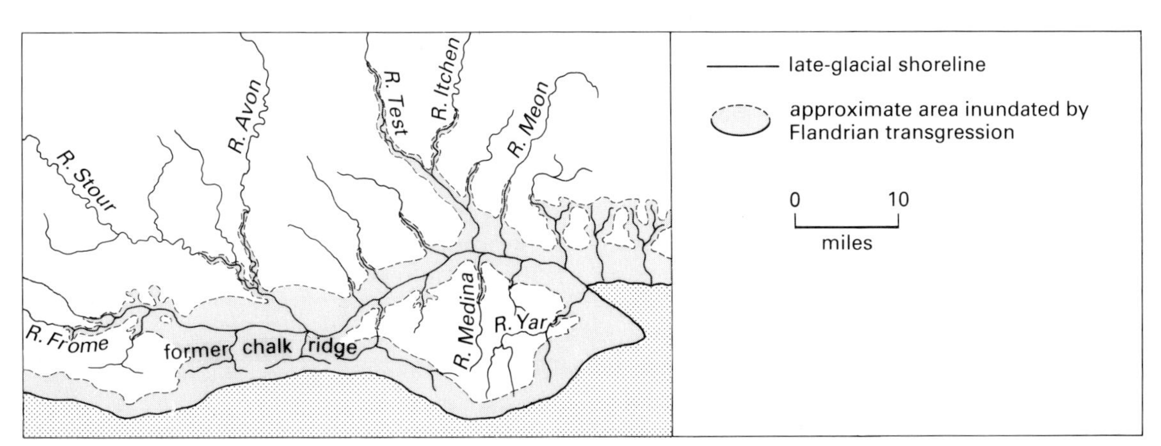

Figure 6.24 *The former Solent River and coastline of Hampshire and Dorset (see p. 154)*

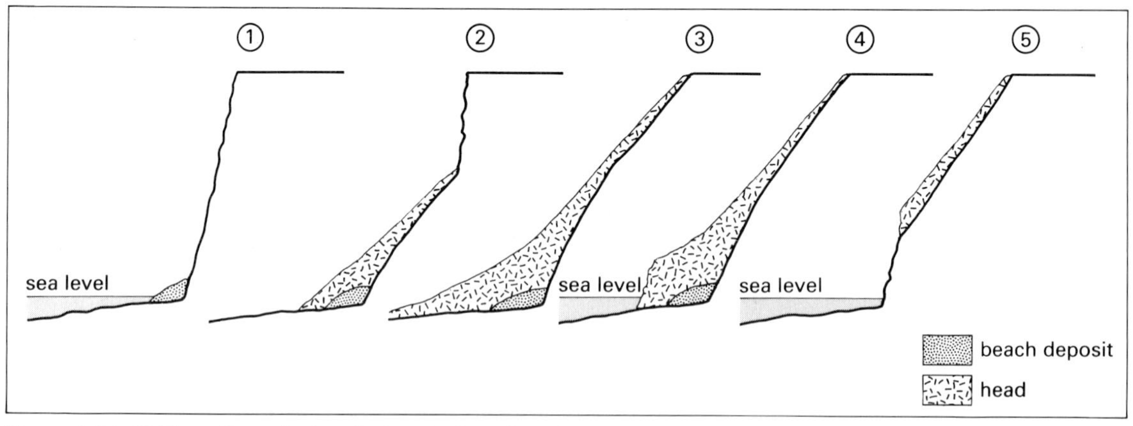

Figure 6.25 *Cliff profile evolution during the last glacial and post-glacial periods (see pp. 155–156)*

on which beach deposits, the raised beach proper, are preserved (Fig. 6.27). The latter is identifiable by the presence of typically rounded beach cobbles and pebbles (p. 139), beach sands and marine shells; for example, the Patella beach of south Wales is named after a type of limpet found commonly within it. Beach deposits are, by their nature, unconsolidated and easily destroyed. They tend to be best preserved either where the beach constituents are naturally cemented together, or where there is protection by overlying deposits. In the Gower peninsula of south Wales, raised beach deposits are quite common, sometimes occurring within caves as at Minchin Hole. This is because calcium bicarbonate dissolved by rainwater from the Carboniferous Limestone cliffs is reprecipitated as calcium carbonate within the beach, converting it into a *beach conglomerate* which resembles concrete. Additionally, periglacial mass wasting of the cliffs has resulted in the build-up of head deposits, themselves often cemented together, lying on top of the raised beach.

In some instances, raised beaches appear to be composite features, related not to one period of high sea-level, but two or three. For example, in Gower three beaches have been identified by some workers in a very narrow height range of only 5 m. Moreover, wave-cut platforms are often of complex form. In addition to the raised beach platform, the 'modern', and usually much more extensive, wave-cut platform may be eroded across at two or three distinct levels at heights between +5 m OD and −1 to −3 m OD. Such a composite platform is seen at Manorbier Bay (p. 155).

The examples of raised beaches and platforms described are all at a low elevation, and reflect the changes of sea-level of the mid and late Quaternary. However, marine fluctuations occurred earlier, for example during the latter part of the Tertiary era. These have led to the formation of extensive *coastal platforms*, often several km across, and separated from each other by slopes which are the product of long continued weathering and erosion of ancient cliff lines. Such platforms are found around the coastal margins of Wales and the south-west peninsula of England. They occur at various heights up to 200 m OD, though the most obvious platforms are at 180 m, 120 m, 100 m and 60 m OD. The platforms appear to have been formed by wave planation during relatively long *stillstands* of the sea, during a period dominated by uplift of the land relative to the sea, probably by tectonic movements. Although controversial, in terms of their origin and age, they are usually regarded as pre-Quaternary features, and possibly date mainly from the Pliocene period.

ASSIGNMENTS

1 Visit a beach within reach of your home or school.
   a. Draw as accurately as you can a series of

Figure 6.26 *A raised beach deposit, comprising rounded pebbles overlain by periglacial head, at Portland Bill, Dorset*

Figure 6.27 *Raised beach platforms, at 2 m and 18 m OD, in Gruinard Bay, Sutherland*

sketch profiles showing the form of the beach in cross-section. (If you have a clinometer, measuring tape and range poles, you can survey the profiles, and draw them on graph paper.)

b. Make notes of the sediments forming the beach (cobbles, pebbles, sand, silt, clay). How is the distribution of these sediments related to your beach profile?
c. Note any evidence of the sorting of beach material along the beach. An appropriate experiment would be to choose at random 50 cobbles/pebbles at opposing ends of your beach. The maximum dimension of each pebble could be measured with a ruler, and its shape recorded as round, partially round, sub-angular or angular. Histograms can then be drawn to show variations in size and shape between the two samples.
d. Attempt to determine, from observing the

processes of wave break and from any other available evidence, the direction of longshore drift of beach sediment. An appropriate experiment would be to paint 100 pebbles red, and to place them on the beach beside a fixed marker. On a subsequent visit (1 or 2 days later), the distance and direction of movement of any recovered pebbles can be recorded. The movements can then be related to records of wind speed and direction during the course of the experiment.

e. Suggest, with reasons, what is the likely source for the sediments forming your beach.

2 Attempt to simulate the growth of a coastal spit, over a period of several centuries, by drawing a series of six maps, representing time intervals of 50–100 years. Make the following assumptions:

a. The coastline is orientated generally west-east but the spit begins to form at a point where the coast changes from WNW-ESE to WSW-ENE.

b. The dominant winds and waves are from the south-west, but occasionally winds and waves are from the south and south-east.

c. During the early stages of spit growth there is an abundant supply of beach sediment from the erosion of cliffs to the west of the spit.

d. For the past 75 years, the sediment supply has been reduced by the construction of a sea wall and associated groyne structures.

Write brief explanatory notes on each of your six maps.

3 Visit a stretch of coastal cliffs within reach of your home or school.

a. Walk along the cliff top and/or cliff base (taking particular care to avoid dangerous situations).

b. Draw a series of sketch profiles of the cliffs, recording any factors, such as rock type, structure, and angle and direction of dip that appear to influence cliff form.

c. Note the detailed form and extent of any wave-cut platforms.

d. What features of the cliffs indicate (i) that erosion is active under present conditions, and (ii) that the cliffs have been affected by past episodes of erosion?

e. Write a brief explanatory account of the form and development of the cliffs in your study area.

4 Choose a stretch of the British coastline, up to 20 km in length, for which you have OS 1:50 000 and geological 1:50 000 maps available.

a. Draw an outline map of the coastline, marking features such as cliffs, beaches and river mouths.

b. Draw on tracing paper an overlay to show (i) the main types of rock outcropping at the coastline, (ii) any structural features (fold lines, angles and directions of dip, faults) that you can identify from the geological map.

c. By superimposing your two maps, attempt to draw conclusions about the influence of geological structure on the form and evolution of this stretch of coastline.

d. Describe any evidence, derived (i) from your maps, and (ii) from any other source available to you, of past changes of sea-level which have affected this coastline.

7

Landforms on a Global Scale

The earth's physical landscape displays great variability, which is, in turn, a reflection of the complex way in which the factors controlling landform development interact. As shown on p. 65, these factors are either external to the earth (mainly climatically determined) or internal to the earth (related to geological structure and earth movements). Indeed, one study which is designed to explain broad landform patterns is that of *climatic geomorphology* (p. 56), in which an attempt is made to define large scale morphogenetic regions. These are characterised by particular geomorphological processes, or groups of processes, which in turn may produce distinctive landform types. An alternative approach, and the subject of this chapter, is that of *structural geomorphology*, in which the major physical divisions of the earth are explained primarily in terms of geological control, although the influences of denudational processes, particularly when operating over a lengthy geological time span, can of course never be totally ignored.

MAJOR STRUCTURAL FEATURES OF CONTINENTAL LAND MASSES

The Pre-Cambrian Shields

In every continent there are broad areas, referred to as *crystalline shields, basement complexes* or (in modern terminology) *cratons*, over which extremely ancient Pre-Cambrian rocks, with an age in excess of 600 million years, are exposed (Fig. 7.1). These are, in effect, the 'cores' of the modern continents, on to which younger rocks have been 'grafted' over a long period of geological time, embracing the three main geological eras (Palaeozoic, Mesozoic and Cainozoic) (Fig. 7.2). Within Europe the principal craton is the Fenno-Scandian or

Figure 7.1 *Dissected Pre-Cambrian schists, forming part of the Arabian Shield, near Al Quwayiyah, Saudi Arabia*

Figure 7.2 *The major structural divisions of Europe (see p. 159 and p. 161)*

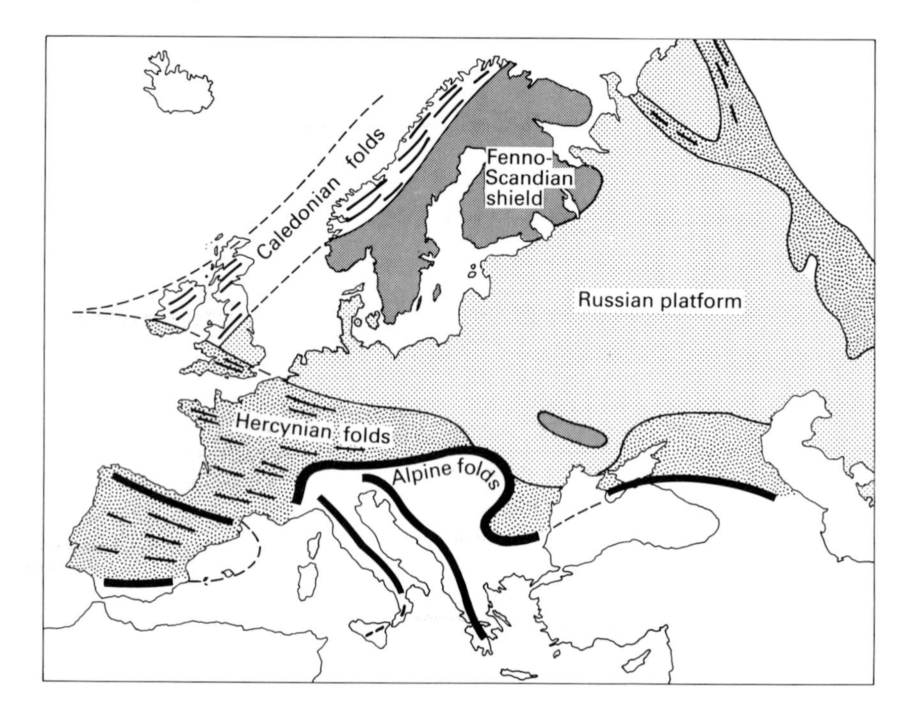

Baltic Shield, which occupies much of Scandinavia and north-west USSR. An equivalent feature in North America is the Laurentian Shield of central and eastern Canada. In Africa, the craton is particularly extensive, and is exposed over much of the southern two-thirds of the continent.

In the early stages of their formation the cratons, comprising mainly granite and metamorphic rocks such as gneiss and schist, experienced powerful folding, faulting and even volcanic activity. However, since Pre-Cambrian times, they have behaved largely as rigid, more or less stable blocks. In response to more recent earth movements, they have undergone either bodily uplift (as over much of east Africa, where the shield forms high plateaus at 1000–2000 m above sea-level) or large scale but gentle warpings, which have given rise to the watersheds between the main river systems. The history of many cratons has, in more recent geological times, been dominated by erosion, in the course of which they have been reduced to near level erosional plains, such as those which extend over much of Africa south of the Sahara. At their margins, the cratons have also been depressed by crustal movements, and the resultant marine transgressions have led to the formation of a cover of younger sediments. Some shields, notably those of Fenno-Scandia and the Laurentide region, have recently experienced ice-sheet glaciation, though this has done little to change the pre-existing landforms on a major scale (p. 96).

The fold mountains

By far the most impressive of the earth's major landforms are the great fold mountain chains, such as the Himalayas of Asia, the Alps of Europe, and the Rockies and Andes of North and South America respectively. These mountains are characterised by their great height above sea-level (in the Himalayas, Everest, Kangchenjunga and K2 attain 8848, 8578 and 8160 m respectively), and in many instances by high jagged peaks, active glaciers, deeply entrenched valleys and torrential rivers.

Fold mountains are the product of powerful compressive forces in the earth's crust, when rigid blocks move towards each other. Intervening sediments will be crumpled, and, in

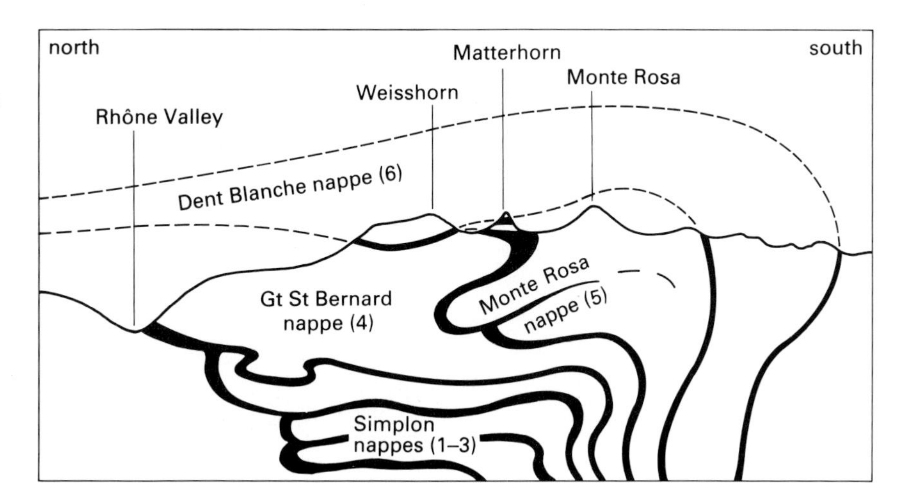

Figure 7.3 *Simplified diagram of nappe structures of the Pennine Alps*

extreme cases, contorted into isoclinal folds, recumbent folds and nappes (Fig. 7.3). The forces involved are so enormous that many strata become metamorphosed; for example, clays are transformed into slate, and sandstones into quartz-schists. Moreover, crustal fracturing may lead to intrusive and extrusive vulcanism (p. 167). In Switzerland, the northern Alpine ranges are dominated by limestones (in the so called High Calcareous Alps) and the southern ones by schists and gneisses (in the Pennine Alps). In the French Alps, Mont Blanc and its subsidiary peaks are fashioned from a block of granite of intrusive origin.

Fold mountains are highly complex geological structures, often formed by a succession of earth movements. Subsequent to their formation, erosion on an enormous scale may remove thousands of metres of rock from the folds, so that reconstruction of the original structure becomes very difficult. Not surprisingly, landform patterns are equally complex, but there is usually evidence of selective erosion by rivers and glaciers or lines of weakness, such as major faults or relatively soft geological strata. The great trench of the Rhône valley, above Martigny in Switzerland, is eroded along the geological junction between the High Calcareous and Pennine Alps.

Since Pre-Cambrian times there have been three great fold mountain building episodes, known as *orogenies*, in Europe (Fig. 7.2). The *Caledonian orogeny*, which took place some 400 million years ago, formed the mountains of Scandinavia and north-west Britain and Ireland. These possess a clear 'structural trend' from north-east to south-west. The *Hercynian* (otherwise *Armorican* or *Variscan*) orogeny occurred some 300 million years ago, and resulted in the formation of uplands such as the Massif Central of France, the Harz Mountains of southern Germany, the Meseta of Spain and the Coalfield Plateau of south Wales. The *Alpine orogeny*, active a mere 30 million years ago, produced mountain ranges such as the Alps themselves, the Pyrenees and the Carpathians. There are counterparts of these various mountains outside Europe, as in North America, where the Appalachians are the equivalent of the Caledonian and Hercynian folds and the Rockies are of Alpine age. However, the timing of the orogenic episodes was not precisely the same between continents. Indeed, taking a world wide view, the Alpine movements were very long lasting, and occupied much of the last 150 million years. Thus, whilst the Himalayas were contemporaneous with the Alps, the Rockies and Andes were largely developed some 20–40 million years earlier.

In terms of geomorphology, there are contrasts between the Caledonian and Hercynian systems on the one hand, and the Alpine on the other. This partly reflects the greater

Figure 7.4 *An ancient upraised peneplain: the Welsh plateau surface at 450–500 m OD south-east of Tregaron, Dyfed*

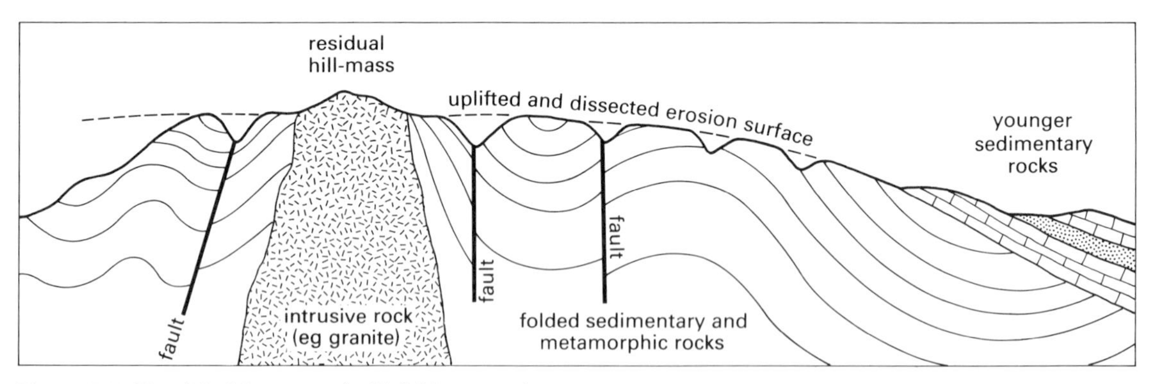

Figure 7.5 *Simplified features of old fold mountains*

amount of erosion suffered by the former. A broad distinction has therefore been made between *young* and *old* fold mountains. The main features of the latter (Fig. 7.4), as exemplified by the uplands of Scotland, northern England, Wales and south-west England, are: clear evidence of past peneplanation of the old structures (p. 77) to give near level *erosion surfaces*; partial or complete burial of the peneplained mountains by younger sediments (for example, it has been suggested that the Welsh uplands were once covered by a layer of chalk, of marine origin); and evidence of more recent uplift during Alpine times, which has led to the removal by erosion of overlying sediments, and deep incision of the river valleys (Fig. 7.5). The resultant landscapes are plateau-like (the Welsh uplands are sometimes referred to as a 'Tableland'), and are often characterised by discordant drainage (rivers cutting across old fold and fault lines). The latter results from the process of *superimposition*, whereby rivers developing on an upper, younger stratum eventually cut downwards into an underlying, older rock structure. Some old fold mountains have been further modified by glacial erosion, which has produced locally a much more rugged landscape of sharp peaks and arêtes, cirques and glacial troughs (p. 91). By contrast, young fold mountains are highly irregular in outline, rather than plateau-like, and are normally of much greater elevation. The latter reflects not only their briefer erosional history, but also active uplift by isostatic movements during the post-folding period. Also, they are much more deeply and intensely dissected by rivers and

Figure 7.6 *Young fold mountains: the mountains of the Bernese Oberland, Switzerland, viewed from the Schilthornhutte*

glaciers, and in general give rise to very spectacular scenery, as in the Alps and Himalayas (Fig. 7.6).

Sedimentary structures

Away from the main orogenic zones, there are more stable areas where considerable thicknesses of sedimentary strata have accumulated and remained relatively undisturbed. Within Europe, such areas include England south-east of the 'Tees-Exe line', and much of northern and eastern France. The sediments, mainly of Mesozoic and Cainozoic age, comprise limestones, chalks, sandstones and clays, resting on an underlying foundation of more ancient rock. The latter is formed either by the depressed southern margin of the Fenno-Scandian shield, as in the Russian Platform of north-east Europe, or by Palaeozoic rocks which were folded by the Caledonian and Hercynian earth-movements, peneplained in early Mesozoic times, and then downwarped. In northern Africa, the Pre-Cambrian and Palaeozoic basement has also been depressed, relative to central and southern Africa, and over wide extents of the Sahara and Egyptian deserts is overlain by Cretaceous strata, including the limestones of southern Algeria and the Nubian sandstones of Egypt.

The foundations on which the sedimentary strata rest have been periodically uplifted and depressed, in a largely gentle fashion, since early Mesozoic times. In effect, this has allowed the sea to spread from time to time over the continental margins, and on some occasions well inland, and then to withdraw again. The resultant cycles of marine transgressions and regressions have resulted in the development of sedimentary sequences comprising alternate marine and continental formations.

Structurally, the sedimentary structures comprise: extensive areas of near horizontal strata; gently dipping strata forming *uniclinal structures*; and broad anticlines and synclines, as in south-east England where the 'Wealden Dome' separates the London Basin to the north from the Hampshire Basin to the south. The lack of severe structural disturbance in these areas reflects the rigidity of the underlying foundation. However, during the Alpine period, even the latter locally experienced renewed movements along ancient fold and fault lines, resulting in some structural dislocation of the overlying strata. This process may have been responsible for the many minor folds in the chalk country of southern England, sometimes referred to as the so called 'outer ripples' of the Alpine Storm.

There are two main types of landscape commonly associated with sedimentary structures (Fig. 7.7). *Dissected plateaux* are characterised by the more resistant strata forming level-topped uplands, mesas and buttes, which are separated by incised river valleys, sometimes displaying structural benches. Good examples are found in the Langres region of eastern France, the Grands Causses of southern France, and the Nubian sandstone region of Libya. In *scarp and vale landscapes* the resistant formations (limestone, sandstone, chalk) form cuestas with bold scarp faces and extensive dip slopes, whilst the weaker layers (clays, sands) are etched by fluvial erosion into strike vales (Fig. 7.8). In the process the river systems become highly adjusted to structure. Excellent examples of scarpland morphology are to be found in lowland England, the eastern Paris Basin, and the Basin of Aquitaine in south-western France.

Landscapes associated with fault structures

Geological *faults* are fractures on either side of

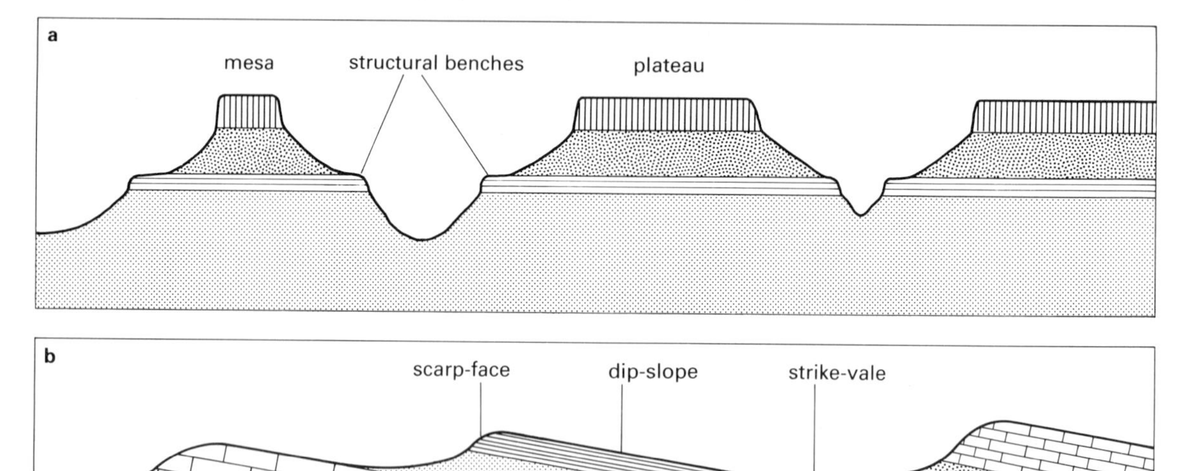

Figure 7.7 *Landforms in horizontal (**a**) and gently-dipping structures (**b**)*

Figure 7.8 *The scarp face, in Old Red Sandstone, of the Black Mountains near Brecon, south Wales*

which there is vertical and/or horizontal displacement of rocks. They are widespread phenomena, and the landforms they give rise to are sufficiently distinctive to merit separate consideration. Faults are of many types, depending on whether they are the result of tensional or compressional stresses in the earth's crust. A *normal fault* is produced by tension, or stretching, and involves the lowering of the rocks on the side towards which the fault plane is inclined. A *reversed fault*, due to compression, has the effect of raising the rocks on the side towards which the fault plane is inclined. Sometimes reversed faults involve the sliding of rocks, along a plane of low angle, a considerable distance over the underlying rocks, to give a *thrust fault*; such faults may accompany powerful overfolding.

In some instances, movement of the rocks on either side of a fault plane is primarily horizontal and parallel to the fault; this is a *tear fault* or, if on a large scale, a *transform* or *transcurrent fault*. Faults rarely occur singly. In any one area, there may be a system of sub-parallel faults, resulting in *step faulting* or *tilted fault blocks*. Where faulting is on a large scale, a series of adjacent crustal blocks may be alternately raised and depressed, giving *horsts* and *graben*. Excellent examples occur in south-west Germany, where the upraised *block mountains* of the Vosges and the Black Forest are separated by the graben of the Rhine Valley.

Faulting is of geomorphological interest for two reasons. It directly creates landforms, often on a spectacular scale, such as fault scarps, fault bounded plateaus and rift valleys. However, faults are also lines of weakness, associated with crushed and broken rock (*fault breccia*) which can be selectively eroded by rivers, waves, glaciers and ice-sheets. *Fault scarps* are common landforms in tectonically active regions, such as California or New Zealand (Fig. 7.9a). However, in areas where the faults are ancient, true fault scarps will be rare. Here, long continued erosion will have led to the destruction of the initial fault scarps (the immediate product of the faulting), and the formation of *fault line scarps*. An important

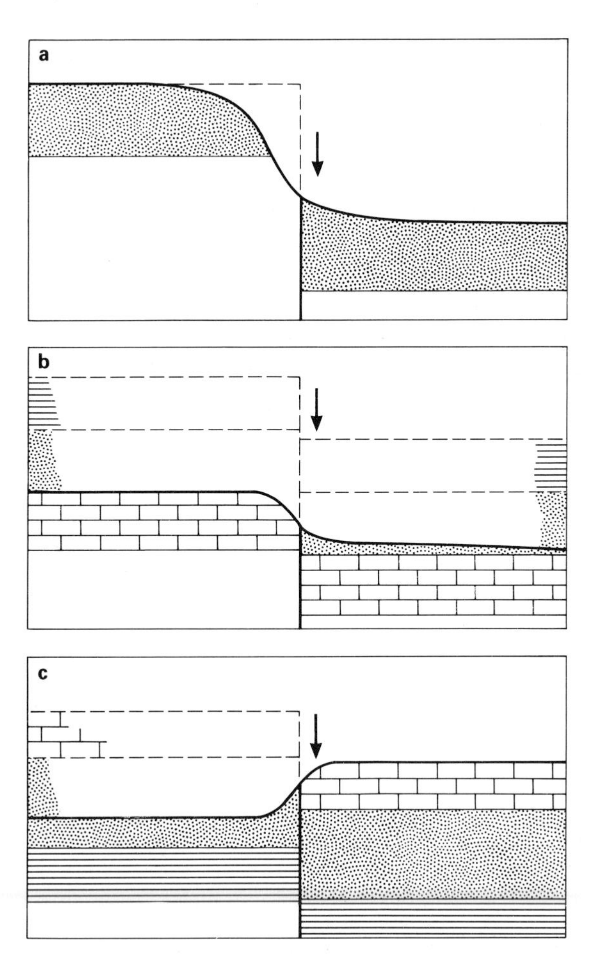

Figure 7.9 *Fault scarp (**a**) and fault-line scarps (**b** and **c**)*

effect of faulting is to bring unresistant rocks against resistant rocks. Where the former are removed or lowered by erosion, the latter will be left upstanding to form an escarpment along the line of the fault (Fig. 7.9b and c). In some instances, depending on the precise arrangement of the rocks at the fault, this scarp may actually face in the opposite direction to the initial fault scarp!

Perhaps the most impressive product of faulting is the *rift valley*; this is the surface landform usually, but not invariably, resulting from a graben structure. Rift valleys occur widely and on a variety of scales. Well known examples in Europe include: the Midland Valley of Scotland, which is a downfaulted synclinal structure lying between the great Highland Boundary Fault to the north, and the Southern Uplands Fault to the south; the Rhine rift valley; and the Limagne depression near Clermont-Ferrand in southern France. However, by far the largest and most important rift valley, the product of comparatively recent crustal movements, is that of east Africa. This extends from Jordan in the north to Mozambique in the south, a distance of 5500 km. In its central part the system divides into two branches, the western (Albertine) rift in Uganda and the eastern (Gregory) rift in Kenya; between the two lies a downwarped area of the African plateau occupied by Lake Victoria. The main features associated with large scale rift faulting are well displayed in central and southern Kenya (Fig. 7.10).

In simple terms, the Kenya rift valley consists of a strip of land, elongated north-south and some 50 km or more in width, which has been lowered between parallel major faults in a series of crustal movements lasting from the Miocene period (20 million years ago) to late Quaternary times. At many points, the boundary scarps are bold and high, standing

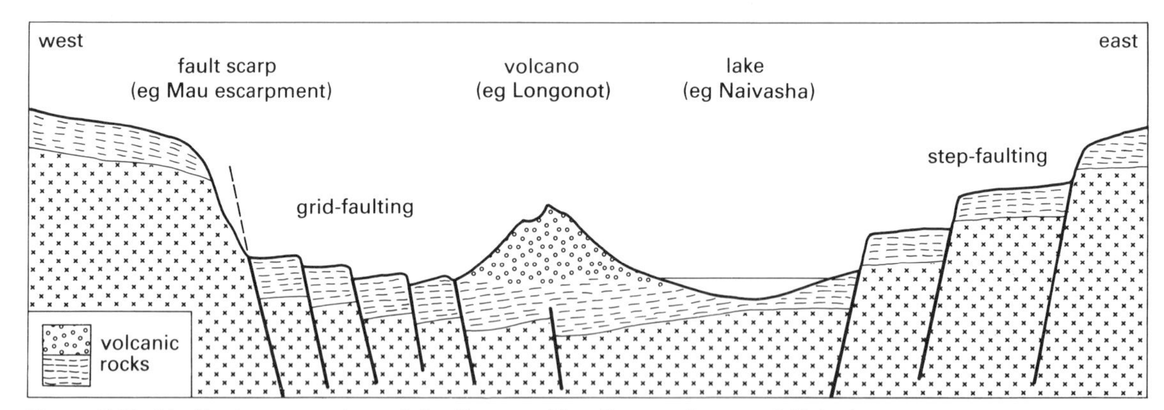

Figure 7.10 *Idealised cross-section of the Kenyan rift valley north-west of Nairobi*

Figure 7.11 *The Kenyan rift valley, viewed from the summit of the eastern fault scarp near Limuru, north-west of Nairobi. The drop to the rift valley floor at this point is over 600 m*

600 m or more above the valley floor (Fig. 7.11). Elsewhere, the scarps bear the clear imprint of step faulting, as to the east of Lake Naivasha; and the floor itself is much broken by small scale faults, known as *grid faulting*. An additional factor has been the massive outpouring of volcanic lavas, both within and on the shoulders of the rift valley. Indeed, although the rift was initiated by fractures in the ancient basement rocks of Africa, as a surface feature today it is developed almost entirely within the volcanic rocks, which underlie the rift floor by hundreds or even thousands of metres.

Landscapes of vulcanicity

Vulcanicity is closely allied to powerful crustal disturbance by folding, faulting and the formation of divergent and convergent plate margins (p. 174). It comprises both the penetration and solidification of magma within the earth's crust (*intrusive activity*), and the escape of lava and associated materials at the earth's surface (*extrusive* or *volcanic activity*). The two types are often closely associated, as in western Scotland. Here, vast thicknesses of basic lava were extruded in early Tertiary times. For example, the basalt flows of Mull still attain a thickness of 2000 m, despite being reduced by late Tertiary and Quaternary erosion Additionally, large masses of granite and gabbro were intruded, and were later exposed by denudation in areas such as northern Arran and Skye.

The forms and scales of intrusive activity vary greatly. Larger features include *batholiths*, which are dome-like intrusions of granite formed at depth in association with mountain-building movements, and *laccoliths*, the product of injection of magma along bedding planes, in such a way as to cause up-arching of the overlying strata. Smaller structures include *sills*, which are concordant sheets of dolerite or similar rocks, again formed along bedding planes, and *dykes*, which are narrow discordant intrusions, cutting across the strata and resulting from crustal stretching. The latter is evident in southern Arran, where the formation of 525 dykes with a total thickness of 1.5 km has involved a crustal extension of 6 per cent. The landforms due to the exposure and modification of intrusive structures also vary considerably, from the high moorlands formed by granite batholiths (as in Dartmoor, south-west England) to the rocky edges related to sills (for example, the Great Whin Sill of northern England) and the groyne-like walls of hard rock formed by dykes at the coast.

The forms of extrusive features are determined by the scale of the eruption, the nature of the vent (central or fissure), and the type of material emitted. Among the largest and most impressive are the *shield volcanoes* of Hawaii, which reach to great heights but possess gentle side slopes of 4° or less, formed from freely flowing basic lava. Other major extrusive features are the vast spreads of 'flood basalts', otherwise known as *plateau basalts*, which have escaped from large linear fractures in the crust. These have been built up as more or less horizontal accumulations in areas such as the Deccan Plateau of southern India and the Columbia-Snake River region of the north-west USA; in the latter, the basalt covers 580 000 km^2. *Composite volcanoes*, comprising alternate layers of lava and ash, are also imposing landforms, with their great height and marginal slopes of 20°–30°. However, their form may owe much in detail to recent erosion. For example, the Tertiary volcanoes of Mont-Dore and Cantal, in central France, have been deeply dissected by a radial pattern of river valleys, and further modified by Quaternary glaciers. Smaller and simpler volcanic cones include steep sided *cinder cones* and convex *acid domes*, formed by the extrusion of viscous acid lava. The two types are to be found together in the Chaine des Puys, in the Massif Central of France. In some instances, the central parts of the large volcanoes have collapsed, as the magma reservoirs have become depleted, to form major craters known as *calderas*, as at Suswa and Menengai in the rift valley of Kenya (Fig. 7.12).

In terms of their global distribution, recent or active volcanoes exhibit a distinct pattern.

Figure 7.12 *The southern margin of the great collapsed volcano, or caldera, at Menengai, Nakuru, Kenya. The floor of the caldera reaches a maximum width of 13 km, and is occupied by numerous lava flows active during the past few centuries*

The major concentrations are developed around the margins of the Pacific Ocean (the 'Pacific Ring of Fire'), along island arcs and mid-ocean ridges (p. 169), in association with the East African rift valley system (p. 166), and in a zone passing through the Mediterranean region into Armenia, Iran and Baluchistan (the Alpine-Himalayan orogenic belt).

MAJOR STRUCTURAL FEATURES OF THE OCEAN BASINS

The continental shelf

In many areas the margins of the continental land masses have become submerged, as a result of crustal depression or rises in the level of the oceans, to form a gently sloping submarine platform which terminates at its outer edge at a depth of 120–360 m. Beyond this is a steep gradient, known as the *continental slope*, leading down to the ocean basin floor. The continental shelf varies in extent; around the British Isles it is well developed, and extends some 300 km westwards from Land's End, but along the Pacific coasts of North and South America it is absent altogether. The continental shelf may be, in part, an extended wave-cut platform, developed over a long time span as the oceans advanced and retreated over the continental margins. However, it is also partly a depositional feature. It is underlain in many areas by the same sedimentary rocks that form the near-by land, and in western Europe is widely covered by tills and glacio-fluvial sediments deposited by the Quaternary ice-sheets. Locally the shelf is crossed by deep trenches, known as *submarine canyons*. These tend to occur opposite the mouths of large rivers, such as the Congo and Hudson River, but are unlikely to be subaerial valleys which were subsequently drowned by a rise in ocean level. One plausible theory is that they were eroded by submarine mud flows, referred to as *turbidity currents*. These have been active where river sediments accumulated on the shelf and then, when disturbed by earthquakes, slid rapidly down the continental slope.

Sea floor plains

Wide areas of the ocean basins are both very deep, at 3000–6000 m, and relatively featureless, owing to the build-up of considerable thicknesses of sediment derived both from the continents (silts and sands from turbidity currents, volcanic dust and aeolian material), and from the oceans themselves (organic oozes, comprising calcareous and siliceous skeletons

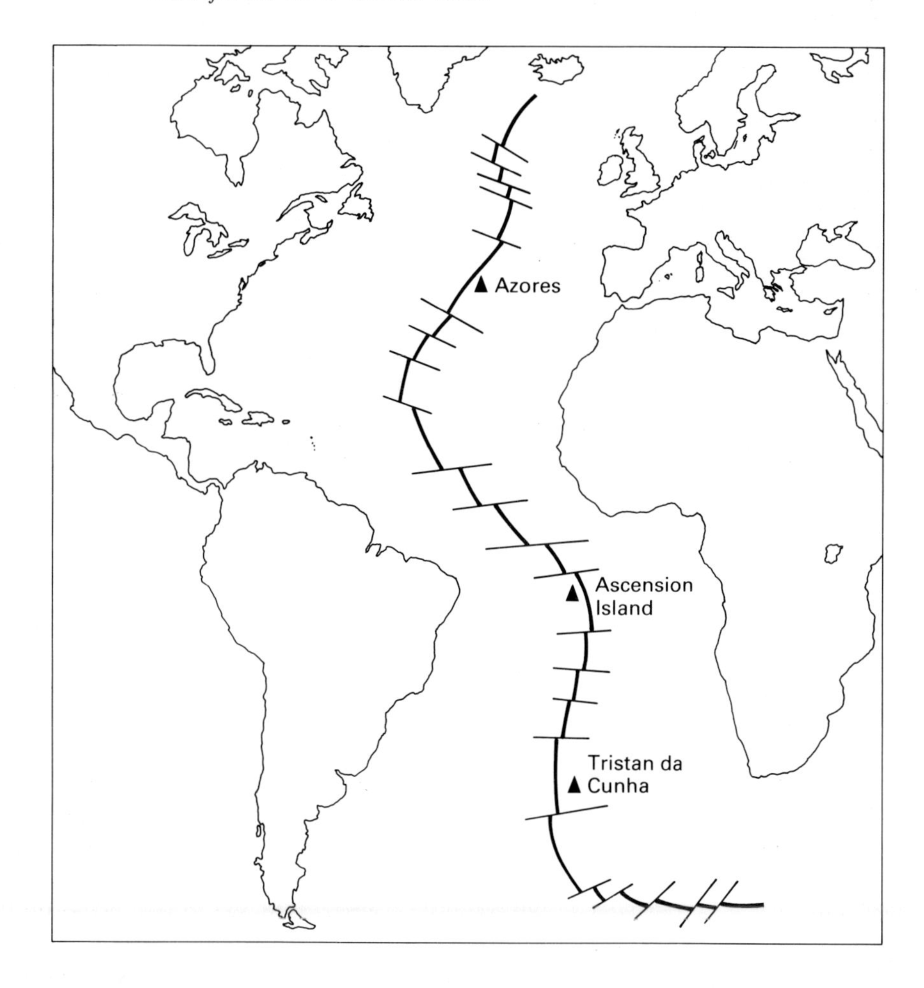

Figure 7.13 *The generalised pattern of the Mid-Atlantic Ridge*

of marine organisms, and chemical precipitates). Occasionally these sea floor plains are interrupted by *sea mounts*, or submarine volcanic cones rising steeply from the sea-bed. These may breach the surface as groups of volcanic islands, as in Hawaii, where Mauna Loa rises from a depth of 5000 m, and then extends a further 4168 m above sea level. In the Pacific Ocean, many sea mounts have been planed across at their summits by marine erosion, giving flat topped submarine hills known as *guyots*.

Mid-ocean ridges

What is in effect a great submarine mountain chain, comparable in scale with the Rockies or Andes, runs approximately north-south along the centre line of the Atlantic Ocean (Fig. 7.13). This ridge, comprising massive extrusions of volcanic lava, mainly basalt, is known as the Mid-Atlantic Ridge. It varies in width, at its maximum exceeding 1500 km, and individual summits rise up to 3000 m or more above the ocean floor. Only the very 'highest' peaks, consisting of huge volcanic mountains up to 6000 m in elevation above the ocean floor, appear above sea-level, as in the Azores, Ascension Island and Tristan da Cunha. In detail, the plan of the Mid-Atlantic Ridge is very irregular, with many offsets related to transform faults, on either side of which the rocks have been displaced laterally.

Equivalent features are found in the other oceans; indeed all these mid-ocean ridges interconnect to form a world wide system. Thus, the

Mid-Atlantic Ridge turns eastwards, past South Africa, to become successively the South-west Indian Ridge, the Mid-Indian Ridge, the South-East Indian Ridge and the Indian-Antarctic Ridge (past Australia). It then turns again north-eastwards as the Pacific-Antarctic Ridge and the East Pacific Rise, which impinges on the coast of North America in Mexico. It is now known that all these mid-ocean ridges represent major fracture zones in the earth's crust (p. 172).

Island arcs and ocean trenches

In some oceanic areas, notably the western Pacific margins, long, narrow and often gently curving ridges rise from the ocean floor. In most instances these give rise to lines of islands, known as *island arcs*, as in the Aleutian Island Arc of the north Pacific and that running southwards from the island of Honshu, Japan, through the Marianas. These islands, containing numerous volcanic cones, constitute dangerous earthquake zones, and clearly mark lines of great crustal instability. Closely allied to island arcs, and running closely parallel to them, are deep, narrow and steep sided *ocean trenches*, also known as *foredeeps*. Good examples are the Aleutian Trench, which is associated with the Aleutian Island Arc, and the Japan, Bonin and Marianas Trench, off Honshu and the Marianas Island Arc. These trenches, at 7500–10 000 m the deepest parts of the oceans, contain relatively little in the way of sediments. Ocean trenches are also developed parallel to some continental margins, as in the Peru-Chile Trench lying immediately offshore from the western coast of South America.

THE STRUCTURAL EVOLUTION OF THE CONTINENTS AND OCEANS

The earth's structure

Structurally, the earth comprises three main components. There is a central *core*, with a radius of approximately 6000 km, consisting of materials of very high density (up to 13.0 g/cm^3), at high very temperatures (up to 5500°C), and in its outer parts made up of a molten layer of iron and nickel. Outside of this, there is a *mantle*, some 300 km in thickness, of lower temperature (up to 3000°C), of lesser density (3.0 to 5.0 g/cm^3), and composed mainly of solid ultrabasic rocks rich in iron and magnesium. Finally, there is a relatively thin outer *crust*, with a maximum thickness of 60–70 km beneath the continents, and made up largely of igneous rocks covered by a veneer of sedimentary rocks. Within the upper part of the mantle, at a depth of 60–200 km, is a zone of much reduced strength, where heat from the radioactive decay of rocks has accumulated. Within this upper *asthenosphere*, very slow flowage can occur under great pressure. The topmost part of the mantle, and the overlying crust (together constituting the *lithosphere*, but separated from each other by the *Mohorovičić discontinuity*, or '*Moho*') behave by contrast as a rigid shell. The crust itself is broadly divisible into two layers: a lower layer of basaltic rock, sometimes referred to as *sima*, from the predominance of silica and magnesium minerals; and an upper layer of granitic rocks, known as *sial*, from the presence of silica and aluminium minerals. The sima has a relatively high density (2.9–3.3 g/cm^3) and is continuous, underlying both the continents and the oceans; the sial, of lower density (2.6–2.7 g/cm^3) is discontinuous, and forms the main continental areas.

Crustal movements

Although the earth's crust constitutes a generally rigid layer, it is subject to both major and minor deformations. It can be locally uplifted, depressed, tilted, folded or faulted. These processes are collectively termed *tectonic activity*. The most simple, though by their nature large scale, tectonic processes involve slow and long continued vertical movements which affect the continental land masses and the ocean floors. These so called *epeirogenic*

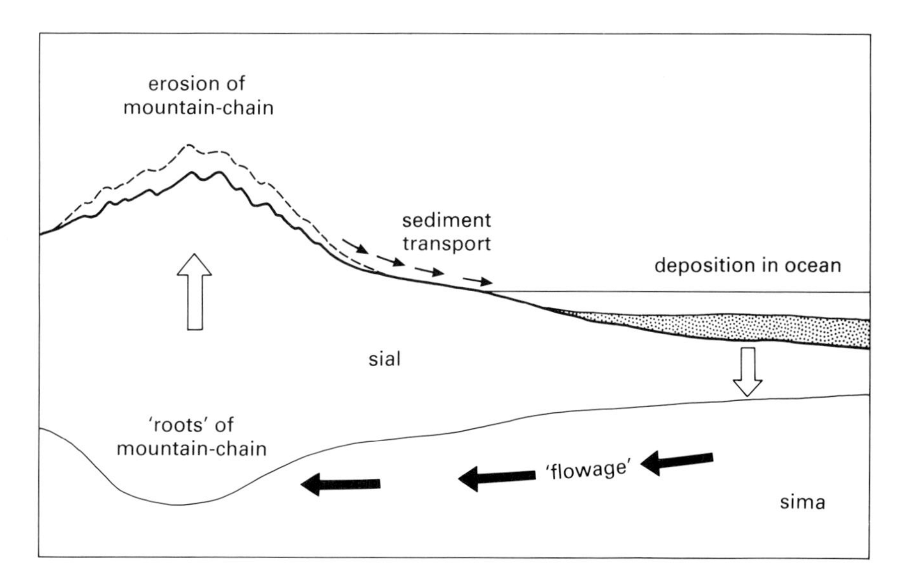

Figure 7.14 *Isostatic movements in response to erosion and deposition*

movements do not cause powerful folding or faulting, but rather lead to the gentle warping and tilting of strata. Among their main effects are the lowering or raising of continental margins. The first process allows the oceans to invade adjacent continental areas; the second results in the expulsion of the seas, and the exposure of newly formed sedimentary rocks. Epeirogenic movements also modify continental relief patterns, and influence major drainage divides and river systems, as in the shield areas (p. 160).

The theory of *isostasy* provides an explanation of vertical crustal movement. This states that there is a state of equilibrium in the earth's crust whereby equal mass at depth underlies equivalent surface mass. In simple terms, where young fold mountains such as the Himalayas (p. 160), comprising mainly sialic rocks, rise high above the average surface level, there must be a compensating root of sialic material penetrating the denser sima. The continents themselves can be likened to 'rafts' of sial floating on a 'sea' of sima (Fig. 7.14). The process of *isostatic uplift* occurs when some of the sialic mass is removed by erosion, and bodily elevation is necessary to maintain equilibrium. Such movements affect both young fold mountains and broad continental areas subjected to long continued erosion. Oceanic floors, by contrast, may experience *isostatic depression* in areas where sediments worn from the land accumulate in vast quantities. Thus, isostatic uplift at one point, and depression at another, can be viewed as interlinked processes. One important type of isostatic adjustment has resulted from the growth and decay of major ice-sheets during the Quaternary period (p. 154).

Other types of crustal deformation, with a more spectacular outcome, result from tangential, or lateral, movements, either of *compression* (where parts of the crust move together) or of *tension* (where parts of the crust move apart). The major process related to compression is *orogenesis*, or the formation of mountain chains; other processes due to compressional and tensional movements are considered below.

Continental drift and plate tectonics

The notion that large masses of the earth's crust are capable of lateral movement, over considerable distances and during long periods of geological time, is by no means new. The hypothesis of *continental drift* was advocated by several authorities, but is associated particularly with the German meteorologist Alfred Wegener. Wegener, writing in 1910, envisaged that the earth's continents were once grouped into one major land area, referred to as *Pangaea*, which itself comprised two main elements: a northern 'supercontinent', which he termed *Laurasia*, consisting of North America, Europe and much of Asia: and a southern supercontinent, *Gondwanaland*, including South America, Africa, southern India, Australia, and Antarctica. The two great continents were themselves separated by the *Tethys Sea*; and, at that time, a greatly expanded Pacific was an even more dominant ocean than at present.

The break-up of Pangaea was believed to have begun in late Mesozoic times, and to have involved three main components: the detachment and drift to the west of the Americas, thus opening up the Atlantic Ocean; the drift of Australia and India to the east; and a movement of the continents towards the Equator, termed by Wegener 'The Flight from the Poles'. This latter drift was especially important in the southern hemisphere, where the northward migration of most of the southern continents in effect left Antarctica behind as an isolated Polar continent. Much evidence was cited in favour of the hypothesis of continental drift, including: the excellent 'fit' of the eastern and western coastlines of the Atlantic Ocean; the remarkable correspondence of orogenic belts across oceans, for example, the Caledonian-Hercynian fold mountains of north-west Europe and eastern North America; and the occurrence of a great glaciation of the southern continents in Carboniferous-Permian times, which could best be explained if, at that time, those continents were continuous with each other, as Gondwanaland, and in a polar location. Nevertheless, continental drift, although an attractive and exciting hypothesis, was for many years viewed with suspicion by scientists, largely because the mechanisms whereby large crustal blocks could migrate over thousands of kilometres could not be explained in the light of knowledge then available.

However, from the 1950s onwards there began an era of exploration of the earth's crust which has added immensely to our understanding of its structure, history and current processes of modification. Much valuable information about the structure of the ocean floors emerged from the deep sea drilling carried out from the ship *Glomar Challenger*, as part of the US National Science Foundation Drilling Program. Of particular importance, too, was the evidence derived from studies of *rock magnetism*. When volcanic lava solidifies, or certain types of sediment are laid down, magnetic minerals such as iron oxide align themselves like magnetic needles (a) in the horizontal plane pointing towards the earth's magnetic pole, and (b) in the vertical plane, dipping at an angle that is dependent on latitude. Measurements of the magnetism preserved by old rocks (*palaeomagnetism*) have revealed three things: that over geological time the magnetic poles appear to have experienced major shifts; that the earth's magnetic field has undergone numerous reversals, just as if the north and south magnetic poles had abruptly changed places; and that the evidence from different continents was not in agreement. For instance, the palaeomagnetic readings from North America and Europe indicated *two* North Poles. This discrepancy could be explained only on the assumption that the two continents were actually some 20° of longitude closer together about 20 million years ago!

Palaeomagnetic evidence was of great help in explaining the form and origin of mid-ocean ridges (p. 169). For example, study of the basaltic lavas of the Mid-Atlantic Ridge revealed a pattern of 'magnetic striping' on either side of the main axis. Moreover, this striping, which records many reversals of the earth's magnetic field, is exactly symmetrical. This phenomenon can be explained by the assumption that, over a lengthy geological period, narrow bands of volcanic rock continually welled up and solidified in the centre of a widening rift in the earth's crust. Each band, carrying a record of the magnetic field at the time of its formation, was in turn split, as the crust on either side pulled apart, thus allowing the formation of yet another, younger volcanic band (Fig. 7.15). Accurate measurements have now confirmed that the crustal blocks on either side of mid-ocean ridges are

Figure 7.15 *Features of a typical mid-ocean ridge (see p. 172)*

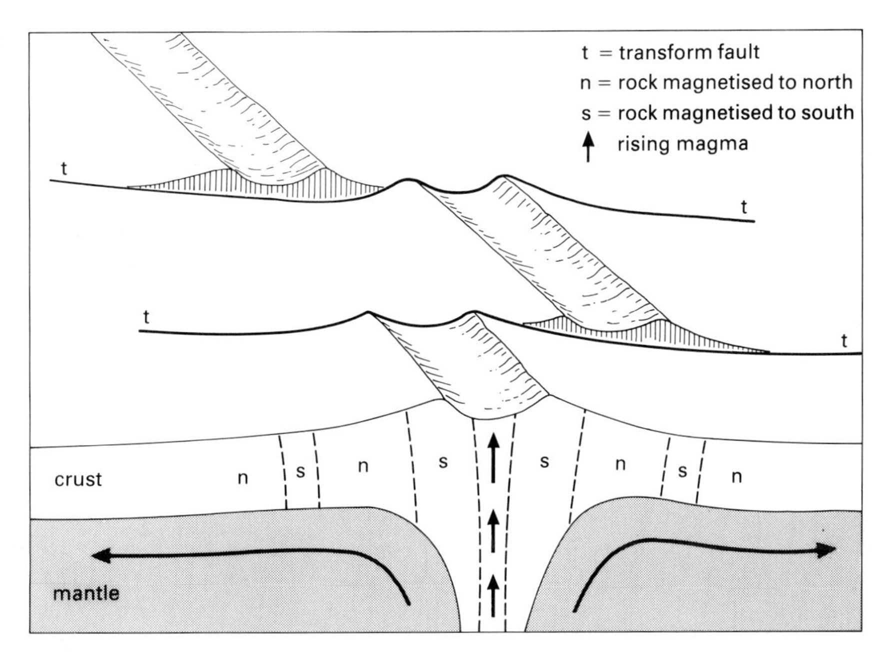

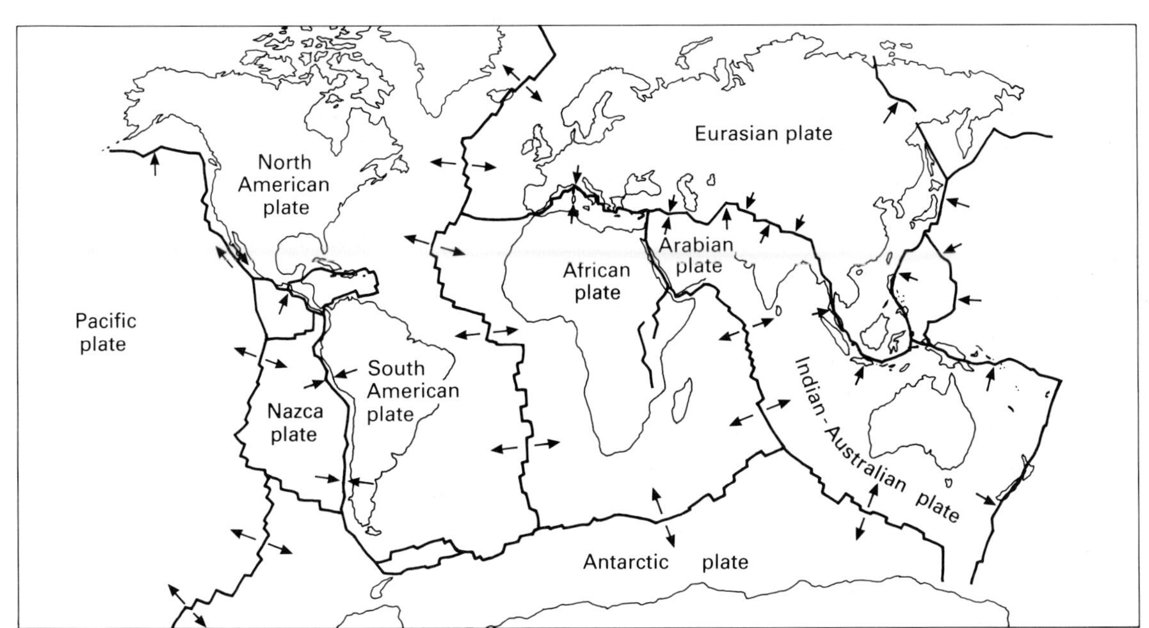

Figure 7.16 *The distribution and movement of crustal plates (see p. 174)*

moving apart at rates of up to 6 cm/annum^{-1}, or 60 km every million years. Such *crustal divergence* is known to be the cause not only of the earth's system of mid-ocean ridges, but also of features such as the great rift valley of east Africa (p. 166), although in this instance the movement of the blocks to east and west has, for some reason, been less pronounced.

Knowledge of this kind has provided the basis for the modern theory of *plate tectonics*, in which it is postulated that large sections of the earth's crust behave as rigid *plates*. These are capable of substantial lateral movement relative to each other, much as in the continental drift hypothesis. Each plate consists of part of the crust and upper mantle, and is thus a lithospheric block, which can migrate across the plastic zone of the asthenosphere (p. 170). Seven major lithospheric plates have been identified (the Eurasian, African, North American, South American, Pacific, Indian, Australian and Antarctic Plates), together with a number of subsidiary blocks (for example, the Arabian Plate, which is separated from the African Plate by the rift valley of the Red Sea, and the Nazca Plate, which is separated from the South American Plate by the Peru-Chile Trench) (Fig. 7.16).

Just as plates move apart, as in the example of the Mid-Atlantic Ridge, which therefore represents a *zone of spreading* or a *divergent plate margin*, so they are also capable of sliding

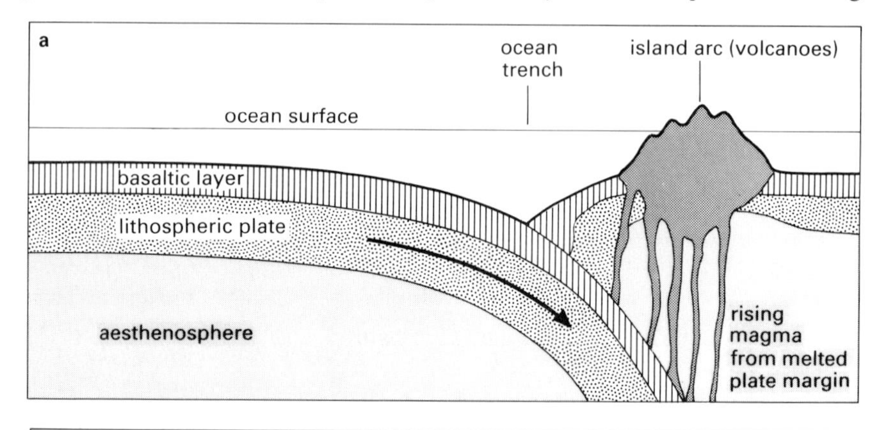

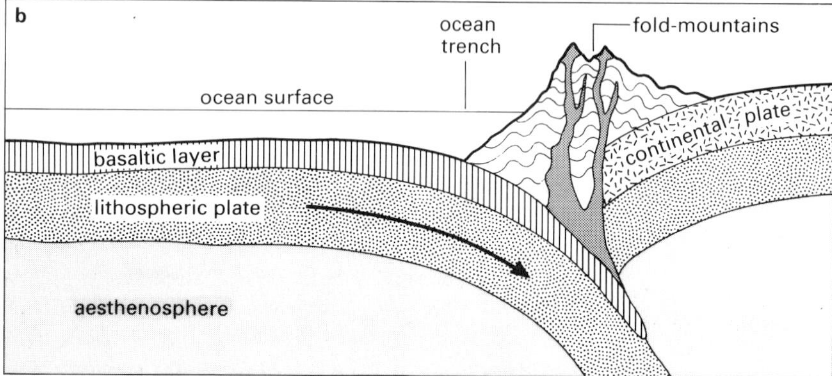

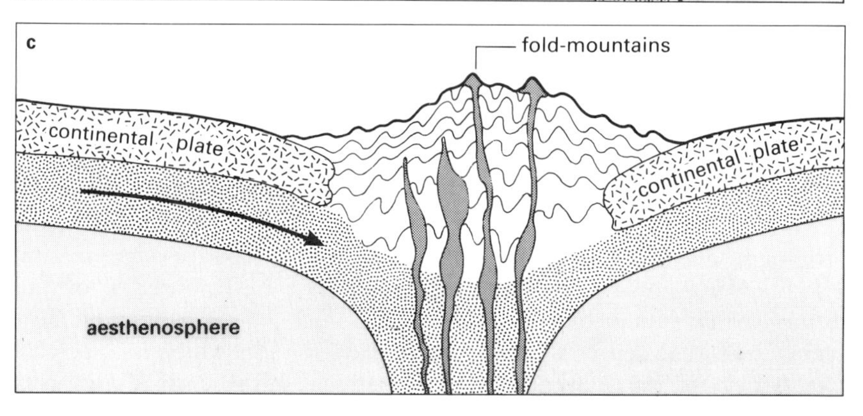

Figure 7.17 *Plate margins, subduction zones and associated landforms (see p. 175)*

past each other or towards each other. The former process involves transcurrent faults, the best known example of which is the San Andreas Fault, or megashear, of California. Along this massive crustal fracture, the Pacific Plate is moving north-eastwards past the North American plate, at about 6 cm/annum^{-1}. Where the latter process occurs, giving rise to a convergent plate margin, it is inevitable either that both plates bend down or that one overrides the other, which is then forced down into the asthenosphere, a process referred to as *subduction*. Since the subducted plate is subjected to destruction by melting at its margin, this is also known as a *destructive plate margin*, in contrast to divergent plate margins which are *constructive*, in the sense that new rock material is constantly being added at the plate edge.

Three types of convergent plate margin have been recognised. First, two oceanic plates may move towards each other, as in the western Pacific, where the major Pacific Plate, migrating north-westwards, passes beneath the smaller Philippine Plate along the line of the Marianas Trench (Fig. 7.17a). Secondly, an oceanic plate may encounter a continental plate, as in the south-east Pacific, where the east moving Nazca Plate passes beneath the west moving South American Plate at the Peru-Chile Trench (Fig. 7.17b). Thirdly, two continental plates may converge, as in northern India, where the western section of the Australian Plate, represented by the Deccan Shield, has moved north-eastwards towards the Eurasian Plate; intervening sediments in the resultant zone of compression have been intensely folded, to form the Himalayan fold mountain chain (Fig. 7.17c). It will be clear that convergent plate margins are associated with highly distinctive major landform types, such as ocean trenches, island arcs and fold mountains, in the manner shown in Fig. 7.17. It also follows that the world pattern of mountain ranges, the distribution of zones of volcanic activity (most notably in the 'Pacific Ring of Fire') and the incidence of earthquake activity (the product of differential movements along fault lines, as at the San Andreas megashear) closely reflect the positions of plate boundaries, and the nature, direction and intensity of plate movements. In that sense, the modern theory of plate tectonics has provided us at last with a means of explaining satisfactorily the large scale landform patterns and crustal processes of the earth.

ASSIGNMENTS

1 Explain how and why the mountains of upland Britain are different from the mountains of Switzerland.

2 Illustrating your essay by selected examples, write an explanatory account of the influence of geological faults on landforms and their development.

3 a. Using an appropriate atlas (such as the New Oxford Atlas), draw an outline map of the world, showing (i) the distribution of the major mountain ranges, and (ii) the distribution of the major mid-ocean ridges.

b. Transfer on to this map the major plate boundaries shown on Fig. 7.10. Note the directions of plate movement, and distinguish between divergent plate margins (show these as blue lines) and convergent plate boundaries (red lines).

c. Write comments on the relationships between mountain ranges, mid-ocean ridges and plate boundaries revealed by your map.

4 Write an explanatory account, with diagrams, of the development of landforms of (i) divergent plate margins, and (ii) convergent plate margins.

Index

ablation zone, 82–8, 86, 88
abrasion, 26, 28, 84, 87–8, 89, 90, 92, 93, 96
accumulation zone, 82–4, 86, 89
active layer, 101, 104
alas, 103–4
alluvial fan, 32, 33, 72, 126, 133
aquifer, 18, 19, 20, 21, 22, 124, 127
arch, 152–3
arête, 59, 93, 162
artesian basin, 22–3, 102
asymmetrical valley, 42, 43, 108, 109–10

backwash, 138, 140
bajada, 133
bank-full stage, 12, 34
barchan, 129–130
barrier beach, 113, 143, 146–7
basal sliding, 86, 87, 92, 96
basal surface of weathering, 58, 115–116, 117, 119, 120, 121, 124
base flow, 14, 29
base-level of erosion, 41, 64, 77
bay head beach, 143
bed load, 28, 29, 30, 32, 35, 37, 38, 41
bergschrund, 92
bevelled cliff, 149, 155
biological weathering, 56
block disintegration, 52, 54, 56, 63, 121, 123, 132
boulder controlled slope, 71, 72, 132
braided stream, 33, 35, 37–8, 107

carbonation, 55, 58, 59, 60, 61
castle koppie, 122, 123, 125
cavernous weathering, 54, 125
cavitation, 28, 29
channel flow, 10, 13–16
cirque, 92–3, 106, 162
cliff recession, 135, 136, 147–8
climatic geomorphology, 56, 159
coastal bar, 145–7
coastal platform, 156
coastal spit, 138, 140, 141, 142, 144–5, 146, 147
cockpit karst, 116
concave slope, 66, 72, 73, 74, 76, 78, 110, 122, 132
constructive wave, 138, 139
continental drift, 171–2, 174
continental shelf, 168
convex slope, 66, 67, 68, 69, 70, 72, 73, 74, 76, 78
corestone, 55, 57, 115, 118, 119, 121, 124, 137
craton, 159–160
crustal movements, 170–1
cuesta, 21–2, 126
cycle of erosion, 25

dead cliff, 150, 151, 154
debris slope, 51, 70–1, 73, 75, 76, 150, 155
deflation, 108, 128
desertification, 112–13
destructive wave, 138, 139
dilatation, 52, 53, 58, 63, 88
discharge, 13–16, 25, 26, 32, 34–5, 36, 37–8, 39, 41, 90, 107, 133
drainage basin analysis, 46–9
drainage density, 47–9
drainage pattern, 44–6
drumlin, 97
dry valley, 22, 48, 107, 108
duricrust, 119–20

equilibrium line, 83, 86
equilibrium slope, 66, 72, 74, 77
erg, 128, 131
esker, 98, 99, 100
eustatism, 153–4
evapotranspiration, 6, 7, 8, 9–10, 14, 17, 20, 21
exfoliation, 52, 53, 54, 58, 63, 73, 121, 122, 123, 125

fault, 21, 38, 40, 42, 44, 46, 64, 81, 128, 131, 133, 152, 161, 163, 164–7, 169, 175
felsenmeer, 53, 59, 60
fetch, 137
field capacity, 10, 17
flash flood, 20, 111, 112, 124, 126
flood plain, 33
flood prediction, 13
fluted moraine, 95
fold mountain, 64, 160–2, 171, 172, 175
free face, 51, 62, 70, 73, 77, 150
freeze-thaw weathering, 37, 43, 52–3, 55, 56, 58–60, 62, 87, 88, 92, 94, 104, 110, 136, 155
frost creep, 105
frost heave, 101, 104, 105

gelifluction, 105
geo, 148, 152
glacial outburst, 90–1
glacial overflow channel, 99
glacial trough, 86, 93, 162
glacio-fluvial stream, 90–1
gorge, 28, 29, 42, 64, 88
graded river, 38, 39, 40
granular disintegration, 52, 54, 61, 128, 132
ground ice, 100, 101–3, 104
ground water, 5, 6, 14, 16–23, 69, 103, 112, 124, 127

hammada, 128, 131
hanging valley, 93
headward erosion, 28, 29, 40, 45, 46, 76, 122
hogs back cliff, 149
hydration, 55, 58, 126
hydrograph, 14–16, 48
hydrological cycle, 5–6, 112
hydrolysis, 55–6, 58, 114, 115

infiltration, 8, 9, 11, 16–17, 49, 66, 67, 117
infiltration excess flow, 11, 66–7
inselberg, 52, 58, 116, 121–2, 123, 124, 128, 130
insolation weathering, 53–4, 58, 125
interception, 9
island arc, 170, 175
isostasy, 154, 155, 162, 171

joint, 19, 22, 29, 40, 42, 45, 51, 52, 54, 55, 56, 58, 59, 62–3, 64, 68, 88, 94, 104, 110, 115, 121, 122, 125, 126, 128, 132, 148, 150

kame, 98
kinetic energy, 26, 138
knick, 132, 133
knickpoint, 40

land slide, 68–9, 117
lateral erosion, 28, 47, 49, 64, 70, 93, 107, 130, 132
lateral moraine, 59, 89, 95–6
laterite, 119–20